MUNIAS AND MANNIKINS

MUNIAS AND MANNIKINS

ROBIN RESTALL

PICA PRESS
SUSSEX

RUSSEL FRIEDMAN BOOKS
SOUTH AFRICA

THE NETHERLANDS
AND BELGIUM

© 1996 Robin Restall
Pica Press (an imprint of Helm Information Ltd),
The Banks, Mountfield,
Nr. Robertsbridge,
East Sussex TN32 5JY

ISBN 1-873403-51-8

A CIP catalogue record for this book is available from the British Library.

Published in Southern Africa by
     Russel Friedman Books CC
     PO Box 73,
     Halfway House
     1685,
     South Africa.

ISBN 1-875091- 08-4
(Southern Africa only)

Published in the Netherlands and Belgium as *Dutch Birding Vogelgids 7* by
     Ger Meesters Boekprodukties
     Vrijheidsweg 86,
     2033 CE Haarlem,
     The Netherlands.

ISBN 90-74345-17-4
(Netherlands and Belgium only)

Editor: Nigel Redman
Copy Editing: Iain Robertson
Production and Design: Julie Reynolds

Computer graphics and typesetting by Fluke Art, Bexhill-on-Sea, E. Sussex.
Film output by PLS Ltd, London.
Printed by Midas Printing, Hong Kong.

TAXONOMY AND RELATIONSHIPS

Munias, or Mannikins? It is the convention to refer to some of the African and all of the New Guinea species as mannikins, and most of the Asian ones as munias. In this book I follow this usage although it is difficult to avoid regarding the two terms as being interchangeable, and both are English synonyms for the scientific *Lonchura*.

The munias have sometimes been subdivided into both supergenera and subgenera. Delacour (1943) gives a comprehensive review of the divisions with various groupings listed and a list of synonyms. He considered there to be three supergenera, *Padda* which embraced the Java and Timor Sparrows, *Amadina*, Cut-throat and Red-headed Finch, now regarded universally as falling within the Estrildidae, and *Lonchura* which contained all the munias, divided into four subgenera. These were *Heteromunia*, *Euodice*, *Lonchura* and *Munia*.

Subsequently Wolters (1957), Steiner (1960) and Guttinger (1970 and 1976) gave further conclusions. Peters' *Check-list of the Birds of the World* (Paynter 1968) uses the nomenclature and sequence – with the relationships implicit – most widely used today. Paynter recognizes two genera *Padda* and *Lonchura*. Goodwin (1982) merges *Padda* with *Lonchura*. Sibley and Monroe (1990) recognise *Heteromunia* (Pictorella Mannikin), *Lemuresthes* (Madagascar Mannikin) and *Padda* in addition to *Lonchura*. Having studied these birds all my life and quite intensely for the last seven years, I find no good reason to subdivide them in this book. Having studied most of the species in the wild and under controlled conditions, I am certain there are no clear lines apparent between each subgenus and several species arguably belong on either side of lines that had been drawn. The new field of genetic analysis, apparently imperfect since each researcher's results differs in detail from the next, will no doubt eventually show the true relationships in due course. Until then it seems pretentious of me, and of little utility, to conclude evolutionary relationships based on superficial morphological details, inconsistent criteria, or received wisdom and so I use the genus *Lonchura* throughout. The supergenera and subgenera are included with the scientific synonyms that are listed in each species account.

In terms of English language names it is not possible to please everybody. I have generally given each species the name that seems most widely recognised, and then listed all the other names that appear in the literature. I have given every subspecies a common English name as well so that terms of reference may be constant and consistent.

To put the *Lonchura* in perspective it may be helpful to first look briefly at the finches as a whole. Traditionally, everything was placed in one of two families. The Emberizidae, embracing not only the buntings and cardinals, but also the tanagers and the true finches, rating each as subfamily, and the Ploceidae. This latter included weavers, sparrows, parasitic whydahs, parrotfinches and mannikins, rating each as a subfamily. More recently, the most widely accepted structuring has been four neatly defined families; the Emberizidae (buntings and allies), Fringillidae (true finches and allies), Ploceidae (weavers and sparrows), with the waxbills, parrotfinches, grassfinches and munias forming the Estrildidae.

This was fine until Sibley *et al.* (1985 and 1988) published the findings of extensive work based on protein and DNA analyses. The implications are still so startling that few yet have grasped the nettle and recognised the redrawn the lines which, for example, place the accentors and wagtails in the Fringillidae. Sibley and Ahlquist then switched to apes and humans and stirred up such controversy in the United States that their methods were called into serious question (e.g. Sarich *et al.* 1988, and Britten 1989), and the controversy is still raging. In Sibley and Monroe (1990) the estrildids are placed in yet another family, the Passeridae (sparrows and allies).

Delacour's (1943) seminal work was the basis of all subsequent revisions for the next few decades. When I first became seriously interested in estrildids it was the first major paper I read. Delacour's work, although obviously vulnerable in some detail, was noteworthy in that it reduced a plethora of genera to a manageable number and unified several species. But Delacour was a lumper and combined several forms that today are widely accepted as being distinct species. In contrast I find myself to be a splitter and I take comfort in Christidis (1987) and Corbin (1977) who point out that there is a genetic distance between subspecies. My preference springs from a desire to see all behavioural observations located in origin precisely so that data can be as comparative as possible. To me the value of separating debatable species such as *L. malacca* and *L. atricapilla* is that field data can be related to its proper geographic location and a full comparative picture of a bird, its behaviour, diet, etc., can be built up. This is true also for recognising subspecies. If the forms are lumped some relevant, and perhaps quite localised behaviour from a

13

single location, may be misguidingly taken to apply to the species as a whole.

The essential weakness in Delacour's revision was that he used a combination of morphology, ecology and ethology to support his case and he was not entirely consistent in how he used these different criteria. He arbitrarily unified some species like the two silverbills, *L. malabarica* and *L. cantans*, in one case and two of the pale-headed munias, *L. maja* and *L. flaviprymna*, in another. A few students who were more familiar with the birds in life leapt upon these details to carry out structured comparative studies (e.g. Harrison 1964) and thereby modify Delacour's structure, so beginning the breakdown of Delacour's revision.

In the years between Delacour's paper and the monumental work of Derek Goodwin (1982) many very able and talented workers such as Steiner (1960), Immelmann and Immelmann (1967), and Guttinger (1970) studied the estrildids and offered the results of their own studies. I commend the student of estrildid history to refer to the definitive list of references at the time of writing, given in Sibley and Ahlquist (1990).

Since Goodwin, a great deal of work has continued, mostly in Germany, studying and breeding individual species. General field work continues, and in particular many publications have appeared based on field work in Indonesia and Papua New Guinea. The extent to which the work of Sibley *et al.* is valid or not I am not qualified to comment on, but I suspect it will turn out to be highly significant as other researchers experiment with molecular engineering, protein analyses and DNA studies. We have become accustomed to the wonders of forensic science in our daily media, from police work in deciding, for example, the parentage of a child, to the reconstruction of chromosome chains of a mammoth unearthed in Siberia. It seems obvious that there are techniques available that can definitively resolve the genetic relationships between living creatures. We are most likely to be confused by social and political issues when we talk about races of *Homo sapiens* or our genetic relationships to the apes, but when we look at birds we can hope to be a little more objective.

The study by Kakizawa and Watada (1985) at the Yamashina Institute in Tokyo is particularly interesting. The authors analysed the genetic variation of 42 species of estrildid by means of protein electrophoresis. They found that by measuring the distances between the gene count they could define the closeness of relationships and suggest a distance in evolutionary terms. Of the many charts showing all these details, one termed a dendrogram is the easiest to read, as it shows at a glance both generic relationships and gives an evolutionary dimension.

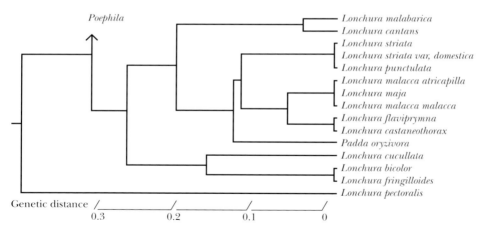

(After Kakizawa & Watada 1985)

Christidis (1987), using a much smaller selection of species, found both *Amadini* and *Erythruri* to be in *Lonchurinae*. He found a clear separation between *L. atricapilla* and *maja* in contrast to the findings of Kakizawa and Watada. But he also found *maja*, *flaviprymna* and *castaneothorax* to be extremely close.

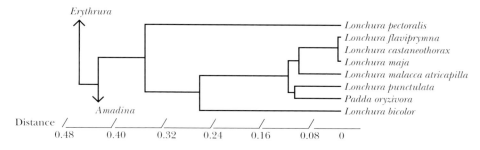

Erythrura

Amadina

Distance

| 0.48 | 0.40 | 0.32 | 0.24 | 0.16 | 0.08 | 0 |

Lonchura pectoralis
Lonchura flaviprymna
Lonchura castaneothorax
Lonchura maja
Lonchura malacca atricapilla
Lonchura punctulata
Padda oryzivora
Lonchura bicolor

(After Christidis 1987)

References

Britten (1989), Christidis (1987), Corbin (1977), Delacour (1943), Goodwin (1982), Guttinger (1970), Guttinger (1976), Harrison (1964), Kakizawa & Watada (1985), Immelmann & Immelmann (1967), Morris (1958), Paynter (1968), Sibley & Ahlquist (1985, 1990), Sibley & Monroe (1990), Sibley *et al.* (1988), Sarich *et al.* (1988), Steiner (1960), Wolters (1957).

NATURAL HISTORY OF MUNIAS AND MANNIKINS

GENERAL DISTRIBUTION

The munias are widespread throughout the Afrotropical, Oriental, Australasian and Melanesian regions. They range from West Africa to the Arabian Peninsula and through Asia to China, southwards to New Guinea and Australia and even beyond to some of the Pacific islands where one species is found on the island of Ponape (Pohnape) in the Carolines. They are not found naturally elsewhere, although some species have been introduced further afield by accident or by design.

HABITAT

Essentially munias are birds of arid savannah and open grassland, and the more primitive species (in evolutionary terms), Pictorella Mannikin *L. pectoralis*, the silverbills *L. cantans* and *L. malabarica*, and Madagascar Mannikin *L. nana* are still found in such habitat. But the genus *Lonchura* is still radiating and adapting. It has responded to opportunity by evolving far-ranging species such as White-rumped Munia *L. striata* and Scaly-breasted Munia *L. punctulata* that populate continuing habitat over thousands of kilometres, modifying marginally in coloration and minor physical details. In areas where the geography is essentially non-munia habitat, but offers locally suitable opportunities such as on the island of New Guinea, the genus has produced a variety of species, sibling species and distinct subspecies, the relationships of which can only be properly sorted out by the kind of genetic analysis referred to in the previous chapter.

Munias are also found in grassy country where the grasses are short, on land cleared by man for arable use, abandoned land where weeds and feral millets grow, and they have occasionally moved into areas inhabited by humans. Some, such as Javan Munia *L. leucogastroides* in Singapore and White-rumped Munia on Hong Kong island, have recently adapted to become common garden birds. Magpie Mannikin *L. fringilloides* has a strong relationship to bamboo and it seems that the distribution of the species may reflect that of the species of bamboo it relates to. Other munias may have bamboo connections, White-rumped Munia and White-spotted Mannikin *L. leucosticta* are two examples, but the bill of White-rumped Munia is a typical munia shape while that of White-spotted Munia is comparatively small. Not enough is known of the bamboo relationships to draw reasonable hypotheses. Considering how widespread and common the genus is, it is surprising how poorly its biology is understood.

MORPHOLOGY

Munias range in size from that of the large Java Sparrow *L. oryzivora* to the diminutive Madagascar Mannikin, by coincidence the only two species with red in their bills, although the red of Madagascar Mannikin is not very noticeable.

Goodwin (1982) pointed out that the bills of estrildids tend to increase in size disproportionally as the birds get larger. I have not seen any behaviour to suggest that this disproportionately greater size is to take advantage of larger or harder seeds. The exception is that of Magpie Mannikin, which has apparently evolved a rather large and long bill to deal with the seeds of the Bindura Bamboo *Oxytenanthera abyssinica*. From personal observations I have no doubt that bill size in munias has a function almost exclusively to do with social behaviour, primarily sexual attractiveness, and only secondarily in aggression, if at all. Male munias tend to have heavier bills than females, a subtlety usually lost to the human observer but one presumably recognised by female munias.

Goodwin (1982) also pointed out that Allen's rule, that extensions of the body tend to be smaller in colder regions, appears to apply within the Estrildidae. The only example of a munia I can find to support this is Alpine Mannikin *L. monticola* which has a noticeably smaller bill and thicker plumage. There are two species that have variation in bill size from one subspecies to another; these are White-bellied Munia *L. leucogastra* and Hooded Mannikin *L. spectabilis*. There are no comparative studies to throw light on why this might be. I have kept two distinct races of the former in captivity but was unable to detect any comparative food preferences.

Many species have large feet, with the central toe as long or longer than the tarsus and significantly longer if the toenail is added. This is a clear adaptation to feeding on and in grasses and sedges, when seeds are taken directly from the plants. A bird will fly at the stems just short of the head, feet outstretched with toes wide and ready to grasp. On impact, the stems usually bend, with several stems coming together, before the bird grasps at and usually clutches several stems at the same time. The long toes and equally long claws make this comparatively easy.

Those species with larger feet, such as Chestnut Munia *L. atricapilla*, usually inhabit marshy grassland, more typically the areas along river edges and marshy country favoured by tall grasses and sedges. Those munias with smaller feet such as silverbills are more likely to feed habitually on the ground, taking fallen seeds. They tend to be birds of more arid habitat, open steppe with scattered bush and scrub, montane grassland or man-occupied lands such as agricultural areas and gardens.

Immelmann (1982) described a wild Chestnut-breasted Mannikin *L. castaneothorax* feeding by reaching out from a grass stem on which it was clinging and grasping with its bill and pulling seeding heads towards it which it then held with its foot while it ate the seeds. Several seeding heads became held in this manner to be released when the bird flew off. I watched several Grey-headed Mannikins *L. caniceps* feeding like this in Papua New Guinea and saw Chestnut Munia do the same in the Philippines. Baptista (1990) describes the Grand Mannikin *L. grandis* using its bill in an unusual manner when he saw it running the bill in one single wipe along the length of a panicle of seeding grass, taking several of the soft green seeds in one go. I have observed this same behaviour in Chestnut Munia in Sulawesi when a feeding bird, having already taken some seeds from a panicle, ran its bill along the rest of the stem thereby taking several seeds at once. The grass was a low-growing species of the *Digitaria* type.

Another aspect that Goodwin (1982) notices is that estrildids with comparatively longer pointed bills also tend to be ground feeders. This generalisation does not hold good for munias. A typical ground-feeding munia that fits this concept is Pictorella Mannikin *L. pectoralis*, but Magpie Mannikin *L. fringilloides*, which has proportionately the longest bill of any munia, is said to seldom feed on the ground (Clement *et al.* 1993). Other ground-feeding species, such as silverbills have short, conical bills.

PLUMAGE AND COLOUR

Adult Plumage

Fresh adult plumage is often brightly coloured and shiny, more so in second-year birds than those in first-year adult plumage which, in contrast, might be without gloss. I have seen a large number of Five-coloured Munias *L. quinticolor* that had highly glossy edges to the breast and flank feathers that reflected brilliantly in the sunlight. A quartet of Streak-headed Mannikins *L. tristissima* that moulted into second-year plumage while in my care also had the edges of the breast and flanks feathers silky shiny, causing the the under-parts to appear in some lights to be scalloped with a paler colour. The African mannikins have patches of metallic gloss, green or blue depending on the species, on the head, wings or breast. Javan Munia will show a purplish gloss on the black of the breast, and Timor Sparrow *L. fuscata* can also have a purple gloss to the brown of the breast. Black-breasted Mannikin *L. teerinki* has a brown gloss to the head and breast, and Grand Mannikin of New Guinea may also have a green gloss to the head feathers. Some species, particularly those in the Chestnut Munia group, have glossy, fine trailing tips to rump, uppertail-coverts and central tail feathers, while others may show paler edges to the feathers of the nape and mantle, especially in new plumage. The Australian races of Chestnut-breasted Mannikin, and the south-east Asian Chestnut Munia *L. atricapilla sinensis* are outstanding examples.

In some species the difference between birds in first adult plumage and adults of two years or more is more than a degree of shine or feather extensions, both of which may be affected by wear or diet. Two examples where the difference between these plumage phases is significant are the Javan Munia and the Black-breasted Munia, and these are illustrated in the identification plates.

Juvenile Plumage

Juvenile munias begin to change the coloration of their soft parts quite soon after fledging. The mandibles are horny-dark upon fledging but soon begin to change once the bird is feeding independently of its parents, although it is known to take up to three months in the case of some Pale-headed Munias *L. pallida*. The lower mandible lightens in every species except those that have an all-black bill when adult. Legs and feet tend to become a little paler as the juveniles change to adult plumage with the exception of those species that have black legs and feet, and the irides, at first dark brown, brighten to become chestnut or deep ruby.

If a series of juvenile munias of a single species from one location is examined carefully, it will be seen that they vary slightly in coloration from one another, whilst all are clearly the same species. In selecting examples for the identification plates, the juveniles I have illustrated are representative guides and should not be regarded as definitive plumages for species-diagnostic differences. One noticeable exception is Black-and-White Mannikin *L. bicolor* where there is a marked average difference between the juveniles of the different races, and another is Chestnut Munia where there are also significant differences between juveniles of some of the races.

The moult from juvenile to adult plumage appears to take place usually between 5 and 7 months from fledging. There are plenty of records of birds in captivity moulting at anything from 3 months to almost 12 months, but about 5 months is normal.

Bill Colour

Immelmann did a lot of work on the significance of bill coloration in Zebra Finches *Poephila guttata*. In his work on imprinting in the Zebra Finch (1962a), which included extensive use of Bengalese, bill colour was a key factor. From this it is possible to infer that the dark bill in fledgling munias functions as an aggression and sexual attraction inhibitor.

In that study, Immelmann also found that bill coloration had most significance in flocking behaviour. I have noticed that the bicoloured-billed birds tend to clump and roost together, as do pale-billed birds, but I believe the all-pale bill has a stronger influence, in that bicoloured-billed birds will more freely clump with pale-billed birds than vice versa.

SEXUAL DIMORPHISM

Only a few munias are sexually dimorphic, that is to say, the sexes having noticeably different body size (as opposed to different coloration or dichromatism). The most notable example is that of Grand Mannikin, where males are usually significantly larger than females and the difference in bill size may be such that the depth (i.e. height) of a male's bill can be 20% more than that of a female. Java Sparrow is a less dramatic but more consistent example; the base of the bill and the eyelids of a male in full breeding condition are noticeably more swollen and redder than those of the female.

In many species the head of the female tends to be rounder and narrower, males being broader at the forehead and at the base of the culmen. There is often a ridge of the slightly more swollen base of the culmen of a male that can usually be felt by the tip of the finger and nail if a bird is examined in the hand.

The Queensland Finch Society (1987) noted that munias can be sexed by the depth of the concavity of the base of the bill, that of females being deeper than in males. I have been able to verify this by personal observation on several occasions but the difference is usually only a millimetre and it is not so constant as to be a reliable indicator. I also often find a difference in the width of the base of the bill which is slightly greater in males than females. Typical measurements would be 8mm for a female and 9mm for a male.

Overall length and wing length may also represent sexual differences, hence these measurements can be used as well in determining the sex of an individual bird. When measuring newly-caught birds in the field I have noticed a consistent grouping of measurements for males, and another for females, but when faced with a choice from very few birds this is not very helpful, for there are not only large females and small males in every population, but a bird of a few years of age might be as much as 10% larger in some measurements.

As a generalisation it seems that males average up to 10% larger. For example, males of a given population of a given species of a given age might average 110mm in total length (from tip of bill to tip of tail in a straight line) and 52mm in length of wing (the closed wing measured from the shoulder to the tip of the longest primary). In contrast, the length of the female might measure 105mm, and the wing 48mm.

The difference in shape and size of tails is usually overlooked. When measuring birds, it is an additional set of measurements worth taking for future reference, since it may prove to be useful for the diagnosis when sexing several birds. Amongst the cases where I have found that this applies, there is a distinct difference in the length of the tail of the male compared to that of the female Scaly-breasted Munia from Kalimantan. The distance from wing tip to tail tip of the dozen or so females measured was invariably 30mm, while the same measurement in a similar number of males was 35 or 36mm. I also found a similar constant difference in some Chestnut Munias and was subsequently able to sex them in this way. In African Silverbill a series of comparative measurements showed that the central tail feathers of the males were not only consistently longer than those of the females, but were narrower as well. In other species with comparatively long and somewhat pointed tails, such as Indian Silverbill and White-rumped Munia, the tail measurement may also be significant.

SEXUAL DICHROMATISM

There is much more sexual dichromatism (different coloration of the plumage) in munias of a given age than the literature records. The details will become apparent under the notes for individual species. When adult birds in fresh comparable plumage are together, males of species with black heads tend to have the black a purer black, shinier than that of the females which tend to have the blacks slightly browner. This distinction is usually lost on old museum specimens.

EFFECTS OF CAPTIVITY

Munias and mannikins are typical estrildid finches in the way they appear to be affected by living under controlled conditions. The fine long extensions to the tails of freshly moulted wild Tricoloured and Chestnut Munias are never seen on birds bred in confinement, nor do the tails of domesticated silverbills grow as long as those of wild birds. Madagascar Mannikins, bred regularly in Germany and elsewhere, appear to lose the reddish base of the lower mandible. Those I saw in England, imported from the Netherlands, were all somewhat melanistic as well. My friend and fellow munia breeder, Colin Rowe in England, tells me that all his cage-bred Chestnut-breasted Munias *L. castaneothorax sharpei* have black legs and feet compared to the grey legs of the wild adults.

There is normally no dramatic change or loss of plumage colour in birds kept in confinement, but cases of melanism do occur. I have seen many cases of melanism among estrildids, when the birds have moulted progressively darker. Among Java Sparrows I have seen several cases where the bird has lost the white on the cheek, leaving the head all black. I have also seen several black or blackish Bronze Mannikins, and two cases of melanistic Scaly-breasted Munias. Leucism is less common. One of the few Streak-headed Mannikins which I kept moulted into its second-year plumage with a pair of white feathers on its breast and a Scaly-breasted Munia grew several white primaries, as did a White-spotted Mannikin. Luis Baptista tells me he often saw fawn sports of Scaly-breasted Munia in Hong Kong many years ago, but I have only heard of one other case of fawn birds which occurred in a shipment of several thousand birds transiting through Singapore.

VOCALISATIONS

The call notes of adult munias fall into several groupings. There are soft notes that are uttered by a bird that is alone and other notes that are uttered when other birds are around. The notes used when calling have considerable, if subtle variation. Soft calls tend to be the same between sexes, but loud calls differ from male to female, often very noticeably. Male contact notes may be up to two whole tones apart from those of the female. The note used when calling a mate is different from that when making contact with others in the group, or the neighbourhood. There are also calls uttered in flight which serve to maintain contact and flock cohesion and may signal certain intentions. In my observations, males have significantly larger and more complex vocabularies than do females. In contrast the actual notes uttered by females are more complex. From studies of Bengalese and White-rumped Munias, it is likely that all juvenile munias have a vocabulary similar to that of the females, with the distinctive call notes of the male only coming with the ability to sing. This may well occur while a bird is still in juvenile pumage. Many species, if not all, tend to form pair bonds while still in juvenile plumage, but after the development of adult voice and the ability to sing.

Song is primarily sexual in function (Hall 1962) and is never used in aggression. There are many variations of song. The sonograms of songs in this book are mostly of the males uttering undirected advertisement song, in cages in my studio. They serve to show the structure of the basic song, and have comparative value. A fully comprehensive study would include subsong or whisper song, usually uttered by a male alone, often at night. There is the undirected song of an unmated male, and the advertisement song by a male accompanied by a female or mate. Males will sing a broadcast song from the entrance of the nest and this may be directed at the mate nearby. He will also sing within the nest when alone. There is also direct courtship song, delivered at a specific female close by or alongside. This may be low intensity or high intensity with clear intention to mating. There will be variations between all these songs, although superficially they appear to be similar.

I had been studying munias for over 20 years before I noticed the difference in voice between the sexes. Suddenly it became apparent when I had several individuals of White-rumped Munia each in a separate cage, each cage a few metres apart. The birds included a bonded pair and the clarity of difference between their loud contact calls was so obvious as not to be ignored. I have since successfully used it as a way to separate the sexes in many species. I should add here that it is not always easy and it is important to note the loud contact call, not the soft notes that sound more as if a bird is talking to itself rather than making deliberate contact. On one occasion I had nine Grand Mannikins, each in a separate cage. After four days of careful attention I gave up in despair. Only subsequent song and display identified a male, and then a comparison of sonograms enabled the identification of the sex of each bird recorded; eight of the nine turned out to be males.

Munias are very sociable birds, often highly gregarious, and most of their behaviour, if not all, seems to have been modified for the benefit of social harmony. As a result they are comparatively dull birds, with no dramatic displays, and no outstanding songs. In some species the song is so quiet to human ears that one may doubt its existence, or only pick up the extended *weeeeee*.

NESTING

Munia nests are naturally roundish bundles that range from neat and compact to untidy and straggly, with the entrance hole at one side, or they are a distinct oval with the entrance at one end. The entrance may have a very slight overhang or porch, or it may have a pronounced porch that effectively obscures the entrance. Nests are made of grasses, strips torn from bamboo or palm leaves or other leaves, rootlets, fibres and similar thin lengths of pliable material. There is not a great deal of detailed information of nests in the wild, and the nests of many species appear to be virtually unrecorded. The literature often refers to the nest of a given species as being a 'typical munia globe' or similar phrase, but this is unfortunate and unhelpful. Nests between species can be quite different in structure and content, and the more detailed any description, devoid of clichés, the better.

The nesting behaviour of munias in captivity should not be taken as representative of natural behaviour in the wild as they will nest in boxes with holes, half-open boxes, wicker baskets, or even rolls of wire mesh in captivity. This is more an indication of the adaptability of the genus in general, and in particular of the adaptability of some species, than an insight into how nests are built.

From their willingness to accept covered, hole-in-side nest baskets in captivity, Goodwin (1982) offers the hypothesis that many estrildids not presently known to do so, may occasionally make use of other species' nests. The only example I have personally found of this practice was in Bali, where a pair of White-headed Munias *L. maja* had taken possession of the nest of a Streaked Weaver *Ploceus manyar*. It seems possible that many species of *Lonchura* may opportunistically take over the covered nest of another species if available.

In most, if not all species, the male brings the nesting material to the nest, while the female inside works it into place by pushing. This pushing may extend to a kind of weaving when a length of grass may be pulled back into the structure and thus loops, catching hold, but the munias are not authentic weavers. In the case of nests built amongst reeds by species such as Chestnut-breasted Munia, when the structure becomes anchored by having some living stems go through the sides of the nest and leaves of the living plant become entwined with the nest material, the effect is similar to that wrought by a true weaver-bird. The African mannikins usually include feathers or down when lining the nest, but the Asian species seldom do. Three Asian species that have regularly included strands of material, such as feathers, strips of newspaper and other soft items in the nest structure and lining, are White-bellied Munia, Streak-headed Mannikin and Timor Sparrow.

Michael Plose (pers. comm. 1987) in England, noticed that when his captive Grey-crowned Mannikins were breeding, the bird flying to the nest always carried a short length of coconut fibre in its bill. I am not sure how widespread or typical this behaviour is. No doubt observations on munias in captivity are imperfect anyway because there may not be any suitable nesting material available once the birds are known to be sitting on eggs, and such behaviour might be inadvertently prevented. In my aviary, coconut fibre was always in short supply due to demand, as were short lengths of raffia. Also, items as fine as a piece of coconut fibre only a few centimetres long would be easy to miss being noticed by all but the most dedicated observer.

The estrildids of the genus *Estrilda* are known for building 'cock's nests', that is a smaller nest cavity on top of the nest and part of the total nest structure. This only occurs habitually in *Estrilda* species. It does not appear to be a characteristic of *Lonchura* but there are instances worth mentioning as further study might have evolutionary implications. I have personal experience of three instances when a cock's nest seems to have been built by a munia, all birds being studied in captivity. The first is a pair of Timor Sparrows that nested in a lovebird nest box. When the birds deserted their clutch of four eggs for the second time I took down the box and thoroughly examined the inside. There was a perfect and well-used cock's nest. I would occasionally enter the bird room during the day, and the male would leave the nest instantly, but the female stayed inside. Upon discovering the double cavity in the structure I watched the birds carefully and concluded that the male had been sitting in this sentinel nest while his mate had been sitting on the eggs in the inner chamber. I had a similar experience with a pair of Java Sparrows apparently building a double tiered, double chambered nest in an artificial log I constructed out of Spanish oak bark. The case of the Timor Sparrow tends to support Goodwin (1982) in his belief that the prime function of the cock's nest would be to thwart a predator.

When breeding Javan Munias in England, one pair appeared to have a built a cock's nest as part of the structure which was in a bank of hay. The Queensland Finch Society (1987) states that a roost nest will sometimes be built above or below the breeding nest, but there is not enough information to infer whether these might be cock's nests in the meaning discussed here.

Eggs

Munias lay white oval eggs, usually wider at one end, but there is considerable variation of shape within a species and even within individual birds. Young females producing their first clutch may lay smaller and more rounded or perfectly oval eggs. Incubation averages 13 days and the clutch is normally brooded by males and females alternately during the day, and probably by the female only at night although the male may roost in the nest with her. Eisner (1963) in her major study of the Bengalese, observed that more males hatch in the spring while more females hatch in the autumn. How this would relate to the breeding patterns of White-rumped Munia is difficult to extrapolate. It is not known if this is normal for other or even all *Lonchura*, or what the significance might be.

Nestlings and fledglings

Nestlings are born naked with their eyes closed. The skin varies from dark to pink depending on the species. They call to be fed and this becomes a clamour as they grow and compete for the parent's attention. They appear to be fed on demand, the call, when it has been recorded, being a repeated *chi-chi-chi-chi* or similar. Young munias are fed by both adults by regurgitation. The young beg in a prone posture, twisting and turning the head up and pointing it at the parent. The parent inserts its beak into the gape and pushes, the youngster clearly grasping the bill and pushing in the opposite direction. The food is regurgitated with a pumping action.

Each species has a distinctive pattern of black and white markings on the palate, with white nodes at the edges of the gape. Eisener (1963) found considerable variation in the palate markings of the Bengalese, but the extent to which there might be variation within a wild population is not known. Two records (Sproule 1994 and pers. obs.) of the palate marking of Five-coloured Munias suggest that there might be more variation than taken for granted. The patterns may change during the period that the chick is in the nestling stage (Payne 1973 and Goodwin 1982), and frequent records of the palate of a nestling Pearl-headed Mannikin over the nestling period (Baptista *in litt.*) show an evolution of the pattern. It seems that the age of the nestling should be noted when the palate marking is recorded. One of the characteristics distinguishing the African mannikins from the Asian munias is held to be the double horseshoe palate marking of the former, but I have found a double horseshoe marking in the palate of Five-coloured Munia from Indonesia. It is relevant that not all species have had the palate markings recorded.

The nestlings usually fledge on the same day even though they may be at slightly different stages in development or age. They are encouraged by the parents to return to the nest to sleep, at least for the first few nights after fledging. When watching a loose colony of Chestnut Munias in the gardens of a hotel near Manado, Sulawesi, I observed the feeding of a crèche of new fledglings. On two occasions there was no doubt that young birds, all recent fledglings from three or four different nests, were being fed by an adult that was not necessarily the parent of the birds being fed. I have referred to this (Restall 1995a) as 'crèche feeding'.

BEHAVIOUR

Little is known, and even less has been published, of munia behaviour in the wild. Most of the little that we know, including much of this chapter, is from the study of individual species in captivity.

Wing-raising

African mannikins will raise the wing on the far side of the body, both when being fed and when threatened by another bird, when the wing-raising bird is unwilling to give way or flee. Australian Pictorella Mannikins will raise the wing on the far side of the body to a parent when begging for food. Fledgling Pearl-headed Silverbills will quiver their wings in solicitation of feeding. I have recorded (Restall 1995a) the same wing-raising by a first-year adult Philippine Scaly-breasted Munia *L. punctulata cabanisi* when it felt threatened by a slightly larger munia of a different species, on another two separate occasions by Chestnut Munia *L. atricapilla brunneiceps* under similar circumstances, and also in Indonesia by a fledgling Chestnut Munia *L. atricapilla jagori* when competing with siblings to be fed.

References

Eisner (1963), Goodwin (1982), Hall (1962), Immelmann (1962a, 1969 & 1982), Immelmann *et al.* (1968-72), Moynihan & Hall (1945), Morris (1957), Queensland Finch Society (1987), Restall (1989 & 1995a), Sproule (1994).

PLATES
1-16

PLATE 1: SILVERBILLS AND AFRICAN MANNIKINS I

2   **African Silverbill** *Lonchura cantans*   **Text and map page 60**

See also Measured Drawing on plate 18.

   2a   *L. c. cantans* **adult** From West and central Africa.
   2b   *L. c. inornata* **adult** From extreme northeastern Africa and the Arabian Peninsula.
            Touch of dark red in the uppertail-coverts and edges of the tail not noticeable in the
            field.
   2c   *L. c. orientalis* **adult** From East Africa. Darker on face and upperparts.

4   **Pearl-headed Mannikin** *Lonchura griseicapilla*   **Text and map page 66**

   4a   *L. griseicapilla* **adult** From East Africa.
   4b   *L. griseicapilla* **juvenile**

3   **Indian Silverbill** *Lonchura malabarica*   **Text and map page 63**

See also Measured Drawing on plate 19.

   3a   *L. malabarica* **adult** From Israel to northeast India and Sri Lanka.
   3b   *L. malabarica* **juvenile**

5   **Bronze Mannikin** *Lonchura cucullata*   **Text and map page 68**

See also Measured Drawing on plate 20.

   5a   *L. c. cucullata* **juvenile**
   5b   *L. c. cucullata* **adult** From West Africa. Green on flanks.
   5c   *L. c. scutatus* **adult** From East Africa. Usually an absence of significant green on flanks.
            Barring on rump, upper- and undertail-coverts much finer.

1   **Madagascar Mannikin** *Lonchura nana*   **Text and map page 59**

See also Measured Drawing on plate 17.

   1a   *L. nana* **juvenile**
   1b   *L. nana* **adult** Madagascar and the Comoros. Reddish on base of bill.
   1c   *L. nana* **adult** Dark type found in captivity.
   1d   *L. nana* **juvenile** Dark type.

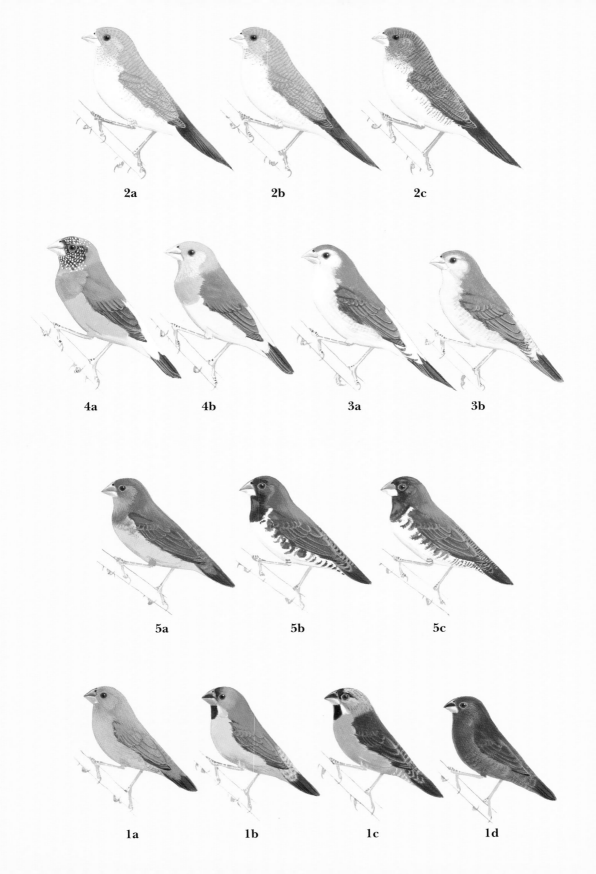

2a   2b   2c

4a   4b   3a   3b

5a   5b   5c

1a   1b   1c   1d

PLATE 2:   AFRICAN MANNIKINS II

6   Black-and-White Mannikin *Lonchura bicolor*   **Text and map page 71**

See also Measured Drawing on plate 21.

6a   *L. b. nigriceps* **juvenile** Paler and browner on back and wings, paler ear-coverts, chin and throat.

6b   *L. b. bicolor/stigmatophora/poensis* **juvenile** Dull earth-brown above, greyish below.

6c   *L. b. bicolor* **juvenile** From Mt. Nimba, Liberia. Richer brown on breast and creamier below.

6d   *L. b. poensis* **adult** From Central Africa, Cameroon to northern Angola. Green gloss on black plumage. Black-and-white barring on rump, uppertail-coverts and wings.

6e   *L. b. bicolor* **adult** West Africa, Senegal to eastern Nigeria and Mt. Cameroon. Green gloss on black plumage. Absence of any barring on the wings or rump. There may be one or more pale vestigial spots on the tertials.

6f   *L. b. bicolor* From Mt. Nimba, Liberia. No barring on the wings or rump. Three white spots on innermost tertials.

6g   *L. b. stigmatophora* **adult** From northern shore of Lake Victoria to southern Ethiopia. Dull black on head, brownish-black on mantle, only a slight purple or bluish gloss.

6h   *L. b. woltersi* **adult** From southwest Katanga and northwest Zambia. Purple or bluish gloss on black plumage. Dark brown back and wings.

6i   *L. b. nigriceps* **adult** From East Africa. Rufous-brown back and wings. White quills to scapulars.

---

7   Magpie Mannikin *Lonchura fringilloides*   **Text and map page 74**

See also Measured Drawing on plate 22.

7a   *L. f. fringilloides* **adult** From West Africa to western Uganda. Broad patches of black on sides of breast and brown on flanks. *L. f. pica* from East and south-east Africa has less black and brown on sides of body and has the mantle slightly paler brown.

7b   *L. f. fringilloides* **juvenile**

6a   6b   6c

6d   6e   6f

6g   6h   6i

7a   7b

PLATE 3:   WHITE-RUMPED MUNIA

8   White-rumped Munia *Lonchura striata*   **Text and map page 77**

See also Measured Drawings on plates 23–26.

8a   *L. s. striata* **juvenile**.

8b   *L. s. striata* **adult** From Sri Lanka and southern India. Black face with very pale belly and rump.

8c   *L. s. striata* **adult** From central and northern India. Face not as black as the birds from the south of the subcontinent.

8d   *L. s. acuticauda* **adult** From Darjeeling. Striations on head restricted to outer ear-coverts.

8e   *L. s. acuticauda* **adult** From Khasia. Striations on rear-crown and nape, and sides of neck.

8f   *L. s. acuticauda* **adult** Type specimen. Pale edges to breast feathers.

8g   *L. s. semistriata* **adult** From the Nicobar Islands.

8h   *L. s. fumigata* **adult** From the Andaman Islands.

8i   *L. s. subsquamicollis* **adult** From Laos and Burma. Plain-coloured thighs and undertail-coverts.

8j   *L. s. subsquamicollis* **adult** From peninsular Malaysia. Ear-coverts well marked and dark edging to the thighs and undertail-coverts.

8k   *L. s. sumatrensis* **adult** From southern Sumatra. Greyish ear-coverts and dingy grey tone to well-marked belly and flanks.

8l   *L. s. swinhoei* **adult** From eastern China. The breast colour graduates into that of the belly, and the edges of the flanks are unlined or lined with paler grey.

8m   *L. s. swinhoei* **adult** From Chingkiang, north-east central China. Brown wash to underparts.

8n   *L. s. phaethontoptila* **adult** From Taiwan. The mask graduates into the breast, and the pale edges to the breast feathers are only bright at the sides of the breast. The bright cream underparts are less boldly lined with grey.

8o   *L. s. swinhoei* **adult** From Hainan. The mask is clearly defined and the ear-coverts are very pale. The lining below is mostly on the flanks.

8p   *L. s. swinhoei* **juvenile**.

8a   8b   8c   8d

8e   8f   8g   8h

8i   8j   8k   8l

8m   8n   8o   8p

PLATE 4: ASIAN MUNIAS I

9   Javan Munia *Lonchura leucogastroides*   **Text and map page 85**

See also Measured Drawing on plate 27.

9a   *L. leucogastroides* **juvenile** From south Sumatra, Java and Bali.

9b   *L. leucogastroides* **first-year female** Creamy breast, with vague horseshoe markings on flanks.

9c   *L. leucogastroides* **first-year male** Creamy breast, with vague lining on breast.

9d   *L. leucogastroides* **adult** White breast and flanks.

11   Moluccan Munia *Lonchura molucca*   **Text and map page 89**

See also Measured Drawings on plates 28–29.

11a   *L. m. molucca* **first-year female** From north Sulawesi and the Moluccas. Entire back is barred.

11b   *L. m. molucca* **first-year male** Distinguished by a paler patch on the sides of the neck.

11c   *L. m. molucca* **adult male** Barring on back is restricted to upper mantle.

11d   *L. m. molucca* **juvenile**

11e   *L. m. vagans* **adult** From southern Sulawesi. There is an irregular bar of white across the upper breast. Barring on flanks broader and black mixed with brown.

11f   *L. m. propinqua* **adult male** A melanistic bird from Timor.

11g   *L. m. propinqua* **adult** From Kangean. This population is very lightly marked on the breast.

11h   *L. m. propinqua* **adult** From the Lesser Sundas. Base colour of underparts light creamy, upperparts earthy-tan. Barring on flanks tends to grey.

11i   *L. m. propinqua* **adult** From Timor. There tends to be fewer markings on the rump.

9a   9b   9c   9d

11a   11b   11c

11d   11e   11f

11g   11h   11i

PLATE 5:   ASIAN MUNIAS II

15   White-bellied Munia *Lonchura leucogastra*   **Text and map page 105**

See also Measured Drawing on plate 42.

15a   *L. l. leucogastra* **juvenile** From peninsular Thailand, Malaysia and Sumatra. Duller version of the adult.

15b   *L. l. leucogastra* **adult** Striations only on mantle, black uppertail-coverts, yellow edges to tail.

15c   *L. l. palawana* **adult** From Palawan and northern Borneo. Striations from crown to back.

15d   *L. l. everetti* **adult** From the northern Philippines. Striations on flanks.

15e   *L. l. manueli* **adult** From the southern Philippines. Black spots on brown sides of breast. The white of the lower flanks is more extensive.

15f   *L. l. smythiesi* **adult** From western Borneo. Earth-brown above without striations on the nape. The flanks are warmer brown.

15g   *L. l. castanonota* **adult** From central south Borneo. Dark chestnut back, black uppertail-coverts.

15h   *L. l. castanonota* **juvenile**

---

10   Dusky Munia *Lonchura fuscans*   **Text and map page 88**

10a   *L. fuscans* **juvenile** From Borneo.

10b   *L. fuscans* **first-year**

10c/d *L. fuscans* **second-year** Showing the variation between individuals; the sexes are similar.

---

32   Cream-bellied Munia *Lonchura pallidiventer*   **Text and map page 161**

See also Measured Drawings on plates 70–72.

32a   *L. pallidiventer* **juvenile** From southeastern Borneo, precise origin unknown.

32b   *L. pallidiventer* **adult female** Rump brownish-orange with whitish barring.

32c   *L. pallidiventer* **adult male** More extensive orange on rump.

---

12   Spot-sided Munia *Lonchura* **sp.**   **Text and map page 93**

See also Measured Drawing on plate 30.

12   **Undescribed form: adult female** Origin unknown.

15a   15b   15c   15d

15e   15f   15g   15h

10a   10b   10c   10d

32a   32b   32c   12

PLATE 6:   SCALY-BREASTED MUNIA

14   Scaly-breasted Munia *Lonchura punctulata*   **Text and map page 97**

See also Measured Drawings on plates 31–40.

14a   *L. p. punctulata* **juvenile** From Pakistan, India and Sri Lanka.

14b   *L. p. punctulata* **adult** This is the only race with orange uppertail-coverts, and pure black-and-white scaly markings on the breast and flanks.

14c   *L. p. subundulata* **adult** From Assam, Bangladesh and north-east India to Burma. The scaly markings are brown and the uppertail-coverts olive-yellow.

14d   *L. p. topela* **adult** From Burma through Thailand to China and Taiwan. Somewhat variable across its range, with salmon uppertail-coverts in western Thailand to yellow in China. Little or no striations on the back.

14e   *L. p. yunnanensis* **adult** From Yunnan in south-western China. Cinnamon back with white striations. Note the brown of the throat merges into the white of the belly.

14f   *L. p. fretensis* **adult** From Thailand. Black bill and more orange on outer ear-coverts.

14g   *L. p. fretensis* **adult** From Sumatra. Note the bicoloured bill.

14h   *L. p. nisoria* **adult** From Java, Bali and Lombok. Distinguished by its dark reddish face, and virtually no striations on the back.

14i   *L. p. holmesi* **adult** From southern Kalimantan. Finely barred on the back, and very pale grey edges to the uppertail-coverts.

14j   *L. p. blasii* **adult** From Flores through Timor to Tanimbar in the Lesser Sundas. Dark reddish-brown face with reddish-brown scaly markings on cream ground colour. Dark above with barring from nape to rump.

14k   *L. p. sumbae* **adult** From Sumba. Paler ear-coverts than other Lesser Sundas races, and white ground colour to the scaly markings.

14l   *L. p. particeps* **adult** From Sulawesi. Cream below, with dark brown vermiculations.

14m   *L. p. baweana* **adult** From Bawean. More earth-brown than other Indonesian races, and the scaly markings are not so strongly defined. The uppertail-coverts have straw edges.

14n   *L. p. cabanisi* **juvenile** From the Philippines. The smallest of the races.

14o   *L. p. cabanisi* **adult** The face mask is very small on this race. The scaly markings are mid-brown, elongated, and double-looped. The bill is all grey in first-year adults, but the upper mandible darkens in the second year.

14p   *L. p. fortior* **adult** From Sumbawa. Warm earth-brown above, striations on mantle only.

14a   14b   14c   14d

14e   14f   14g   14h

14i   14j   14k   14l

14m   14n   14o   14p

PLATE 7:   STREAK-HEADED AND WHITE-SPOTTED MANNIKINS

16   Streak-headed Mannikin *Lonchura tristissima*   Text and map page 111

See also Measured Drawings on plates 43–44.

16a *L. t. tristissima* **juvenile** From western Irian Jaya.

16b *L. t. tristissima* **adult female** Slightly more spotted than male. Thin black bar above buff on rump.

16c *L. t. tristissima* **adult male** Buff of rump extends further upwards.

16d *L. t. calaminoros* **juvenile** From north-central New Guinea.

16e *L. t. calaminoros* **adult** Note wing-bar and absence of black above rump.

16f *L. t. calaminoros* **adult** From Karkar Island. Note the prominent white wing-bar.

16g *L. t. hypomelaena* **adult** From west-central Irian Jaya. Almost entirely black below, lemon-buff rump with broad black bar above. The female is more likely to have pale streaks on the sides of the breast, with the edges of the median and greater wing-coverts dark brown instead of black.

16h *L. t. bigilalei* **juvenile** From southern Papua New Guinea. Well spotted, especially breast.

16i *L. t. bigilalei* **adult female** More spotted than male, especially on breast.

16j *L. t. bigilalei* **adult male** Note long uppertail-coverts dark brown on both sexes. Absence of bar over rump.

17   White-spotted Mannikin *Lonchura leucosticta*   Text and map page 115

See also Measured Drawing on plate 45.

17a *L. l. moresbyi* **adult male** From Port Moresby. White spotting less extensive on breast. Note dark greyish-brown undertail-coverts.

17b *L. l. leucosticta* **juvenile** White chin, may have pale edges to undertail-coverts.

17c *L. l. leucosticta* **adult female** Whiter on face, and less white on chin than the male. Brown undertail-coverts diagnostic.

17d *L. l. leucosticta* **adult male** The yellow rump is more extensive. Black undertail-coverts.

16a   16b   16c

16d   16e   16f   16g

16h   16i   16j

17a   17b   17c   17d

18   Tricoloured Munia *Lonchura malacca*

Text and map page 119

See also Measured Drawings on plates 46–47.

18a   *L. malacca* **adult** From India and Sri Lanka.

18b   *L. malacca* **adult** This variant has irregular and uneven edges to white flanks.

18c   *L. malacca* **adult** The brown edges to the white feathers of the breast and flanks may be on a white or light cinnamon ground colour.

18d   *L. malacca* **adult** Variant with cinnamon breast and flanks. The strength of cinnamon may vary from one individual to another, or within individual populations of normal birds.

19   Chestnut Munia *Lonchura atricapilla*

Text and map page 122

See also Measured Drawings on plates 48–55.

19a   *L. a. atricapilla* **adult** From lowland northeastern India (black to blackish belly and undertail-coverts), to most of Burma (dark brown belly and undertail-coverts) as illustrated here. The uppertail-coverts and fringes of the tail are orange or yellowish.

19b   *L. a. rubroniger* **adult** From the foothills of the Himalayas of India and Nepal. Rich chestnut brown, belly and undertail-coverts black. No yellow or orange on uppertail-coverts.

19c   *L. a. deignani* **adult** From Indochina to China. Chestnut to mahogany-red; note lack of orange and yellow on rump and uppertail-coverts.

19d   *L. a. sinensis* **adult** From peninsular Burma and Thailand to Malaysia (northern populations). Light chestnut above, often with paler scalloping on mantle; orange to yellowish on uppertail-coverts. The belly is dark brown to blackish.

19e   *L. a. brunneiceps* **adult female** From south Sulawesi, Muna Butung and Ambon. Browner on head than male, broader brown band across breast.

19f   *L. a. brunneiceps* **adult male** Smaller, brown of body less rich than other races, rich maroon rump, some orange edging to uppertail-coverts.

19g   *L. a. jagori* **adult female** From the Philippines and northern Borneo, and Sulawesi. Usually browner on the rear head and has a broader brown band across the breast than the male.

19h   *L. a. jagori* **adult male** Highly variable race, males average darker heads than females in any given population. Rich maroon rump, orange uppertail-coverts becoming yellow on edges of tail.

19i   *L. a. formosana* **adult female** From Taiwan and northern Luzon. Paler than male, particularly on head; may have sulphur edging to feathers of nape.

19j   *L. a. formosana* **adult male** Orange on uppertail-coverts and edges of tail.

19k   *L. a. batakana* **adult** From the northern highlands of Sumatra. Chestnut is even above and below. Note maroon from rump to tail.

19l   *L. a. sinensis* **adult** From peninsular Malaysia and Sumatra (southern populations). Pale edges on the mantle are almost whitish. This population is very rarely black on the underparts.

19m   *L. a. obscura* **adult** From central south Borneo. Very dark brown.

19n   *L. a. selimbauensis* **adult** From western Borneo. Only slight orange edging to tail feathers.

18a 18b 18c 18d

19a 19b 19c 19d

19e 19f 19g 19h 19i 19j

19k 19l 19m 19n

PLATE 9: ASIAN AND AUSTRALASIAN MUNIAS I

20 **Black-throated Munia** *Lonchura ferruginosa*   **Text and map page 130**

See also Measured Drawing on plate 56.

20a *L. ferruginosa* **adult** From Java and Bali. This is the male variant with the entire underparts black.

20b *L. ferruginosa* **adult male** Type specimen. Narrow brown band across breast.

20c *L. ferruginosa* **adult female** Type specimen. Broad brown band across breast.

31 **Yellow-rumped Mannikin** *Lonchura flaviprymna*   **Text and map page 159**

31a *L. flaviprymna* **adult** From northern Australia. The sexes are alike.

31b *L. flaviprymna* **juvenile**.

22 **White-headed Munia** *Lonchura maja*   **Text and map page 135**

See also Measured Drawings on plates 60–63.

22a *L. m. maja* **adult male (second-year)** From peninsular Thailand to Bali. Clean whitehead.

22b *L. m. maja* **adult male (first-year)** Suffusion from nape extends to crown.

22c *L. m. maja* **adult female** Breast colouring merges into flanks.

22d *L. m. vietnamensis* **adult male** From the Mekong Delta, Vietnam. Head tawny except for white around eye.

22e *L. m. maja* **juvenile**

23 **Pale-headed Munia** *Lonchura pallida*   **Text and map page 139**

See also Measured Drawing on plate 55 and 64.

23a *L. p. pallida* **adult female** From the Lesser Sundas and Sulawesi. Paler belly than male, usually with subtle grey edging to feathers near breast.

23b *L. p. pallida* **adult male** Richer colour than female on belly and paler face.

23c *L. p. subcastanea* **adult** From the Palu Valley, central Sulawesi. Rich cinnamon belly.

23d *L. p. pallida* **juvenile**

25 **Grey-banded Mannikin** *Lonchura vana*   **Text and map page 145**

25a *L. vana* **adult** From the Vogelkop, western Irian Jaya.

25b *L. vana* **juvenile**

20a   20b   20c   31a

22a   22b   22c   22d

23a   23b   23c   25a

23d   22e   31b   25b

33   Chestnut-breasted Mannikin *Lonchura castaneothorax*   **Text and map page 162**

See also Measured Drawings on plates 73–74.

33a   *L. c. castaneothorax* **juvenile** From eastern Australia.

33b   *L. c. castaneothorax* **adult**

33c   *L. c. assimilis* **adult** From northern Australia. Richer breast and cream ground colour to belly and flanks.

33d   *L. castaneothorax* **adult** From Tahiti. Most populations on Tahiti were apparently descended from *L. c. castaneothorax*. They are distinguished today by having paler underparts and by the scalloping of the nape extending onto the mantle.

New Guinea forms

33e   *L. c. ramsayi* **adult** From southeastern Papua New Guinea. Distinctive black head with faint scalloping which may be more noticeable on the head of the female.

33f   *L. c. boschmai* **adult** From the Lake Wissel area in Irian Jaya. Brown scallops on the flanks and paler to straw on the uppertail-coverts.

33g   *L. c. sharpii* **adult** From Hollandia, Irian Jaya and Papua New Guinea. Very pale grey on the head, and dull uppertail-coverts.

33h   *L. c. uropygialis* **adult** From the head of Geelvink Bay in western Irian Jaya. Grey of the head not so pale, and note orange on the long uppertail-coverts.

21   Five-coloured Munia *Lonchura quinticolor*   **Text and map page 132**

See also Measured Drawings on plates 57–59.

21a   *L. q. quinticolor* **juvenile** From the eastern part of the Lesser Sundas; juveniles of all races are similar.

21b   *L. q. quinticolor* **adult** Distinguished by the yellow to golden uppertail-coverts.

21c   *L. q. sumbae* **adult** From the central Lesser Sundas. Orange uppertail-coverts.

21d   *L. q. wallacii* **adult** From the western part of the Lesser Sundas. Brick-red uppertail-coverts.

33a   33b   33c   33d

33e   33f   33g   33h

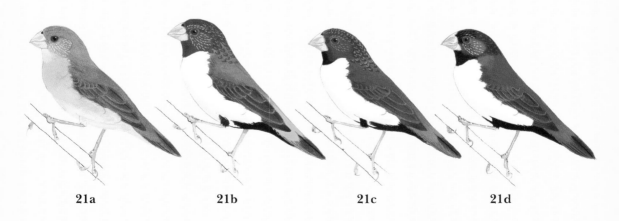

21a   21b   21c   21d

24 Grand Mannikin *Lonchura grandis*   **Text and map page 141**

See also Measured Drawings on plates 65–66.

24a ***L. g. grandis* juvenile** From southern Papua New Guinea.

24b ***L. g. grandis* adult male** Back rich cinnamon, uppertail-coverts orange.

24c ***L. g. destructa* adult male** From Hollandia in northern New Guinea. The largest race. Back rich, deep chestnut. Three colours of rump and uppertail-coverts graduate into each other. Yellow long uppertail-coverts.

24d ***L. g. destructa* adult female** Usually smaller but not always significantly so.

24e ***L. g. heurni* juvenile** From northwestern Irian Jaya.

24f ***L. g. heurni* adult male** Similar to *destructa* but slightly smaller, more brown on flanks and three colours of rump and uppertail-coverts clearly separated. Long uppertail-coverts and edges of tail straw-coloured.

24g ***L. g. ernesti* adult male** From northern Papua New Guinea. Back cinnamon-rufous, uppertail-coverts deep orange. Flanks irregular.

38 Thick-billed Mannikin *Lonchura melaena*   **Text and map page 174**

38a ***L. m. melaena* juvenile** Cinnamon rump and uppertail-coverts.

38b ***L. m. melaena* adult male** From northern New Britain. The brown of the back begins from the mid-crown and covers the back of the head.

38c ***L. m. bukaensis* adult male** From Buka Island, Solomons. Entire head is black, the uppertail-coverts are darker and richer coloured, and the salmon of the belly extends to the flanks.

30 New Ireland Mannikin *Lonchura forbesi*   **Text and map page 158**

30 ***L. forbesi* adult male** From New Ireland. Creamy-orange rump and uppertail-coverts.

24a   24b   24c   24d

24e   24f   24g

38a   38b   38c   30

PLATE 12:   AUSTRALASIAN MANIKINS II

26   Grey-headed Mannikin *Lonchura caniceps* Text and map page 146

See also Measured Drawing on plate 67.

26a   *L. c. caniceps* **adult female** From southern Papua New Guinea.

26b   *L. c. caniceps* **adult male** Orange extends further up rump than on the female.

26c   *L. c. kumusii* **adult male** From northern Papua New Guinea. Olive-grey of the breast merges into the dark grey of the flanks and belly.

26d   *L. c. scratchleyana* **adult male** From mid-montane Papua New Guinea. Olive-grey of nape becomes cinnamon-grey on belly and flanks. Uppertail-coverts are yellow.

26e   *L. c. "myolae"* **adult male** Head smoky-grey, rump and uppertail-coverts buff.

26f   *L. c. caniceps* **juvenile**

29   Hunstein's Mannikin *Lonchura hunsteini* Text and map page 156

29a   *L. h. hunsteini* **adult female** From New Hanover.

29b   *L. h. hunsteini* **adult male** Orange of rump extends further up than on the female.

29c   *L. h. minor* **adult male** From Pohnpei in the Caroline Islands. Whiter nape and darker rump.

29d   *L. h. nigerrima* **adult male** From New Ireland. Browner head and paler rump.

29e   *L. h. hunsteini* **juvenile**

29f   *L. h. nigerrima* **juvenile**

26a   26b   26c   26d

26e   26f

29a   29b   29c   29d

29e   29f

PLATE 13: HOODED MANNIKIN

28   Hooded Mannikin *Lonchura spectabilis*   **Text and map page 152**

See also Measured Drawing on plate 69.

New Britain

28a/b   *L. s. spectabilis* **juveniles** Showing typical variation, probably influenced by the age of the bird, the second bird being older.

28c   *L. s. spectabilis* **adult** Type specimen with white breast; shows black edging on the mantle.

28d   *L. s. spectabilis* **adult** Variant with barring on sides of the breast and flanks.

New Guinea

28e   *L. s. mayri* **juvenile** From northern Irian Jaya and northwestern Papua New Guinea.

28f   *L. s. mayri* **adult** Type specimen. The breast may also be white, and older birds have whiter breasts.

28g   *L. s. mayri* **adult** Variant with grey barring on the sides of the breast and flanks.

28h   *L. s. wahgiensis* **adult** From the foothills of Herzog, Saruwaged and Bismarck Mountains of Morobe and Madang provinces. Note yellow rump and some blackish edging to the upper mantle.

28i   *L. s. sepikensis* **adult** From the Sepik plains. With cinnamon breast and flanks.

28j   *L. s. gajduseki* **adult** From the eastern part of Chimbu province. With cream breast and uniform rump and uppertail-coverts.

28k   *L. s. "karimui"* **adult** From the western part of Chimbu province. This undescribed form has a dark chocolate brown head, and yellow long uppertail-coverts that contrast with the orange rump.

28l   *L. s. "korobae"* **adult** From Koroba near Lanke Kopiago. Tawny breast and flanks.

28m   *L. s. "guariae"* **adult** From Guari in the Prince Edward Albert Mountains. Distinguished by the dark brown nape.

28n   *L. s. "guariae"* **adult** This variant has dark brown barring on the sides of the breast and flanks.

28a   28b   28c   28d

28e   28f   28g   28h

28i   28j   28k   28l

28m   28n

PLATE 14: AUSTRALASIAN MANNIKINS III

34 **Black Mannikin** *Lonchura stygia* **Text and map page 167**

See also Measured Drawing on plate 75.

34a *L. stygia* **juvenile** From south-central New Guinea.

34b *L. stygia* **adult female** Slightly browner with black edges to the brown feathers on the head and mantle. Yellow uppertail-coverts not so bright.

34c *L. stygia* **adult male** Rump and uppertail-coverts tend to be brighter and more extensive. First-year males are much like females.

27 **Grey-crowned Mannikin** *Lonchura nevermanni* **Text and map page 149**

See also Measured Drawing on plate 68.

27a/b *L. nevermanni* **juveniles** Showing typical variation within the species.

27c *L. nevermanni* **first-year female** Underparts duller and may be edged with paler scalloping on the mantle.

27d *L. nevermanni* **first-year male** Cleaner forehead.

27e–h *L. nevermanni* **adult females** Showing the range of variation. The deeper-coloured rump with the black marks could also occur on a male. In general, the white on top of the head ends at the crown.

27i–k *L. nevermanni* **adult males** Showing range of variation possible. In general, the white on the head extends past the crown. The black spots on the breast of 27k could also occur on a female.

27l *L. nevermanni* **adult male** Showing melanism. As demonstrated by this plate, the species has a propensity to show black feathers on areas that are normally cinnamon or orange. In my experience only males exhibit this amount of black, but females could well do so.

34a   34b   34c

27a   27b   27c   27d

27e   27f   27g   27h

27i   27j   27k   27l

PLATE 15: NEW GUINEA MANNIKINS

37 Alpine Mannikin *Lonchura monticola*   Text and map page 173

37a   *L. m. monticola* **juvenile** Fine striations on chin and throat, warm rump and uppertail-coverts.

37b   *L. m. monticola* **adult** From the Wharton Range in Papua New Guinea. Brownish suffusion on breast and yellow tinge to belly.

37c   *L. m. myolae* **adult** From the Owen Stanley Range. White breast and belly with richer yellow on rump and uppertail-coverts.

36 Snow Mountain Mannikin *Lonchura montana*   Text and map page 172

36a   *L. m. montana* **juvenile** From the Snow Mountains in Irian Jaya, extending to western Papua New Guinea. Warm flush on breast and light barring on undertail-coverts.

36b   *L. m. montana* **adult female** Clean division between throat and breast, black of forehead ends mid-crown.

36c   *L. m. montana* **adult male** The black edging of the throat is slightly diffused and the black of the forehead ends at the rear-crown.

35 Black-breasted Mannikin *Lonchura teerinki*   Text and map page 169

See also Measured Drawing on plate 76.

35a/b *L. t. teerinki* **juveniles** Showing variation in age, the bird on the right being older. From Grand Valley and the northern slopes of Mt. Wilhelmina in the Orange Mountains, Irian Jaya.

35c/d *L. t. teerinki* **first-year adults** Showing degrees of plumage variation, regardless of sex.

35e   *L. t. teerinki* **adult female (second-year)** Broken line of brown and black along the flanks typical of the older female.

35f   *L. t. teerinki* **adult male (second-year)** Continual line of black along the flanks. Note also the amount of tan on the sides of the breast.

35g   *L. t. mariae* **adult male** From Bokidini, north of the Baliem Valley, Irian Jaya. Darker, more earth-brown back.

37a   37b   37c

36a   36b   36c

35a   35b   35c   35d

35e   35f   35g

PLATE 16: ASIAN AND AUSTRALIAN MUNIAS

13 Hill Munia *Lonchura kelaarti*   **Text and map page 94**

> **13a**   *L. k. kelaarti* **juvenile** From Sri Lanka. Richly coloured breast, uniform colour from mantle to uppertail-coverts.
>
> **13b**   *L. k. kelaarti* **adult female** Less well-defined breast markings, more white flecking on rump.
>
> **13c**   *L. k. kelaarti* **adult male** Striations absent from rear crown.
>
> **13d**   *L. k. vernayi* **adult** From the Eastern Ghats in Andhra Pradesh. Pinkish-cinnamon breast, cinnamon short uppertail-coverts.
>
> **13e**   *L. k. jerdoni* **juvenile** From southwestern India. Paler uppertail-coverts.
>
> **13f**   *L. k. jerdoni* **adult** Striations on breast and upper flanks.

39 Pictorella Mannikin *Lonchura pectoralis*   **Text and map page 175**

> **39a**   *L. pectoralis* **adult male** From northern Australia. Almost clear white breast.
>
> **39b**   *L. pectoralis* **adult female** Distinguished by the black crescents on the white breast.

41 Timor Sparrow *Lonchura fuscata*   **Text and map page 182**

See also Measured Drawings on plates 79–80.

> **41a**   *L. fuscata* **juvenile** Drab, but bulkier than other munias with larger bill and dark lores.
>
> **41b**   *L. fuscata* **adult** Unmistakable, bold plumage.

40 Java Sparrow *Lonchura oryzivora*   **Text and map page 177**

See also Measured Drawings on plates 77–78.

> **40a**   *L. oryzivora* **juvenile**
>
> **40b**   *L. oryzivora* **adult male** In breeding condition showing swollen and increased redness of the eyelids and base of the mandibles. Adult female in breeding condition does not have the base of the mandibles and the eyelids so swollen or as red.

13a 13b 13c 13d

13e 13f 39a 39b

41a 41b

40a 40b

SYSTEMATIC
SECTION

1 MADAGASCAR MANNIKIN
Lonchura nana   Plate 1

Described as *Lonchura nana* Pucheran.
Former scientific names: *Pyrrhula nana*, Pucheran, 1845, Rev. Zool. (Paris), 8, p.52. *Lepidopygia nana*, Reichenbach, 1862 - 63. *Lemuresthes nana. Spermestes nana, Munia nana.*
Other common names: Dwarf Mannikin, Madagascar Munia, African Parson Finch, Bib Finch.

Madagascar Mannikin.

FIELD CHARACTERS One of the smallest of the mannikins, a compact brownish-grey bird, with a blackish bib and a short dark tail. It is the only estrildid to be found on Madagascar and is unlikely to be confused with any other species. It is possible that the juvenile could be confused with a juvenile Bronze Mannikin, or vice versa, on the island of Mayotte but probable that either would be identifiable by association with adults.

STATUS Common, or locally common.

HABITAT This little munia is found in a variety of habitats but is essentially a bird of arid scrub. It is found in grassland where there is scattered scrub cover, or palm trees, edges of forests and in forest clearings, from high plateau prairies to cultivated areas, including rice paddies and villages, from eucalyptus forests to marshes. It occurs from sea level to above 2,000m.

HABITS AND BEHAVIOUR Madagascar Mannikins are gregarious, flocking at all times of the year in groups of from a few up to about 50. These may be family groups, which may include members of all the broods in the season. They keep together when they fly and perch closely together when they alight in a tree or bush.They have also been observed in mixed species flocks.

FOOD AND FEEDING It feeds on seeds of growing plants such as retops *Rhychelytrum*, wild millets, and other sedges and grasses. It also freely feeds upon the ground. It probably takes some insect food, based on avicultural experience, but is apparently more opportunist than particular in its feeding habits.

MOVEMENTS It is both resident and sedentary.

CALL The voice has not been adequately described and I regret not recording it in detail in my own birds. The contact note is a soft *zit* or a louder *zitsy*. Also given as a soft *pit* and a metallic *pitsri* (Clement *et al.* 1993)

SONG The song is performed in an upright position but without any noticeable feather erection. It is a short burbling *whirr*, repeated several times and usually followed by some chasing of the (intended) female.

COURTSHIP AND DISPLAY In courtship the male holds a length of grass, fibre or other nesting material in his bill and performs a bobbing dance, caused by alternately stretching and bending his legs. I have not seen this so vigorously that the bird actually jumps off the perch. The song is uttered during this effort. A responsive female will crouch and solicit with quivering tail. If copulation occurs it is followed by bill fencing and usually allopreening.

Madagascar Mannikin in high intensity song.

BREEDING In breeding it is opportunistic, building in any suitable vegetation from a shrub at 1m off the ground to as high as 5m up in a palm. It will occupy and refurbish the nest of the local weavers (e.g. Madagascar Fody *Foudia madagascarensis*), narrowing the entrance and building a porch over it. One nest described in detail by Rand (1936) was a well-built structure made entirely of grasses and lined with chicken feathers; another was lined with plant down, and another with palm fibres.

The nest is an oval structure with the entrance at one end, with a projecting porch. Rand (1936) describes one as looking like a flask lying on its side. It was placed on a horizontal palm leaf supported by leaflets on each side, and was made largely of the thread-like fibres from palm leaves. Another was described as being oval with a porch roof over the entrance made from a few dead grass blades but mostly dead grass heads very finely put together. The floor cavity was lined with hen feathers. It measured 110mm tall and 140mm deep (from entrance to the back). The entrance measured just 35mm, and the walls were 20mm thick. Another nest was lined with cotton.

Two–eight eggs form the clutch, although 5 seems to be the common number. Both sexes incubate and sleep together in the nest at night. Incubation, as recorded in domestic birds, is 11 or 12 days, and the nestling period is 24–31 days. The fledglings are dependant upon their parents for the following 10 days or so before becoming self-feeding.

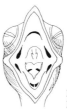

Palate markings of nestling Madagascar Mannikin.

DISTRIBUTION Madagascar and the island of Mayotte in the Comoros. It is widely distributed and common or local in the north of Madagascar, but local to scarce south of Tulear and the south-east (Dee 1986).

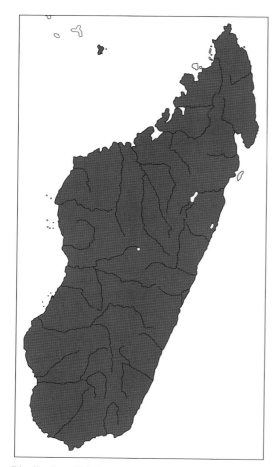

Distribution of Madagascar Mannikin.

DESCRIPTION   Plate 17
Monotypic.

Adult 87–92mm (one exceptional male measured 98mm).
Wing length 45–47mm, culmen 8–9mm, tarsus 11mm. It
is grey on top of the head, palest on the forehead, with
the centres of the feathers darker, giving a faintly scaled
appearance. The nape, mantle, back and wings are brownish-grey, including the tertials and leading edges of the
secondaries; otherwise the primaries and secondaries are
brownish-black. The rump is ochreous barred with yellowish edges and the uppertail-coverts are yellowish. This
is variable and is never striking. It is described by some
writers as being olivaceous. The tail is brownish-black,
short but graduated. The lores, bib and throat are black
and the bib has a purple sheen in fit birds. The mesial is
pale creamy-grey and the ear-coverts grey. The underwing-
coverts are pale buffy-grey. The underparts are light brown
with a pinkish wash, slightly vermiculated and barred. The
undertail-coverts are barred fawn and brown. The bill is
conical; the upper mandible is black, the lower is pink to
reddish, particularly on some old males. The legs and feet
are pink to flesh. I have been quite unable to establish
any distinction between the sexes.
Juvenile Drab brown above, slightly paler below. It is a
warmer colour than the adult. The upper mandible is

blackish, the lower is pinkish or whitish. The olive of the
rump does not appear until the bird is 6 months old, and
full adult plumage is not acquired until the second year.

In some dozen or so juveniles of domestic birds I have
examined, they were darker than wild birds, and showed
a distinct tendency to melanism. Of some 22 domestic-
bred adults examined, they too were all darker and greyer
than wild birds. They also lacked the pink or reddish tinge
to the lower mandible. In these birds the yellow barring
of the rump showed before any olive or ochreous ground
colour. Neville Brickell in South Africa (pers comm.) examined some 40 birds and found only 10% of them to
have any pink on the lower mandible, and these were
young birds. These birds were found to all be domestic in
origin, originally imported from The Netherlands.

HYBRIDS Nothing recorded in the wild. It has cross-bred
several times in captivity, four or five times with Bronze
Mannikin, and also with Indian Silverbill *L. malabarica*,
Scaly-breasted Munia *L. punctulata*, White-rumped Munia
L. striata and the Bengalese (Gray 1958).

CONSERVATION Apparently there is no cause for concern. There is no trade in wild birds from Madagascar.

REFERENCES Clement *et al.* (1994), Dee (1986), Gray
(1958), Rand (1936).

2   AFRICAN SILVERBILL
Lonchura cantans   Plate 1

Described as *Lonchura cantans* Gmelin.
Other common names: Silverbill, Warbling Silverbill,
Black-rumped Silverbill.

African Silverbill

TAXONOMY Most early literature treats African Silverbill
Lonchura cantans and Indian Silverbill *L. malabarica* as
being conspecific and Delacour (1943) firmly made them
synonymous in his revision of the Estrildinae. Harrison
(1964) first studied the two in a strictly comparative manner and concluded they were two good species. He showed
that while the call notes were similar the songs are distinctly different in form, although they appear to share a
common basic pattern. The two silverbills are sympatric
in the south of the Arabian Peninsula and there is no
record of natural hybridisation, and from personal observations of birds in captivity each of the two forms evince
preference for its own kind. Kakizawa and Watada (1985)
confirmed Harrison's conclusion in their study of genetic
distances by means of protein electrophoresis, and Sibley
and Monroe (1990) accept the two as distinct species.

FIELD CHARACTERS It is a sandy, light brown bird lightly
speckled on the head, barred on the body, with partially
black wings, black rump, somewhat longish pointed tail,

and with a pale silver-blue bill. All other estrildid finches that it might be confused with in the field have red or black bills. In the limited area of the Arabian peninsula where it overlaps with Indian Silverbill, the latter is readily identified by its white rump and uppertail-coverts and whitish ear-coverts. At a distance it might appear similar to Pale Rock Sparrow *Petronia brachydactyla* but this slightly larger bird has white spots on the tips of the tail feathers that are obvious when the bird takes flight.

STATUS Locally common.

HABITAT This is a widespread species of savanna country, arid landscape with thorn bush, or more grassy land with acacias, or simple scrub with sparse grass. It may also be found in cultivated areas and watered grassland and will settle in the vicinity of homesteads and gardens. It is by nature a bird of dry country and can be found far into desert country. It breeds in Atar, Mauritania (Etchécopar and Hüe 1967) which is very dry and arid. It is primarily a lowland species but may be found up to 2,000m.

HABITS AND BEHAVIOUR Mackworth-Praed and Grant (1960) describe it as common, tame and sociable, perching in trees in dense flocks, the birds almost touching one another, "... being not particularly active birds... and sitting huddled together for long periods." It is described in Cramp (1994) as being sociable but secretive, hiding in tall grass and thorn scrub.

It stays in flocks all the year round and usually breeds in a loose colony. The population of the communal roosts increases at the end of the breeding season.

FOOD AND FEEDING It feeds largely on grass seeds, mostly picked from the ground but also taken from the growing plants if easily available. It will cling to grass stems to take seeds from the inflorescences and will also take seeds from weeds and small shrubs. It seems that it feeds exclusively on vegetable matter, rearing its young on seed and green food, but there is a record of it taking aphids from water mint (Meinertzhagen 1954) and Gallagher and Woodcock (1980) say it also takes invertebrates. Birds bred in captivity invariably reared their young on a totally vegetarian diet despite there being a variety of invertebrates available.

MOVEMENTS Irregular and seasonal (Gallagher and Woodcock 1980), and chiefly sedentary (Cramp 1994). When conditions are favourable silverbills are sedentary. Small flocks of juveniles wander. The onset of rains prompts migration to drier areas.

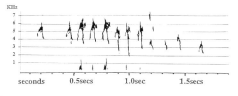
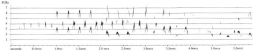

Above, part of the song, after Guttinger (1970). Below, sonogram of the complete song of African Silverbill (Courtesy of Dr. Luis Baptista).

CALL The call note is a clear *tseep*! and other contact notes have been recorded, including a harsh *tchwit*! (Clement *et al.* 1993). The contact call of the male is a single *tseep* or *pseet*, while that of the female is a double-noted *tsiptsip*. Birds in flight keep up a constant *tseep tseep tseep*.

SONG The species has been called the Warbling Silverbill on account of its song which is a rising then falling cadence of rapidly repeated notes forming a sweet trill that is repeated often, with noticeable variation from male to male. It sounds quite different from the song of the Indian Silverbill.

African Silverbill displaying to female. On the left the head-jerk display while holding a straw. On the right the inverted curtsey display with the tail twisted towards the female. (After Baptista and Horblit 1990).

COURTSHIP AND DISPLAY All five component parts of the full straw display may be performed by African Silverbill. These are described in detail by Baptista and Horblit (1990). They are, in sequence, grasping a straw or similar length of grass or fibre, an upward jerking movement of the head, twisting of the tail towards the female, the inverted curtsey (Morris 1958) and the song.

The male displays by grasping a stem of grass at one end, and hops or flies to be near the female. At once he sleeks down his feathers, stands rather upright with tail straight down, and jerks his head upwards a few times. He then leans forward, twists his tail somewhat towards the female and fluffs his flank and belly feathers. At this stage he usually drops the straw and begins to 'sing and dance' with a bobbing curtsey. The flank and ventral feathers are not always fluffed out, and the intensity of the display probably depends on the relationship of the two birds, for example, opportunistic display to a known bird mated to another is less likely to contain full feather erection. The neck is stretched and slightly puffed, and the legs bend and stretch as the bird continues singing. If the female seems receptive the male will attempt copulation. However, most displays come to an end before this final phase is reached. Successful mating is usually followed by a little bill fencing and mutual preening.

Male African Silverbill singing to female. The male is twisted slightly in the direction of the female with tail twisted towards her.

The male will also display in undirected advertisement song, or to an unpaired or lone female to which it is attracted. In this event he usually begins with a side to side twisting movement of the body, the body is slightly stretched and the flanks are only slightly slightly fluffed, if at all. He may hold a straw or is as likely to sing and sway, curtsey or twist without this preliminary.

BREEDING The nest is usually built as a structure in its own right, in the form of a roundish bundle of grasses, soft pliable plant stems and the inflorescences of grasses, with a side entrance. It is lined with soft fibres and sometimes feathers, and may be placed in a thick bush or hedge or amongst the creepers on houses (Rutgers and Norris 1980). African Silverbills will opportunistically adopt the used or deserted nest of a weaver or take posession of a similar structure. It regularly uses old weavers nests in Oman (Gallagher and Woodcock 1980). Archer and Goodman (1961) mention that in northern Nigeria they often nest in the eaves of houses like sparrows, but can be found right out in the bush as well. Archer also reports taking a nest that was made of the fine points of grass in seed, and built in a bush 1.2m from the ground. Another nest was likewise composed of the upper stems of seeding grass about 37cm long, with a bedding "of multitudinous white flake-like seeds and a few white feathers." Buxton (in Bannerman 1949) describes observing the building of a nest in the rolled edge of one of the large mats hung round the house as protection from the sun. In captivity African Silverbills show a marked preference for boxes or baskets to making their own nest from scratch.

The male is recorded in the wild as collecting all the nesting material (Meinertzhagen 1954), the female only sharing in the construction. This is certainly the case in captive birds, but it is not a guarantee of sex. I have observed on three separate occasions a known female in captivity carrying grass when she would fly to the male she was paired to. She did not perform any display, but dropped the grass quite soon.

The clutch varies from 3–6 oval, smooth white eggs, but 5 seems to be the usual number. Up to 12 eggs have been recorded in a nest (Goodwin 1982) but these are almost certainly the product of two or more females. The female incubates during the day, and though the male may relieve her when she leaves the nest to feed, it has been suggested he does not actually brood (Soderberg 1956). They are both in the nest at night. The incubation period is 11–13 days, with the young fledging in about 21 days and becoming independent within a month of fledging. Newly hatched young are dark and have waxy-looking yellow gape swellings. The palate has a single heavy black circle, just inside the white mouth-flange which embraces the upper and lower parts of the gape.

Palate markings of recently hatched African Silverbill.

DISTRIBUTION It is a mainly African species. The race *L. c. cantans* ranges from Senegal and Mauritania on the west coast across Africa south of the Sahara where it reaches 17° N in Mali (Clement *et al.* 1993) to the Central African Republic and Uganda. It has occurred in Algeria (Hall, in Cramp 1994), but this is taken to be an accidental. The 'red-rumped' race *L. c. inornata* occurs in a small wedge from south of Khartoum to Berber in Sudan eastwards to the Red Sea. The Arabian form, *L. c. orientalis*, extends into East Africa to Kenya, where it is scarce and into north-western Tanzania. Eastwards it reaches Oman in the Arabian peninsula, where it is a common breeding bird around Dhofar and overlaps with Indian Silverbill.

The African Silverbill has been introduced to the Hawaiian Islands from Kauai to Maui. It has also been introduced into Puerto Rico, where it is breeding in sufficient numbers as to be the source of supply of the species for the bird trade in the United States. It is apparently breeding on Merrit Island, off the eastern coast of Florida, USA, although recent reports indicate that its status there is now uncertain.

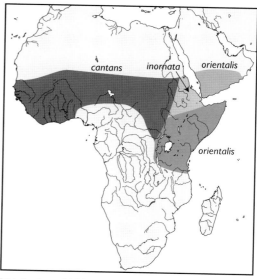

Distribution of African Silverbill

DESCRIPTION   **Plate 18**
There are three subspecies. The West African Silverbill is a light sandy above with soft barring on the upper parts, the East African Silverbill is noticeably darker above, with darker barring. The Arabian Silverbill is very similar to the West African race, although it tends to be a little darker, and has a distinct propensity to show red in the fuscous of the uppertail-coverts.

WEST AFRICAN SILVERBILL
Lonchura cantans cantans
Former scientific names: *Loxia cantans,* Gmelin, 1789, syst. Nat., 1 (2), p. 859. *Euodice cantans, Uroloncha cantans.*
Adult male 114–115mm. Wing length 53–54mm, culmen 10–11mm, tarsus 11–12mm. Light sandy brown above with darker centres to the feathers on forehead and crown and paler edges, giving a somewhat speckled appearance to the head. On the nape the browner centres become bars and the entire upperparts are finely barred, most noticeably on the wing-coverts, secondaries and lower back. The primary coverts, outer greater coverts and primaries are blackish,

browner on the inner webs. The underwing-coverts are buff. The rump, uppertail-coverts and tail, which is graduated with the central tail feathers longer and slightly pointed, are black. The face and throat are also light sandy brown but less noticeably speckled, buffish on the breast and flanks, faintly barred, buffish to white on the belly and undertail-coverts. The bill is a silvery bluish-grey, almost silvery-pink in some birds, the eyelids are similarly coloured. The legs and feet are mauve-grey or mauve-pink.

Adult female 109–113mm. Wing length *c*.53mm, culmen 9.5–10mm, tarsus 10–11mm. It is similar to the male but has the central tail feathers slightly broader and rounded at the tips.

ARABIAN SILVERBILL
L. cantans inornata
Former scientific name: *Aidemosyne inornata* Mearns 1913, Smiths. Misc. Coll., 61 (14), p.3.
This race was dropped by both Mackworth-Praed and Grant (1955) and Goodwin (1982). However, in view of the propensity to show red on the tail and uppertail-coverts it is worth describing here. It is similar to *L. c. cantans* but has the uppertail-coverts darker brown to fuscous. Individuals show a variable amount of dark reddish on the edges of the uppertail-coverts and edgings to the tail. There is no information on any differences between the sexes.

EAST AFRICAN SILVERBILL
L. cantans orientalis
Former scientific names: *Aidemosyne orientalis* Lorenz and Hellmayr, 1901, *Ornith. Monatsb.*, 9, p.39. *Aidemosyne cantans meridionalis* Mearns, 1913. *Aidemosyne cantans tavetensis* van Someren, 1921.
This race is the same size as *L. c. cantans* but it is darker and much more noticeably barred on the upperparts. From the rump to tail it is fuscous, appearing almost black. The sexes are alike but for the same differences in tail measurements that are recorded for *L. c. cantans.*

Juveniles of all three races are like the adults, but are noticeably softer and warmer in colouring above, lacking the barring of the adult. They are less spotted on the head and have a light barring on the chin, compared to faint spotting in the adult.

The bill is dark on fledging but gradually lightens over the first few weeks and the dark wavy barring of the adult plumage begins to appear.

Charles Fleming of Exeter (*in litt.* and pers. comm.) bred the species in captivity for several years, having bred well over 200 birds at the time we talked (1988). I am grateful to him for a series of measurements of central tail feathers. He has established that the central rectrices of the adult male are invariably narrower and pointed compared to those of the female which are broader and more rounded. Colin Rowe (*in litt.*) also studied the tail measurements of his birds and found the same sexual distinction. This difference can also be seen in young birds which have buffish edges to these feathers. Abrahams (in Butler 1899) said that the "first long feathers" of the wings in the male are almost black, while the hen's are more grey.

I first noticed the presence of red in the uppertail-coverts and tail feathers of this species when I was once presented with a dead pair for painting. The red was not exactly outstanding and is certain to be overlooked in an active, living bird. Goodwin (1982) mentions a specimen of *L. cantans* from Oman which shows pink feathers on the edges of the rump feathers. I aquired two live male birds with the same characteristics from Michael Plose in England, but I was unable to breed from them. Steiner (1966) mentions the propensity of the species to show red in the rump and Rutgers and Norris (1980) say it is possible to produce the race by cross-breeding African Silverbill with Indian Silverbill, which also conceals red in the black edgings to the uppertail-coverts. Fleming found quite a few to have red or chestnut red on the edges of the tail and uppertail-coverts of his birds, but could not say from where these birds, or their parents, had originated.

HYBRIDS I am not aware of any hybrids occurring in the wild but the list of estrildid finches it has cross-bred with in captivity is significant. Gray (1958) lists the following munias: Black-and-White Mannikin *L. bicolor*, Bronze Mannikin *L. cucullata*, Magpie Mannikin *L. fringilloides*, Indian Silverbill, White-headed Munia *L. maja*, Chestnut-breasted Mannkin *L. castaneothorax*, and the Bengalese. Among other estrildids he lists Pin-tailed Parrotfinch *Erythrura prasina*, Red Avadavat *Estrilda amandava*, Common Waxbill *E. astrild*, Orange-breasted Waxbill *E. subflava*, Black-rumped Waxbill *E. troglodytes* and Red-browed Firetail *Aegintha temporalis*.

CONSERVATION African Silverbills are regularly trapped for the cage bird trade, but the quantities apparently caught from local areas of its considerable range seem unlikely to have any impact on the species' survival.

REFERENCES Archer & Godman (1961), Bannerman (1949), Baptista & Horblit (1990), Butler (1899), Cramp (1994), Clement *et al.* (1993), Etchécopar & Hüe (1967), Gallagher & Woodcock (1980), Goodwin (1982), Gray (1958), Harrison (1964), Kakizawa & Watada (1985), Mackworth-Praed & Grant (1960), Meinertzhagen (1954), Rutgers & Norris (1980), Sibley & Monroe (1990), Soderberg (1956), Steiner (1966).

---

3 INDIAN SILVERBILL
Lonchura malabarica   Plate 1

Described as *Lonchura malabarica* Linnaeus.
Former scientific names: *Loxia malabarica*, 1758, *Syst. Nat.*, ed. 10,1, p.175. *Euodice malabrica*, Reichenbach, 1862-3.

Other common names: Silverbill, Common Silverbill, White-rumped Munia, White-rumped Silverbill, White-throated Munia (Sri Lanka).

Indian Silverbill

TAXONOMY The taxonomic status of Indian Silverbill was unclear, and it was regarded as synonymous with the African Silverbill *L. cantans* by Delacour (1943). Harrison (1964) described *L. malabarica* and *L. cantans* as distinct species with careful comparative studies that serve as a good example for similar cases. Kakizawa and Watada (1985) confirmed Harrison's conclusion by the use of electrophoresis techniques and Sibley and Monroe (1990) accept the two as good species.

Steiner (1966), Rutgers and Norris (1977) and Goodwin (1982) all mention the propensity of the species to produce pink or red from the black of the uppertail-coverts. This characteristic is shared with the African Silverbill.

FIELD CHARACTERS This is a small to medium-sized munia. It is drab brown above with partly black wings, white rump and black tail, white below from chin to undertail. It is unlikely to be confused with other species in its habitat. In Arabia it can be separated from the African Silverbill by its white rump and this difference holds for juveniles as well. The white rump is also the obvious distinction from Pale Rock Sparrow *Petronia brachydactyla* and Trumpeter Finch *Bucanetes githagineus* if either are seen fleetingly at a distance. In India it might be confused with juvenile White-rumped Munia *L. striata*, but this latter species is significantly darker if the two can be compared.

STATUS Common or locally common, or scarce (Sri Lanka).

HABITAT It is a bird of open country, semi-desert, arid scrub, open dry woodland, cultivated areas and farm settlements and villages. While it is a bird of towns, villages and gardens in India, it is a bird of open country in Sri Lanka.

HABITS AND BEHAVIOUR Whistler (1928) described it as one of the dullest of the Indian birds "... it has no migrations, no changes of plumage, no habits of interest, and in its breeding arrangements it has some of the failings that one generally expects to find amongst domesticated birds." In contrast Roberts (1992) says "it exhibits many fascinating traits unusual in small passerines." It is a highly sociable species. Clumping and allopreening occur. It gathers in groups or flocks in trees before roosting, and will roost socially. When not breeding, several birds will roost together in one nest. Like the White-rumped Munia it has a longish tail that is full and wedge-shaped when expanded, and indulges in much side-to-side tail-flicking.

FOOD AND FEEDING It feeds most usually on the ground, taking fallen seeds from grasses and weeds, but regularly takes seed from growing grasses, millets and sedges, etc. It has been recorded as taking rice and cultivated millet when available (Henry 1955). Whistler records it feeding on the heads of pampas grass, millet and dari and Roberts records it feeding on the male flowers of maize. They have also been recorded as taking some insects, "ants, beetles and other small insects" (Ali and Ripley 1974, and Roberts 1992), and Salim Ali notes them occasionally feeding on the nectar of the Coral Tree *Erythrina*. Mason and Le Froy (1912) examined the stomach contents of eleven specimens and found that nine had been feeding only on small unidentified seeds, presumably of grasses and weeds although one was identified as rice. Of the other two, one had consumed an insect in addition to seeds and the other a batch of insect eggs.

Phillips (1948) records it as being frequently associated with the Ashy-crowned Finch-Lark *Eremopterix grisea ceylonensis* in Sri Lanka, where it feeds mainly on grass seeds in arid sandy pastures around lagoons and in dry paddyfields.

MOVEMENTS Both irregular and seasonal. It is a migrant in northern Pakistan.

CALL The loud contact call is a complex *tchrip*! or *tchreep*! similar in structure in both sexes, but usually a tone higher in the female (although I have heard it sounding almost identical), and often more complex in the male. Flight contact calls are a rapid high-pitched, much repeated *chirrup*! sounding like *zip*! in flight. There is a soft alarm note *tchek*! and a more harsh *tch wit*!, and an excited *trititit*. I have recorded a soft twittering conversation between birds in a social situation, described as *seesip seesip* by Gallagher and Woodcock (1980), but sounding more like a multiple soft *tsheep tsheep* to my ear.

SONG The song is described as a short trill (Gallagher and Woodcock 1980). It is quite distinct from that of the African Silverbill being a series of shorter and apparently tuneless, abrupt phrases. Harrison (1964) points out that spectrograph analysis shows each burst to be a short song with repeated notes, slurred notes and a terminal phrase.

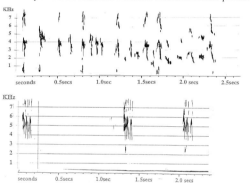

Drawings made from sound spectrographs of vocalisations of the Indian Silverbill. Above, song after Guttinger (1970). Below, call notes of male.

COURTSHIP AND DISPLAY In simple advertisement song the male will perch across a branch or stem singing while facing forward in a fairly upright position.

Breeding behaviour, as with most *Lonchura*, is triggered by the onset of the rainy season. In low intensity display the male will stretch upright and sing with little movement, but will twist towards the female. He displays by holding a length of nest-building material by one end, perching nearby or alongside the female, bobbing up and down by stretching and bending the legs in the inverted curtsey, jerking the head up thereby moving the straw. He will drop the grass and twist from side to side edging close and bowing before attempting copulation.

An unpaired female in breeding condition may take a stem of grass to a male, but will not normally display, although she might well perform a head jerk or shortened version of the curtsey. She may even solicit copulation. A female in the collection of Baptista (Baptista and Horblit 1990) regularly performed both the head jerk and the straw display, but without any song. She ceased displaying once paired to a male.

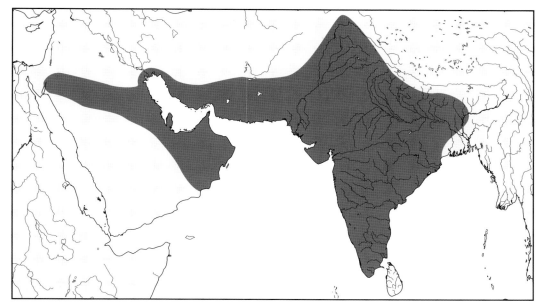

Distribution of Indian Silverbill

BREEDING The nest is an irregular to somewhat ovoid sphere, depending on the location. It is usually made of straws and grasses with the entrance hole at one end. Fine grasses, fibres and sometimes feathers are used as lining. The nest is built largely by the female with the male bringing material to the site.

Nests have been found low in thorn bushes, in trees up to 3 metres from the ground, in holes and among the sticks and rough base structures of the nests of birds of prey. Baker (1934) refers to Silverbill nests in the foundations of eagles and Scavenger Vulture nests. Henry (1955) found in Sri Lanka that the usual site for the nest was the crown of a Screw Pine, where he deemed it fairly safe from most marauders because of the spiny leaves. The natural nest in Pakistan is often built in a bare thorny bush, patently obvious to any passer-by (Roberts 1992).

Probably the most favoured site is a second-hand weaver's nest. In India, according to Whistler (1928), Silverbills are usually to be found using old weaver nests to breed in. In Pakistan, Roberts (1992) describes birds flying into and inspecting occupied nests of both Baya Weaver *Ploceus philippinus* and Streaked Weavers *P. manyar*, looking for a nest to take over, but he says they normally build their own nests.

The clutch varies from 3–8, oval white eggs. Whistler says he found 22 eggs in one nest with a record of 25. Theobald (in Butler 1899) found two pairs building and sharing the same nest, but Burgess (in Butler 1899) says he never found more than 6 eggs in a clutch. The newly-hatched young are black, and remain silent in the nest until the parents cease to brood them, usually around 10 days. Both parents brood the eggs and the precocial young. The nestlings fledge in around 19 days and are feeding themselves within the week. It is a prolific breeder producing up to 4 broods in a season. The nestlings are fed on seeds and other plant matter, and also ants, beetles and other insects (Ali and Ripley 1987). In captivity it has bred successfully on an all-seed and lettuce diet (Restall 1975).

DISTRIBUTION This species ranges from the eastern province of Saudi Arabia, the United Arab Emirates and Oman, southern Baluchistan, Pakistan and Nepal across the Indian subcontinent to eastern Bengal and southwards to the dry zone of Sri Lanka. It ranges altitudinally from sea level up to at least 2,000m. Baker (1934) describes it as the most widespread of all munias (in India). Its range is spreading westwards and it has been found breeding in some of the desert oases as far as Eilat in Israel and has been recorded in Jordan (Clement *et al.* 1993). It is quintessentially a bird of dry, arid and barren country and as such is a great wanderer. In northern Pakistan it is a breeding migrant (Roberts 1992).

DESCRIPTION   **Plate 19**
Monotypic.

Adult male 113–116mm. Wing length 53–54mm, culmen 9.5–12mm, tarsus 10–11mm. Drab brown without any speckles or bars from forehead to upper rump, with some fine barring on the lower back that quickly becomes white on the lower rump. The central uppertail-coverts and the inner webs of the long uppertail-coverts are white, the outer webs and tail feathers are black. There is sometimes a touch of dark pink or reddish in the edges of the black of the uppertail-coverts. The central rectrices are longer and more pointed than the rest of the tail. There is a narrow stripe above the eye, whitish to buff. The face, throat and entire underparts are whitish with some fine barring on the flanks. The supercilium of the male is whiter and stronger, and the barring on the flanks is usually bolder than on the female. Sometimes the base of the lower mandible of the male is pale blue. The male usually has a larger or broader head than the female. The bill is pale slate-blue or pale grey. The legs and feet vary from vinous to pale grey-brown.

Adult female 109–114mm. Wing length 52–53mm, culmen 9.5–10.5mm, tarsus 10–11mm. Resembles the male but has the white of the supercilium a little less clear, and the flanks are less barred. The differences are clear when birds of similar age and known sex are compared, but it is not easy to tell the sex of a single bird.

Juvenile Only slightly softer and paler in colouring, being a little creamier below. It has the rump and uppertail-coverts mottled with brown. The central rectrices are shorter and slightly rounded.

HYBRIDS No hybrids have been recorded in the wild, but in captivity it has often been cross-bred with the African Silverbill. The resulting hybrids are fertile and the feathers of the rump have reddish edges. The species has hybridised with many other munias including African Silverbill, Bronze Mannikin *L. cucullata*, Chestnut Munia *L. atricapilla*, and Chestnut-breasted Mannikin *L. castaneothorax*. Among other estrildid finches it has cross-bred with are included Cut-throat *Amadina amadina*, Long-tailed Grassfinch *Poephila acuticauda* and Zebra Finch *P. guttata castanotis*.

CONSERVATION No apparent cause for concern in India and to the west; indeed the species is actively increasing its range, having reached Israel. There is cause for attention in Sri Lanka, where it appears to be becoming scarcer. There is little or no trade in birds on the island, and certainly not enough to have any impact on the silverbill population. The cause for the decline in Sri Lanka is unknown.

REFERENCES Ali & Ripley (1987), Baker (1934), Baptista & Horblit (1990), Butler (1899), Clement *et al.* (1993), Delacour (1943), Gallagher & Woodcock (1980), Goodwin (1982), Gray (1958), Harrison (1964), Henry (1955), Kakizawa & Watada (1985), Mason & Le Froy (1912), Phillips (1948), Restall (1975), Roberts (1992), Rutgers & Norris (1977), Sibley & Monroe (1990), Steiner (1966), Whistler (1928).

---

4 PEARL-HEADED MANNIKIN
Lonchura griseicapilla Plate 1

Described as *Lonchura griseicapilla* Delacour.
Other common names: Pearl-headed Silverbill, Grey-headed Silverbill, or Grey-headed Mannikin (inadvisable because of confusion with *Lonchura caniceps*). Baptista (1979) argues convincingly that this species is closer related to the African mannikins of the subgenus *Spermestes* and proposed that for this reason Pearl-headed Mannikin is a more appropriate common name.
Former scientific names: *Pytila caniceps*, Reichenow, 1879, *Ornith. Centralbl.*, 4, p.139. *Munia caniceps*, (incorrect, being preoccupied by *Munia caniceps* Salvadori, 1876, for the Grey-headed Silverbill) *Lonchura griseicapilla* Delacour, 1943, Zoologica (New York), 28, p.82.

Pearl-headed Mannikin.

FIELD CHARACTERS A stocky bird with a grey head studded with white dots, body warm greyish-brown, partly black wings and tail, white rump. It is unlikely to be confused with any other species. The juvenile can be readily told from the juvenile African Silverbill *L. cantans* by its white rump which is especially noticeable when the bird takes flight.

STATUS Locally common or uncommon.

HABITAT It is a bird of savanna, arid grassland, and open thorny scrub country and is never found far from water.

HABITS AND BEHAVIOUR It is gregarious, moving in small flocks and often mixing with African Silverbill. It roosts in old nests in captivity, several birds roosting together. Goodwin (1982) speculates that it may well do so in the wild as well. Koepff (1984) is adamant in stating that Pearl-headed Silverbills in captivity resist abitrary pairing, and will breed only rarely under such conditions. It is highly probable that pairs are formed while the birds are still in juvenile plumage.

FOOD AND FEEDING It feeds upon various seeds but so little has been published of the behaviour in the wild that nothing can be extrapolated with certainty from observations of behaviour in captivity. It is reasonable to say that it takes insects opportunistically, as it seems doubtful this food source is critical to its survival. It may be that insects are more a source of (incidentally nourishing) moisture than dry seeds. Birds in captivity readily feed insects to their nestlings.

MOVEMENTS When not breeding it wanders widely, influenced by weather and shifting availability of sources of water.

CALL The contact call is described as a high-pitched weak trill, the alarm a long drawn-out version of this note (Clement *et al.* 1993). Guttinger (1970) describes a contact call that is used both in flight and when feeding. When a large supply of food is discovered, a bird gives a quick series of these calls apparently to attract other Pearl-headed Mannikins to share it. Newly fledged young have a double-note call described by Langberg (1963) as *peed yee-eh*.

SONG The song is a long, gentle chirping uttered with the head stretched upwards, and the bill horizontal, opening and closing while singing. It begins softly and gradually gets louder.

Male Pearl-headed Mannikin at start of straw display.

COURTSHIP AND DISPLAY The courtship display was first described by Guttinger (1970) and is described and discussed in detail by Baptista (1979). The male, holding a length of straw by one end, will fly to the female and then drop the grass, twists head and tail towards the female and begins to sing. While singing he performs a bobbing leg-stretch or inverted curtsey dance. This display has not been observed to result in copulation, and Guttinger (1970) suggests its prime function is the formation of pair bonding and to synchronise mating activity. Copulation apparently only follows song and display if the female responds with a tail quivering display. There is a similar display referred to by Baptista (1979) as submissive courtship when the male sings leaning slightly away from the female, with the tongue protruding. In this behaviour the far-side wing may be flicked open and closed. Baptista also recorded this behaviour when a male sang at a male newcomer in this way.

Baptista notes that peering has not been observed in this mannikin. I came across a photograph (in *Cage and Aviary Birds* August 10, 1991) of a Pearl-headed Mannikin singing in undirected or advertisement display with a couple of other Pearl-headed Mannikins apparently peering. It shows that the feathers of the ear-coverts and mesials are erected to show the 'pearls' as part of the display. This is the only species of *Lonchura* to erect the facial feathers in display that I am aware of.

Male Pearl-headed Mannikin showing erection of mesial and lower face feathers, taken from a photograph of unknown origin. The bird appears to be singing but is probably soliciting allopreening (Luis Baptista pers. comm.).

BREEDING The only references to nests in the wild are of nests built in trees, when it is described as being a sphere of grasses and similar materials, lined with finer material including feathers. Scally (1967) found that a supply of feathers in the aviary stimulated the birds to complete nest building. Copulation has been observed both in the nest and outside. The white oval eggs number from 3–6 and hatch in 14 days. Both sexes take turns in brooding, and both share the nest at night. At changeover, the arriving bird calls to its mate inside the nest, entering only after hearing a reply (Kujawa, in Immelmann *et al.* 1968-72). The arriving male usually brings a small item of nest lining when he relieves the brooding female.

Newly hatched young are pink or dark flesh, have no papillae at the gape but have light blue gape-edging and the bill itself is pink. The palate markings are complex, and change slightly as the nestling grows (Baptista *in litt.*)

Nestlings and fledglings beg in the usual munia way by twisting the neck and pointing towards the feeding

Palate markings of nestling Grey-headed Mannikin. Left after Immelmann *et al.* (1968-72), right, courtesy of Dr Luis Baptista.

parent. This probably probably evolved as a function of breeding in a domed nest which obviously prevents the nestlings reaching straight up. They fledge in 24 - 35 days based on reports of breeding in captivity, seemingly an unusual length of time, and are independent in two weeks. Flicking or partial raising of the far-side wing by fledglings begging to be fed has been observed by both Guttinger and Baptista.

Langberg (1963) bred the species in Denmark. His birds fed quantities of mealworms to their nestlings, and also took germinated seeds, soft food, bread and milk and a vitamin supplement. On one occasion he watched while the cock took a beakful of fresh grit to the nest, apparently to feed the young. He says the young birds were fed "... for a considerably long time after leaving the nest." The newly fledged young appear to be quite precocious, young males were performing non-directed singing within two or three weeks of leaving the nest. The young males assumed the pearl spotting on the throat at 8 weeks from fledging. Koepff (1984) says they require live food to rear the young, and suggests ant pupae, mealworms and waxmoth larvae.

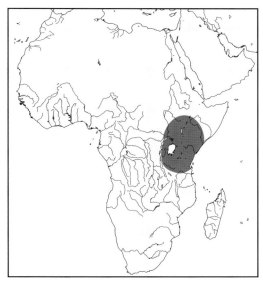

Distribution of Pearl-headed Mannikin.

DISTRIBUTION East Africa, from Southern Ethiopia around Lake Turkana and south-eastern Sudan, to the east and south-east of Lake Victoria, through Kenya and Burundi to northern Tanzania.

DESCRIPTION

Monotypic.

Adult male *c.*115mm. Wing length 58–62mm, culmen 10mm, tarsus 15mm. It has the entire head leaden-grey with the lores blackish, forehead and supercilium have pale grey spots whilst the feathers of the face and chin have white spots. There is a subterminal black spot or bar before each terminal white spot, thus giving each pale spot a 'shadow' or extra dimension which apparently inspired the use of the word 'pearl' in the common name. The back, mantle, scapulars and entire underparts are vinous-biscuit, whitest around the vent. The wing-coverts are pinkish-brown but the flight feathers and tail feathers are black, and the colour of the rump graduates quickly from straw to white. The upper mandible is dark grey, the lower silvery-grey. The legs and feet are dark grey.

Female *c.*110mm. Wing length 55–58mm, culmen 9mm, tarsus 13–15mm. The sexes are alike.

Juvenile Paler, more buffish version of the adult, lacking the white speckles on the head. The colour plate shows the distinction well and also shows that the juvenile cannot be confused with any other species.

I have been unable to detect any visual distinction between male and female, but have not had the opportunity of studying live birds in known pairs. Walther Langberg successfully bred them several times in Denmark during the 1960s and from his observations he became certain that males were distinguishable by having darker breasts than females. Rutgers (1980) refers to a behaviour peculiar to the male, "..a defensive attitude which he takes up when approached: leaning forward a little he opens his beak and shows his tongue". This is undoubtedly the submissive display referred to by Baptista.

HYBRIDS Nothing recorded.

CONSERVATION There appears to be no cause for concern. There is an ongoing trade in birds from the region, but few Pearl-headed Mannikins are trapped.

REFERENCES Goodwin (1982), Guttinger (1970), Immelmann *et al.* (1968-72), Koepff (1984), Langberg (1963), Rutgers & Norris (1980), Scally (1967).

---

5   BRONZE MANNIKIN
Lonchura cucullata   Plate 1

Described as *Lonchura cucullata* Swainson.
Other common names: Bronze-wing, Bronze-winged Mannikin, Bronze-shouldered Mannikin, Swainson's Bronze Mannikin, Hooded Finch, Hooded Weaver-Finch, Hooded Mannikin (Bond 1971).

Bronze Mannikin.

FIELD CHARACTERS This is a small bird with a blackish bill, one of the smallest munias. It is greyish-brown above with blackish head and throat, greenish glint on the shoulder, and irregularly barred on the rump and flanks. There are other mannikins within its range it might be confused with. Magpie Mannikin *L. fringilloides* is similar but is distinguished by its larger size and longer, heavier bill and it lacks barring on the rump and uppertail-coverts. Black-and-White Mannikin *L. bicolor* occurs in different forms according to the subspecies but should be instantly detected by having a pale blue bill. The brown-backed races of *L. bicolor* are distinguished by all-black heads and black-and-white barring on the wings. The juveniles are readily confused in the field and can only be identified with certainty when seen with their respective adults. However, young Bronze Mannikins are earth-brown above and thus much lighter than young Black-and-White Mannikins which are a sooty grey-brown. The juvenile is very similar to the juvenile Madagascar Mannikin *L. nana*. The two species overlap in the Comoros.

STATUS Common and widespread.

HABITAT It is a bird of farms, gardens, thornveldt and light woodland (Clancey 1964), and may be found usually on the ground in open bush country, edges of forest, cultivated land, parks and gardens. Benson & White (1957) found it common in existing and abandoned cultivation, feeding on the ground. In Puerto Rico in the West Indies it is a bird mainly of open lowland country where it is often encountered along streams, and in or on the borders of grassy fields and lawns (Bond 1971). It is said to have become a nuisance in the rice fields where it does serious damage (Lever 1987).

HABITS AND BEHAVIOUR It is a tame and gregarious little bird, feeding on the ground in small flocks of 8–20 birds looking just like tiny sparrows around villages and cultivation. It wanders far and wide in search of food and may be found in open bush country, edges of forest, cultivated land, parks and gardens. Clancey (1964) found it to be wide-ranging and abundant throughout Natal and Zululand from sea level up to "quite high altitudes in the interior". I found it in small groups or loose small flocks in suburban areas in northern Durban where it seemed to behave much like the House Sparrow *Passer domesticus*. Bronze Mannikins sometimes roosts in communal nests outside the breeding season. These structures are put together by various members of the flock and are truly a communal effort but are not finished nests in the accepted sense. They may be pulled apart and the elements used in constructing a new nest, often in a different place each night. The nest is described by Bond (1971) as being "decidedly slovenly." Brickell (1994) says the roosting nests are thinner and more flimsy than those built for breeding.

Before roosting for the night, mannikins will gather at a watering hole, preferably one where the grasses bend over to touch the water (Bannerman 1949).

Most aggression seems to stem from defence of the nest, the actual jealously-guarded territory being only the immediate vicinity of the nest. However, a bird will pursue the offending individual for some distance. Newcomers to the flock may be attacked or courted intensely, but are usually soon accepted. When attacking, the male will lift its far wing, apparently increasing its visual size and showing more of the shiny green of the wings. This is also a behaviour of a begging fledgling that will twist its head toward its parent, while raising the far wing.

Morris (1957 and 1973) has written at considerable length on the behaviour of the species.

FOOD AND FEEDING It takes seeds from small seeding grasses of the millet type, bristle grasses, which include the Italian millet, of the genus *Setaria*, and the common *Digitaria* and *Panicum*. Brickell (1986) and Brickell and Konigkramer (1994) describe some 14 species of plant favoured by the bird in South Africa in the wild and another 16 species taken in captivity. It apparently favours the Antelope Grass *Echidnochloa pyramidalis*. It is not particularly agile at climbing grasses to get at the heads, preferring to bite out seeds it can jump up at, but will cling to stems of seeding grasses, even upside down (Clement *et al.* 1993). It is recorded taking rice and other grains in central Africa. It will also eat soft greens, biting bits out of lettuce and tender shoots.

It naturally takes a little live food, favouring termites of the genus *Microcerotermes* which it can capture in flight. When the termites swarm, mannikins will flock to the area with other estrildid finches and other birds, taking the insects from the ground or wherever they might land. In captivity it will take wood ant pupae (ants 'eggs'), mealworms, buffalo worms, and white worms etc. It has been seen taking nectar and strands of filamentous green algae (Clement *et al.* 1993).

MOVEMENTS Somewhat nomadic, wandering far in search of food.

CALL The call is a wheezy or buzzing *tsek* or *chik chik chikka*. It utters low churring notes when flushed (Bond 1971). When flocks gather in tall grasses to roost, they utter a lively twitter (Bannerman 1949).

SONG The song is a series of *chi-chiu che-ri-hit* notes run together or frequently repeated (Clement *et al.* 1993).

Inverted curtsey display, bobbing and twisting towards the female.

COURTSHIP AND DISPLAY The most succinct description of the display of Bronze Mannikin is by Morris, and I can do no better than refer to it as described in his 1957 paper: "male courtship performed with beak open wide, tongue protruding, beak pointing downwards; body feathers ruffled except for throat region and head; legs bent; tail twisted towards the female; inverted curtsey dance at low intensity, with pivoting added in at higher intensities; displacement beak-wiping is absent almost entirely and its place taken by displacement preening; no straw carrying, no low twist, no preening, mandibulating immediately before each song phrase, but not accompanied by dipping or bowing.

"The female quivers her tail in ruffled oblique posture

instead of usual horizontal sleeked posture. If the male is not ready to copulate, he performs the leapfrog sequence, vaulting back and forth over the female, with a quick displacement preen between each vault."

Male singing to female with head and tail twisted in her direction.

BREEDING It is generally a communal breeder, often with several nests being built in close proximity of each other, but it is not strictly colonial. Breeding may occur at almost any time of the year, but is usually during the rainy or wet season. The nest may be built in any one of a large variety of sites. Trees, shrubs, the thatch of huts, re-lined abandoned weavers' or other estrildid nests may all be chosen. Bannerman (1949) says that many nests are built under the eaves of a house. Holes in buildings are used, creepers as well as on the sides of houses.

Brickell and Konigkramer (1994) list it as occupying the old nests of the Red Bishop *Euplectes orix*, Red-headed Weaver *Anaplectes rubriceps*, African Masked Weaver *Ploceus velatus*, Blue Waxbill *Uraeginthus angolensis* and Common Waxbill *Estrilda astrild*. Mr and Mrs Carlson, in an article in *Cage and Aviary Birds* in 1989, described the species building within a few inches of wasps nests, and how they were attacked and stung when they tried to inspect the mannikins' nest. This is not unique among estrildids, being well known, for example, among the *Uraeginthus* waxbills. Brickell (1986) says it is known to build its nest close to the nest of the vicious Red Tree Ant *Oecophylla longinoda*.

This species is prolific, producing several broods in a year. It is a choice prey for a lot of predators. Brickell (1986) lists coucals, drongos, kingfishers, shrikes and a Wahlberg's Eagle *Hieraaetus wahlbergi* eating nestlings. Nest predation in the tropics is much higher than in temperate zones, and no doubt lizards, snakes, monkeys and spiders all take their toll. The hornets, wasps and ants obviously help the mannikins by providing some protection but it is difficult to see if this is true symbiosis for it is doubtful what benefits the insects derive from having these neighbours. Bannerman (1949) says a Woodland Kingfisher *Halcyon senegalensis* will sweep up the young, presumably recently fledged mannikins, in its bill one after another and gobble them up.

Nest-building is performed initially by the male who carries the grasses to the nest site and begins the structure. The female usually takes over, twisting and turning the strands into place, with the male continuing to bring material. It is a large untidy structure, lined with finer strands and feathers. Brickell and Konigkramer (1994) give mean measurements from a series of nests as, height 163mm, width 125mm, depth 155mm, height of entrance hole 39mm and entrance width 42mm. Nests were made from about 600 or more pieces of grass.

Copulation may well take place in the entrance to the nest. Presumably this offers a degree of privacy, as birds which are in the final stages of mating behaviour often hold a great fascination for other sexually active males who will approach the mating pair, striking them off balance and successfully interrupting the proceedings.

The clutch may be from 4–8 small, white, oval eggs. They vary in size from 12.3–15.5mm x 9.5–11.0mm. The clutch is brooded by both sexes in turn. Both birds are together in the nest at night.

Palate markings of nestling Bronze Mannikin.

Incubation lasts 12 days. The young fledge in about 21 days and are independent within three weeks. In their dull brown plumage they can move around the colony, escaping attack by irate adults. They soon begin to show adult plumage and are fully moulted by six months, by which time the young males are singing and beginning breeding behaviour.

A successful pair may produce up to four broods in a season, if climate and food supplies are favourable. The nestlings are fed on soft green seeds and other vegetation matter, and usually some insects, termites, etc.

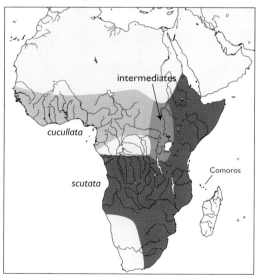

Distribution of Bronze Mannikin.

DISTRIBUTION Ranges widely over Africa south of the Sahara, from Senegal south to Angola, from the Sudan south to the eastern Cape Province. It occurs regularly from sea level up to 1,500m and occasionally up to 2,150m. Offshore it occurs on Fernando Po, Pemba, Mafia, Zanzibar and the Comoros.

Bronze Mannikin has been introduced to Puerto Rico where it is established as a breeding bird (Bond 1971).

DESCRIPTION   **Plate 20**

There are two subspecies recognised. The Southern Bronze Mannikin differs by an almost total absence of green patches on the flanks, and having the barring on the tail-coverts fine and narrow. The two intergrade over a large area resulting in birds with intermediate plumage. I have been unable to study either live birds or specimens from the Comoros.

BRONZE MANNIKIN
L. cucullata cucullata (Swainson)

Former scientific name: *Spermestes cucullata*, Swainson, 1837, Birds W. Africa, 1, p.201.

Other English name: Swainson's Bronze Mannikin (Bannerman 1949).

Adult male 87–92mm. Wing length 48–50mm, culmen 9–10mm, tarsus 10–11mm. The face, throat and centre of the breast are brownish black, with a slight green sheen on the upperparts and a purplish sheen on the cheeks and throat. The mantle and wings are earth-brown to brownish-grey with some slight barring or scaling due to the edges of the feathers being a little paler. The lesser wing-coverts are variable in the extent to which they are shiny green or bronze. The rump and uppertail-coverts are barred brown, grey, black and white, an irregular and not clearly distinct barring. The sides of the breast and entire underparts are white with a bottle-green or bronzy patch on the upper flanks, with irregular bars of grey-brown and black. The underwing-coverts are pale salmon or flesh. The tail is short, black and somewhat rounded. There is much variation in plumage between individuals and it is impossible to isolate any plumage characteristics that help to tell the sexes apart. The bill is fairly conical in shape, the upper mandible is black while the lower is pale greyish-blue. The legs and feet are greyish-brown but this is variable.

Adult female 85–88mm. Wing length 85–88mm, culmen 8–9mm, tarsus 10mm. In other respects resembles the male.

Juvenile Earth-brown above, darker on the head, brownish buff on the flanks and buffish below. The bill is black, but the lower mandible soon becomes paler.

SOUTHERN BRONZE MANNIKIN
L. cucullata scutata

Former scientific name: *Spermestes scutatus* Heuglin, 1863, *Journ. f. Ornith.*, 11, p.18.

This race has not been satisfactorily described because its discriminating characteristics are variable, and not totally predictable. It is more finely barred on both rump and uppertail-coverts, and the undertail-coverts, and I think this is a distinction. Goodwin (1982) describes the discriminator of this race as "...usually lacks the glossy green patch at the side of the breast, having this area barred black and white, and its rump is usually less clearly barred." And he adds "...there is also much minor individual variation..." Brickell (1986) says of *L. c. scutata* simply "male: browner." Bannerman (1949) says that it has a browner throat, is less heavily barred on the rump and "less evident patch of green on the sides of the breast, which is often entirely absent."

It is difficult to maintain this race on the absence of green on the flanks, and whilst undoubtedly many more West African birds have green on the flanks than birds from south-east Africa. Those live birds that I studied in a bird reserve in Durban all had green patches on the flanks. I have illustrated birds representative of both races. An excellent photograph of *L. cucullata scutata* in Sinclair (1984) clearly shows the absence of the glossy green patch on the side of the breast.

There is a possible third race, *L. c. tressellata* (Clancey 1964b), but its validity is questioned by Paynter (1968), and Goodwin (1982) fails to recognise it. Brickell and Konigkramer (1994) say it is distinguished by having the lateral greenish black patches more prominent. I was unable to distinguish it from specimens in the Natural History Museum at Tring and so follow Goodwin's example.

Two races of Bronze Mannikin. Left, *L. cucullata scutata*, **right** *L. c. cucullata*, **showing the bronze patches on the flanks.**

HYBRIDS I am not aware of any hybrids occurring in the wild. In captivity Bronze Mannikin has hybridised with several species of *Lonchura*, including both Black-and-White Mannikin and Magpie Mannikin. It has also been crossed with Madagascar Mannikin and both African and Indian Silverbills. A hybrid produced with Common Waxbill *Estrild astrild* is listed by Gray (1958), but no reference for this is given.

CONSERVATION This species is trapped for the bird trade, in varying quantities, in some of the countries in which it occurs. The market is apparently stable at current levels of price (at each stage in the supply chain), and quantities recorded are unlikely to have the slightest effect on population levels. Being a bird primarily of rough and open grassland there is no likely threat to habitat.

REFERENCES Benson & White (1957), Bannerman (1949), Bond (1971), Brickell (1986), Brickell & Konigkramer (1994), Clancey (1964a,b), Clement *et al.* (1993), Goodwin (1982), Gray (1958), Lever (1987), Morris (1957 & 1970), Paynter (1968), Sinclair (1984).

---

6   BLACK-AND-WHITE MANNIKIN
Lonchura bicolor   Plate 2

Described as *Lonchura bicolor* Fraser
Other common names: Blue-billed Mannikin, Rufous-backed Mannikin.

FIELD CHARACTERS This is a small mannikin with several distinct races, distinguished by the colour of the back, which is black, brown or rufous depending on race. Otherwise, it has the head and breast black with a blue or green gloss, and is white below. The bill is a distinctive pale lavender blue and this feature will separate it,

regardless of the race, from the other small African mannikins. Most races of Black-and-White Mannikin have white dots along the leading edges of the flight feathers which gives a distinctive black-and-white barring to the wings.

It may be seen in the company of Magpie Mannikins *L. fringilloides* in cane grass. The latter is a larger bird and has the upper mandible black. In cleared land adjoining forest or open scrub near woodland it may be found feeding with Bronze Mannikin *L. cucullata* which is about the same size, but the latter may be definitively separated by having the upper mandible blackish.

The juvenile is less easy to identify if seen away from adults of its own species. It is more sooty-brown than juveniles of either Magpie Mannikin or Bronze Mannikin and in southern Africa it may be distinguished from juvenile Bronze Mannikin by having a more chestnut-like back and the distinctive black-and-white spotting on the edges of the primaries.

STATUS Whilst it is a widespread species it is not numerous. It is uncommon in Zambia and is only locally common over much of its range, but is generally described as common in southern Africa.

HABITAT It is primarily a bird of forest clearings and undergrowth. Small flocks may be found among tall grasses, sedges and bushes alongside waterways and in marshy country; it may also be found at forest edges and clearings, and secondary growth near water or forests. It is found in cultivated areas, but whilst not usually around villages or human habitation, Kunkel (1965) found it in the rainforest of the Congo Basin to be one of the commonest species in native gardens. In southern Africa it is common in moist, broad-leaved forest, and coastal forest (Sinclair 1984) and evergreen forest (Maclean 1985). Small flocks occur in open bushveld and open dune forest, feeding on the seeds of grasses (Newman 1983). It ranges altitudinally at least up to 2,150m, on Mt. Ruwenzori.

HABITS AND BEHAVIOUR It may be found in small family groups or parties up to about 12 birds. It is shy, and when disturbed in the open will retreat into the shelter of the forests. It occurs in the grassy undergrowth of gallery forests and may join the feeding parties of birds that work their way through the forests (Bannerman 1949). It is often found in the company of Bronze Mannikins in suitable areas on the edge of woodland or in open scrub, but the latter is primarily a bird of open grassland. Flocks of up to a hundred are known (Clement *et al.* 1993) but it never gathers in the numbers of Bronze Mannikins. It is most likely to be seen in large numbers when flocks visit rice fields, at the time before the rice fully ripens. At this time it will join with Bronze Mannikins, Magpie Mannikins and other estrildid finches, the total flock size becoming quite numerous.

Black-and-White Mannikins will gather together in numbers for communal roosting in cane grass and reeds. They will also build nests for roosting in. These are large and loosely-made, usually without lining, but may be lined with soft material. These roosting nests are the work of several birds together, and several birds will roost in one.

The species will raise its far-side wing when in an aggression/defence situation against another bird. Similarly, fledglings soliciting food will also raise the far-side wing. This behaviour occurs in Bronze Mannikin as well. How it evolved in these two situations and why is an interesting subject that Morris (1957) discusses at length in a lengthy and absorbing paper about Bronze Mannikin. In adult aggression it seems likely that the act of raising the wing gives an illusion of the bird being a larger size and thus more formidable than in reality it is; this is the equivalent of raising hackles in dogs and gill flaps in frilled lizards, etc. The reason for the begging juvenile to raise the far wing is less easy to speculate about. It could be an action to conceal a sibling who may be competing for the food, but I feel it is more likely to be the size factor – the larger the youngster the greater the stimulus to the parent to feed it.

Brickell (1986) notes that it is preyed on by the Fork-tailed Drongo *Dicrurus adsimilis*, and praying mantises *Miomantis* spp.

FOOD AND FEEDING It feeds on grasses of the millet type and flocks to the rice fields as they are coming into seed. Brickell records the natural food as including grass seeds, nectar and small insects, petals of the Weeping Boer-bean *Schotia brachypetala* and the leaves of the water weed (Frog-spittle) *Spirogyra*. Maclean (1986) says it will feed on the nectar of *Schotia* flowers. Kunkel (1965) found that in the Kivu Highlands its food consisted mainly of the seeds of *Setaria* grasses (it readily takes *Setaria homonyma* and *S. pallidefusca* in captivity) and of various millets including *Panicum deustum*. It has been observed taking filamentous algae from puddles, a habit observed in several species of munia. It has also been seen feeding on oil-palm, crop content analysis showing that the fruit had been eaten.

Clement *et al.* (1993) record it as taking more insects than Bronze Mannikin. Bannerman (1949) mentions a bird being shot which was in full breeding condition and had its stomach crammed with insects. It is known to capture termites in flight. Brickell and Konigkramer (1994) record it taking termites *Macrotermes bellicosus* and ants *Myrmicinae* and *Oecophylla longinoda*. In captivity, Black-and-White Mannikins have taken mealworms, moths, fish-moths, *Diptera* larvae, gnats, termites and spiders.

MOVEMENTS Generally sedentary but some wandering, particularly first-year birds. Some altitudinal movements in season, and vagrancy at the edges of the range.

CALL The close contact call is a *tsip* with a louder *pseet*. Twittering and whistling call notes are given as *tsik tsik* by Maclean (1985) and Mackworth-Praed and Grant (1960) give a plaintive *kip*!. There is a clear whistling note given in flight (Newman 1983).

SONG The song is a short series of soft contact notes run together (Clement *et al.* 1993) and is described as sweet by Bannerman (1949).

COURTSHIP AND DISPLAY The courting male performs with the feathers of the head smoothed down, but the body feathers are fluffed out. The bill is opened wide, pointing downwards with the tongue protruding. The legs are bent and the tail is turned towards the female. He performs an inverted curtsey dance at low intensity without any lowering or twisting. At high intensity he pivots, turning towards the female and then away again. There is no straw-carrying to my knowledge. If ready to mate, the female fluffs her feathers and quivers her tail. If the male is not ready, he leap-frogs over the female, quickly performs a displacement preen and hops back again. There is a nest ceremony of bowing, mandibulating, gaping and tongue protruding which may occasionally lead to copulation inside the nest.

Male Black-and-White Mannikin in advertisement song.

BREEDING The breeding nest is usually in a tree or bush, or a stand of reeds 2–8m from the ground. It is constructed of both dry and green grasses and is a large globular structure (Brickell 1986) with a side entrance. The outside may contain leaves (Bannerman 1949). Bates (1930) says that it builds its nest in trees with dense foliage, and a bird may be seen flying into the trees with a great bunch of beard lichen *Usnea* sp., trailing behind it in the air. This plant grows on and hangs from tree branches from which the birds pull it free. In examples like that given by Bates, this material forms the outside of the nest. The main lining of the nest is formed of fine grass stems. It is finished off with the flowering heads of grasses and feathers. (Maclean 1985) says that the roosting nests may sometimes be used for breeding.

The clutch ranges from 3–6, usually 4–5 (Brickell 1986). The eggs are snow white and measure 14 x 10.5mm (Bannerman 1949). Incubation lasts 12–13 days. Both sexes incubate during the day, while the female incubates at night. The young fledge 16–22 days later. They attain adult plumage 65–70 days after leaving the nest. The young are reared on a mixed diet of unripened seeds, presumably some green food, and insects such as small grubs, termites, small spiders, etc.

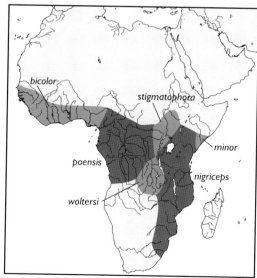

Distribution of Black-and-White Mannikin showing approximate boundaries between the six subspecies.

DISTRIBUTION *L. b. bicolor* ranges widely and erratically from Senegal in West Africa eastwards to eastern Nigeria and Mt. Cameroon. *L. b. poensis* ranges from Cameroon east to southern Sudan, eastern Congo and Rwanda, south to northern Angola, Kasai, Kivu and Fernando Po. *L. b. stigmatophora* occupies a narrow spur northwards from Lake Victoria to southern Ethiopia. *L. b. woltersi* is found in south-western Katanga and north-western Zambia. *L. b. minor* is found only in southern Somalia. The southern race *L. b. nigriceps* ranges from Kenya in East Africa, south to eastern Transvaal, Natal and eastern Cape Province, west to eastern Katanga; north and east Zambia, eastern Zimbabwe, Zanzibar and the Mafia Islands.

DESCRIPTION   Plate 21

There are six races recognised, and they fall conveniently into a black-and-white group and a brown-and-white group. In the first group the Black-and-White Mannikin is simply black and white and is the only race without any white barring on the wings and uppertail-coverts. In the Mt. Nimba area of Liberia the population is distinguished by having three white dots on the innermost tertial. This characteristic gradually disappears in a cline that reaches Cameroon. The Fernando Po Mannikin is also black and white but has black-and-white barring on the wings, rump and uppertail-coverts. Dark-backed Mannikin has the back a dull blackish-brown.

In the brown-and-white group, Wolters' Brown-backed Mannikin has a dark brown back whereas the Rufous-backed Mannikin has the back rufous. The Lesser Brown-backed Mannikin has a brown back midway between the two, and it is smaller than either.

A look at the distribution map and the plates show the cline from Senegal to Natal, and one cannot help but wonder how one species like the Bronze Mannikin can cover virtually the same range with no significant change, yet *L. bicolor* has evolved a dramatic change of plumage from one end of its range to the other. This suggests a sporadic and disjointed distribution pattern rather than a continuous one, and a tendency for the populations to be small, local and sedentary.

Sibley and Monroe (1990) separate *L. b. bicolor* and *L. b. nigriceps* into two parapatric species, but leave the intermediate dark brown-backed races unmentioned and by implication included in *L. bicolor*. I find this illogical and prefer to see stronger evidence than that offered before following their example.

BLACK-AND-WHITE MANNIKIN
L. bicolor bicolor
Former scientific names: *Amadina bicolor*, Fraser, 1843, *Proc. Zool. Soc.* London, 1842, P.145. Spermestes punctata Heuglin, 1871. *Spermestes bicolor permista*, Neumann, 1907.
Other common names: Blue-billed Mannikin, Two-coloured Mannikin.
Adult 96–102mm. Wing length 47–52mm, culmen 9.5–10mm, tarsus 11mm. The head to chest, mantle, wings, rump and tail are shiny black with a slight green gloss. Some birds in Cameroon bordering Liberia may have one or two small white spots on the innermost tertials, those from the Mt. Nimba region of Liberia have three clearly-defined spots in a triangular pattern on the innermost tertial. The lower breast to undertail-coverts are white. The flanks are black with irregular broad white scallops. The underwing-coverts are white with some fine black barring near the alula. The irides are brown. The bill is lavender-blue,

pale bluish-horn or pale grey. The legs and feet are horn to blackish. The sexes are alike.

Triple spot pattern on tertials of Black-and-White Mannikin from the Mount Nimba region in Liberia.

Juvenile Dull earth-brown above, blackish on primaries and tail. The ear-coverts and sides of the neck are grey-brown, shading to greyish on the throat and upper breast. The underwing-coverts and remaining under-parts are dull buff. Birds from the Mt. Nimba region tend to be paler on the bib and darker on the breast.

Black-and-White Mannikin *L. b. bicolor* on the left, Fernando Po Mannikin *L. b. poensis* on the right.

FERNANDO PO MANNIKIN
L. bicolor poensis
Former scientific names: *Amadina poensis*, Fraser, 1843, *Proc. Zool. Soc.* London, 1842, p.145. *Pseudospermestes goosseni* Dubois, 1905.
Other common name: Black-breasted Mannikin (should not be used, as it is confusable with *L. teerinki*).
Adult 98–105mm. Wing length 48–54mm, culmen 10mm, tarsus 11mm. The head is glossed with green. There are white spots on the outer edges of the primaries and basal outer edges of the secondaries which give a barred effect to the base of the flight feathers. The rump and uppertail-coverts are barred with white. The white scalloping on the flanks is broader than that of *L. b. bicolor*.
Juvenile Similar to that of the juvenile *L. b. bicolor* but has faint barring on the primaries and secondaries.

DARK-BACKED MANNIKIN
L. bicolor stigmatophora
Former scientific name: *Spermestes stigmatophorus* Reichenow, 1892, *Journ. f. Ornith.* 40, p.46.
Adult 98–103mm. Wing length 48–52mm, culmen 10mm, tarsus 11mm. This race has the head and breast a less intense black, more a dirty dark brown-black with a little purple-bronze gloss. The mantle and back are dark brown. In other respects it resembles *L. b. poensis* with the same white barring on the wings and

rump. There is no difference between the plumage of the sexes.

Juvenile Identical to the juvenile *L. b. poensis*.

LESSER BROWN-BACKED MANNIKIN
L. bicolor minor
Former scientific name: *Spermestes nigriceps minor* Erlanger, 1903, *Ornith. Monatsb.* 11,p.22.
Adult 94–96mm. Wing length 45–46mm, culmen 9mm, tarsus 10mm. In other respects it is like *L. b. stigmatophora*.

WOLTERS' BROWN-BACKED MANNIKIN
L. bicolor woltersi
Schouteden, 1956, *Rev. Zool. Bot.* Africa, 54,p.272
Other common name: Wolters' Mannikin
Adult 97–100mm. Wing length 47–48mm, culmen 9.5–10mm, tarsus 11mm. Visually it is similar to *L. b. nigriceps* but has a darker brown back, intermediate between *L. b. nigriceps* and *L. b. stigmatophora*.
Juvenile Not recorded. It is probably similar to juvenile *L. b. stigmatophora*.

RUFOUS-BACKED MANNIKIN
L. bicolor nigriceps
Former scientific names: *Spermestes nigriceps*, Cassin, 1852, *Proc. Acad. Nat. Sci.* Philadelphia, 6, p.185. *Spermestes rufodorsalis*, Peters, 1863.
Other common names: Red-backed Mannikin, Brown-backed Weaver-finch.
Adult 97–100mm. Wing length 47–48mm, culmen 9.5–10mm, tarsus 11mm. Visually it is similar to *L. b. stigmatophora* but the mantle, back and wing coverts and parts of the secondaries are rufous or chestnut.
Juvenile Like the immature *L. b. poensis*, but is paler and browner on the mantle and wings.

HYBRIDS No natural hybrids are recorded. In captivity it has cross-bred with other munias. Gray (1958) lists Rufous-backed Mannikin as having crossed with Bronze Mannikin, Magpie Mannikin and the Bengalese.

CONSERVATION There seems to be no cause for concern for this species. The numbers trapped for the bird trade appear to be insignificant, the birds coming from only a few localities out of a wide distribution.

REFERENCES Bannerman (1949), Bates (1930), Brickell (1986), Brickell & Konigkramer (1994), Gray (1958), Kunkel (1965), Mackworth-Praed & Grant (1960), Maclean (1985), Newman (1983), Sinclair (1984).

---

7 MAGPIE MANNIKIN
Lonchura fringilloides   Plate 2

Described as *Lonchura fringilloides* Lafresnaye
Other common name: Pied Mannikin, Giant Mannikin, Pied Weaver-Finch and Pied Grass-finch.

INTRODUCTION Magpie Mannikin has been well known to both ornithologists and aviculturists for a long time. It was described by Lafresnaye in 1835 and was in the collection of Dr Russ in Germany by 1868 (Butler 1899). According to Butler, it not only bred well in captivity but hybridised with other mannikins. In contrast, the natural history of the species is poorly documented and little understood. The association of Magpie Mannikin with

Bindura Bamboo *Oxytenanthera abyssinica* was first recorded by Vincent in Rhodesia in 1936. It was collected among bamboo by Benson (1941 and 1952) in Rhodesia, and Irwin (1956) having collected the species in the bamboo zone on Gorongosa Mountain in Mozambique observed that throughout the eastern and southern parts of its range, it seemed to be associated with bamboos. Bannerman (1949) quotes from Vincent at length, but makes no attempt to explore the subject of a bamboo relationship. Instead, one gets the impression from his notes that it is a rice-dependent species.

Magpie Mannikin.

FIELD CHARACTERS It is a medium-sized munia with a heavy, long pointed bill, black head, brown back and wings, black tail, and white below with some brown and black barring on the flanks. It could only be confused with the much smaller Bronze Mannikin *L. cucullata* but the proportionately larger bill and darker head are good discriminators. Juveniles of these two species, together with juvenile Black-and-White Mannikin *L. bicolor*, are all similar in the field, but the greater size and proportionately larger bill are useful features.

STATUS Irregular and local to extremely local or rare.

HABITAT It is a bird that is never found far from water, and shows a preference for roosting in reedbeds. It frequents bushes alongside rivers and streams, bamboo thickets and rice fields. In some, if not all the parts of its range where it is common, it is found in and around bamboo thickets.

HABITS AND BEHAVIOUR It occurs in the vicinity of native villages, cultivated lands and gardens (Brickell *et al.* 1986), but is a shy bird and will fly to thick cover immediately it is disturbed. It travels in pairs, small family parties or small groups of up to ten or so birds all year round. In exceptional circumstances flocks of up to 500 birds may gather (Maclean 1993). This is most likely to occur when the Bindura Bamboo is seeding (see Feeding below). Breeding birds will join feeding flocks when not attending nest duties. They are great bathers and have been observed to bathe up to seven times or more a day after rain showers, or if exposed to running water (Brickell *et al.* 1986). Even in captivity they will bathe three times a day or more. Magpie Mannikins build nests for roosting in.

FOOD AND FEEDING Jackson (1972), Benson and Benson (1977) and others suggest that the primary natural food of the species is seeds of the Bindura Bamboo, *Oxtenanthera abyssinica*. Mrs D. Searson of Highlands, Rhodesia, quoted in Jackson, describes how the indigenous bamboos in her garden began seeding in profusion in 1967; within the month a flock of 30 to 40 Magpie

Mannikins appeared and apparently fed exclusively on these seeds. The mannikins remained in the neighbourhood in strength for a couple of years and must have found other food, but by 1971 they had all gone. The extraordinary thing about this species of bamboo, like so many bamboos, is that it seeds only rarely. Searson said her plants had not seeded for 20 years or so and they died after seeding. McClure (1993) says it is considered in Malawi to have a flowering cycle of 30 years. It also seems that this bamboo flowers and maybe seeds, every year for the first three years of its life. It then lives for a further 20 or 30 years before flowering, seeding and dying. Such a variable and uncertain source of supply of food certainly explains the peripatetic nature of Magpie Mannikin and its changing pattern of distribution and status. That it is not totally dependent on bamboo seeds is obvious, but it seems equally obvious that it does have a strong relationship with this food source. It also seems that the bird has evolved a particularly strong bill to take advantage of this food.

Seeds of Bindura Bamboo *Oxytenanthera abyssinica* (left), cultivated rice *Oryza sativa* (centre) and Guinea Grass *Panicum maximum* (right) to show the comparatively large size of the bamboo seed.

The large bill of Magpie Mannikin is reminiscent of that of Pin-tailed Parrotfinch *Erythrura prasina*, although it lacks the visual eccentricity. The parrotfinch also has a very close relationship with bamboo and has also adapted its behaviour to exploit rice cultivation. Bamboo seeds are large and hard. The seed of the Bindura Bamboo is from 12.5–16mm in length, excluding the style, and 2–2.5mm in diameter. This compares to a size range of 6–8 x 3–5mm for cultivated rice grains, and an average 3 x 2mm for the common Guinea Grass *Panicum maximum*. Bamboos in Africa have been very poorly studied, and even their distribution is poorly documented. The key question in the context of a bamboo-related bird, such as Magpie Mannikin, is what advantage there are in feeding on the seeds of a plant that has a seeding cycle so out of line with the life cycle of the bird. Assuming the birds actively seek the bamboo when it is seeding, how the birds find seeding bamboos is a mystery. Studies of the nutrition of bamboo seed in India (Mitra and Nayak, in Tewari 1993) suggest that careful attention to this factor could be significant. The seed of *Bambusa bambos* in India has about double the crude protein of rice, and about double the true protein. It has virtually none of the crude fat, but has high levels of calcium, phosphorous, some ash, and thiamine, riboflavin and niacin. It has a nutrition profile more like wheat than rice. If the seed of the Bindura Bamboo is similar it is obviously an excellent survival strategy to have a mandible adaptation that allows exploitation of this first class source of nutrition.

Magpie Mannikin clearly has a liking for rice, and several writers note its readiness to pick up spilled polished rice. Goodwin (1982) notes its liking for areas where dry-soil rice is grown in tropical forests. They are agile feeders on grasses, alighting on the stem in the manner of many munias, and quickly working up to the seeding heads.

Stalks that are broken and fallen to the ground are held by the foot while the seeds are eaten. When given seeding grass in captivity they have been observed to chew the sap from the stems before eating the seeds. I have noticed this in several species of munia. Brickell *et al.* (1980) lists many seeds taken in the wild, including *Panicum aequinerve*, *P. deustum*, *P. maximum* and also the seeds, buds, petals and leaves of Dwarf Marigold *Schukhria pinnata*. It has also been seen feeding on green algae *Spyrogyra* from dry ponds (Brickell and Konigkramer 1994).

This apecies appears to be highly vegetarian. Brickell *et al.* (1980) described the food preferences of birds kept in very large well planted aviaries in South Africa. The leaves of a giant-leaved fig in the aviary had its dying leaves stripped and the pieces eaten. This was a daily occurrence, but no attempt was made to eat the living leaves. These birds also relished water cress and spinach.

It will eat alate termites readily, will take small brown ants, and in captivity, mealworms, but Soderberg (1956) says the taste for live food varies with individuals.

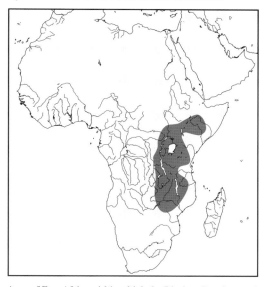

Area of East Africa within which the Bindura Bamboo and similar species are found. The Bindura Bamboo is apparently found throughout tropical Africa (Napper 1965) but only the region shown here appears to be recorded in the literature. The map is based on Kigomo (1988).

MOVEMENTS Irregular and unpredictable. In at least some parts, if not all, of its range it travels in search of seeding bamboo. Whether this searching is exclusively for the Bindura Bamboo or whether the seeds of other bamboos are also taken, is not known. The extent to which paddy rice or dry-soil rice cultivations replace bamboo seeds in the bird's diet, and thus influence the propensity to wander in search of preferred food is not known.

CALL The flight call is a loud *pee-oo pee-oo* (Mackworth-Praed and Grant 1960), rather like a serin's chirrup (Bannerman 1949) or *peu peu peu* (Maclean 1985) or a cheerful *pee-up pee-up*. There is a shrill alarm call (Maclean 1985) described as a thin *cheep!* (Sclater and Moreau 1933). The call of the nestling is a simple series of *cheep*. The call of the fledgling as it begs for food is a shrill *ssi, ssi*.

SONG The song is short, lasting only a few seconds, and may be repeated within a minute. Brickell (1986) describes it as a soft *chi chi chi chi*, and Maclean (1985) describes it as soft and bubbling. Whether it is undirected song or in sexual display the bird keeps the bill wide open, mandibulates and raises and vibrates its tongue.

Magpie Mannikin in full courtship song.

COURTSHIP AND DISPLAY The male does not sing or display while holding nesting material but will fly to the female, holding a straw, then fly to the nest site as if to lead her on. In advertisement song the male stands fairly upright, body close to the perch, head slightly downturned with the bill open while singing. The head may be turned slightly from side to side. In directed advertisement song the body is held clear of the perch. In direct courtship display the male holds its body at an angle of about 45°. As he sings he bobs up and down in the inverted curtsey display, but does not move side to side, or does so very slightly.

BREEDING The nest is built in a bush, tree or bamboo thicket within 3–5m from the ground. In Tanzania it seemed to have a preference for nesting in exotic conifer plantations (Sclater and Moreau 1933). The nest is generally round with a side entrance but may be ovoid with the entrance at one end. It is made of grasses, leaves, and soft bents, lined with finer material, bamboo flowers and feathers. Outside measurements given by Maclean (1985) are from 12.5–20cm, entrance to rear, 11–13cm wide and 12–13cm high. Jackson (1972) gives measurements of one nest as 200 x 130 x 130mm, with an internal diameter of 65mm. Another nest measured 125 x 120 x 125mm with an entrance tunnel 30mm wide x 21mm high and 15mm long. The individual items used in the construction of these nests were mostly 50–150mm in length. Six nests that were pulled apart by Brickell *et al.* (1980) were found to contain between 335 and 370 pieces. They also contained 52–83 feathers in a nest. In some 18 nests recorded by Brickell (1986) the entrance faced west in every case. On leaving the nest the incubating bird will pull some feathers to block the entrance hole.

Nests may be solitary or a few may be built near enough to each other to form a small colony.

The dull white oval eggs form a clutch of 4–6. Eggs in the British Museum collection average 15.3mm x 11.3 mm. Measurements given by Jackson (1972) include an egg 16 x 11mm and 14.7 x 10.9mm. Incubation lasts an average of 15 days. The newly hatched chick is pink, and has the bill white with a black tip, becoming black by the time the birds fledge. The young fledge in 21–26 days (Brickell *et al.* 1980).

The nestlings are fed on both vegetable matter and

Palate markings of nestling Magpie Mannikin.

some insects, but the extent to which animal matter is essential in rearing is uncertain and the advantage, if any, of the inclusion of bamboo seeds in the rearing diet is unknown. Birds have been reared satisfactorily in captivity on an all vegetarian diet, and particularly well in Germany where breeding munias are regularly provided with ripening wheat. In some cases where the species has bred in captivity the parents have taken mealworms, ant pupae and alate termites "...in great quantities" (Brickell *et al.* 1980).

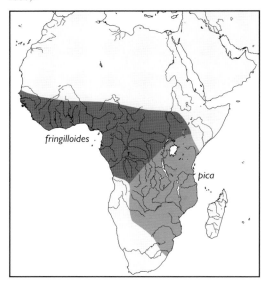

Distribution of Magpie Mannikin.

DISTRIBUTION This species occurs in suitable habitat from Senegal and Gambia on the west coast of Africa south of the Sahara, eastwards across the continent to southern Sudan, south to Cameroon, Gabon, northern Zaïre, and western Uganda (*L. f. fringilloides*), then on through southern Zaïre, western Kenya, Tanzania, Mozambique and Natal (*L. f. pica*).

DESCRIPTION   Plate 22
There are two races of Magpie Mannikin. It would be difficult to identify the race of an individual bird in isolation without knowledge of its origin.

NORTHERN MAGPIE MANNIKIN
L. fringilloides fringilloides
Other scientific names: *Plocus fringilloides*, Lafresnaye, 1835, *mag. zool.* (Paris), 5, cl.2, pl.48. *Spermestes fringilloides*, Swainson, 1837.
Adult male 115–120mm. Wing length 59–62mm, culmen 15–17mm, tarsus 14–15mm. It has the entire head and throat black with a blue or sometimes

greenish gloss. The mantle is brown with paler edges to the feathers, barred somewhat with black and noticeably streaked with pale quills on the scapulars. The lower rump, uppertail-coverts and tail are black and are also slightly glossed with bluish. The underwing-coverts and the trailing edges of the flight feathers are salmon-buff. The sides of the breast and entire underparts are white with alternate irregular bars or patches of salmon-brown and black along the flanks. The irides are brown or chestnut. The upper mandible is blackish, the lower mandible pale bluish or silvery grey with a dark tip. The legs and feet are dark grey to blackish.

Adult female 112–115mm. Wing length 56–58mm, culmen 13–15mm, tarsus 13–14mm. The sexes appear to be similar but the black and brown markings on the flanks of the female are often less prominent and smaller. In a group of several birds it is fairly easy to pick out obvious males and females.

Juvenile Dusky brown above, buffish below with flight feathers and tail darker brown to blackish, the bill blackish-horn. At about four weeks after fledging there are signs of the metallic sheen on the head, face and throat, and the adult plumage begins to show increasingly until full adult plumage is attained at about eight weeks. There are records in captivity of this taking from 3–12 months. The birds come into breeding condition shortly after attaining adult plumage. The wing-coverts have paler edges, giving a slight impression of wing bars. When first fledged the bill is shorter than that shown in the plate.

SOUTHERN MAGPIE MANNIKIN
L. fringilloides pica
L. fringilloides pica Clancey, 1986, *Le Gerfaut*, 76:301-305.

This race differs from the nominate in being less dark and less saturated with colour over the mantle and scapulars. The metallic blue-black patches at the sides of the breast are smaller. The small patches of brown and blue-black on the flanks have less extensive blue-black streaks to the outer edges, and the inner brown is paler, less reddish. The bill is marginally smaller than on the northern and west African birds.

Comparison between *L. fringilloides pica* **(left) and** *L. f. fringilloides* **(right), showing the different flank markings.**

HYBRIDS No hybrids have been reported from the wild. Hybrids have been obtained in captivity, with Rufous-backed Mannikin *L. b. nigriceps* by Steiner in 1945, apparently with ease. The offspring were fertile, both when bred back to either parent or with each other.

It has also cross-bred with Bronze Mannikin in captivity many times. The offspring have been about intermediate in size and apparently infertile (Steiner 1952). There are several records of cross-breeding with African Silverbill *L. cantans* (Gray 1958).

CONSERVATION There is little information upon which to draw any conclusions. Populations seem to be small, and the species has a relationship with bamboo that has not been analysed. It is regularly trapped in small numbers for the bird trade, and is a popular species among estrildid enthusiasts. Neither the demand nor supply are significant. Nonetheless it is not a species to be overlooked or taken for granted.

REFERENCES Bannerman (1949), Benson (1941), Benson (1952), Benson & Benson (1977), Brickell *et al.* (1980), Brickell (1986), Brickell & Konigkramer (1994), Butler (1899), Gray (1958), Irwin (1956), Jackson (1972), Kigomo (1988), Mackworth-Praed & Grant (1960), Maclean (1985), McClure (1993), Napper (1965), Sclater & Moreau (1933), Soderberg (1956), Tewari (1993).

8   WHITE-RUMPED MUNIA
Lonchura striata   Plate 3

Described as *Lonchura striata* Linnaeus
Other common names: Sharp-tailed Munia, White-backed Munia, Striated Munia.

FIELD CHARACTERS This is a medium-sized munia, dark brown all over but for a pale to white rump which shows in flight, and a whitish belly. Indian Silverbill *L. malabarica* is the only other small white-rumped bird in India and Sri Lanka, but is so much paler on the head, breast and mantle that it would not easily be confused with White-rumped Munia.

White-rumped Munia overlaps with White-bellied Munia *L. leucogastra* in Malaysia and Sumatra but can be distinguished by its white rump, and White-bellied Munia has yellowish edges to the tail. The latter is scarce in Malaysia and is much more likely to be seen in forest clearings compared to *L. striata* which frequents open spaces. It overlaps with Javan Munia *L. leucogastroides* in southern Sumatra, but is rare or only locally common there. The two species look surprisingly alike when on the ground, but again the white rump of the former in flight is a positive discriminator.

The juveniles of all these species are each duller versions of their respective adults.

When on the ground, the white rump does not show at all and White-rumped Munia looks very much like Javan Munia.

STATUS Widespread but apparently uneven in its populations. In India *L. s. striata* is common but *L. striata acuticauda* is uncommon except in Assam where it is abundant (Ali & Ripley 1987). It seems to be common to locally common or uncommon over most of its range, usually scarce in Sumatra and rare, probably declining in Singapore. It is increasing in southern China, becoming locally common (Viney *et al.* 1994) and in the New Territories, Hong Kong, fairly common and widespread (Viney *in litt.*).

HABITAT This munia may be found in a wide variety of habitats, from open dry grassland to suburban gardens. It is generally not as tolerant of man's presence as Scaly-breasted Munia *L. punctulata* but runs it a close second in its range and habitat. It is primarily a bird of shrubby open country, forest clearings with young bush, village gardens and parks but is found less frequently in rice fields than other munias (van Marle & Voous 1988).

HABITS AND BEHAVIOUR White-rumped Munias move around in small flocks, at all times of the year. Flocks are commonly recorded during the breeding season. It is a bird that ranges opportunistically wherever grasses and seeding weeds occur, being found in open woodland and forest clearings, scrub, secondary growth, cultivated land and waste land, and even human habitation being a regular visitor to urban gardens in some areas.

FOOD AND FEEDING This adaptable bird feeds both on the ground, picking up fallen seeds, and on growing plants. It feeds mainly on the seeds of grasses of every kind from tiny *Poa* and ground millets to paddy rice. It will alight on a grass stem and approach the panicle from below. In my own garden in Hong Kong I have seen a small flock of about 10 birds working their way through the undergrowth of the hillside feeding on seeds of shrubs, weeds and grasses of all kinds. It normally travels in small groups but it will flock in large numbers to the paddy fields when the rice is ripening. Goodwin (1982) quotes separate sources for at least two races feeding on a filamentous green algae *Spyrogyra* from the edges of drying pools and Burton (1993) records it feeding on algae in puddles in Hong Kong. Avery (1978) found that in Bumbong Lima in Malaysia, rice and puddle algae appear to be the main foods of the species there.

Smythies says it takes seeds of the bamboo *Bambusa polumorpha* and other *Bambusa* spp. The genus *Bambusa* is large and widespread throughout Asia and elsewhere. Most species grow in tall, dense clumps, but a few are comparatively short and light. Several are regular, even constant flowering, but seldom produce seeds. There is very little information on the seeds of any species of bamboo since virtually all propagation in horticulture is by division of culms, layering and other similar processes, due to the habit of bamboos fruiting only rarely. *B. polumorpha* only fruits after 55 to 60 years of life, whereupon it dies (Tewari 1993). Of three species of *Bambusa*, the seeds of *B. blumeana* are 4mm long, those of *B. multiplex* 14mm long and those of *B. longispiculata* 16mm long (McClure 1993). The latter two are very large and as bamboo seeds tend to be hard it is doubtful if they could be managed by White-rumped Munias. Magpie Mannikin *L. fringilloides* has a strong association with the bamboo *Oxytenanthera abyssinica* which has large hard seeds. In this case the bird has a long, large and heavy bill that enables the opening and shelling of the seed. There is no such adaptation in White-rumped Munia, and it is possible that the consumption of

bamboo seed by this species is of an opportunistic nature. However there is such variety of bamboo throughout the range of White-rumped Munia that assumptions on this subject must remain tenuous in the absence of detailed study.

There is not a great deal of information on the nutritive content of bamboo seed, but the work of Mitra and Nayar (1972) and information collected by Tewari are significant. The seeds of the bamboo *Bambusa bambos* have twice the amount of protein than rice. In addition this bamboo seed contains ash, high levels of calcium, phosphorous, thiamin, riboflavin and niacin. It has virtually no crude fat, compared to rice, and has a nutrition profile more similar to that of wheat than of rice. It is possible, perhaps likely, that most *Bambusa* bamboos, and maybe most or all bamboo seeds are similarly nutritious. It is obvious that there is a significant advantage to a species that can exploit this food source.

Reports of White-rumped Munias taking insects in the wild are dubious in my opinion and it almost certainly feeds its young exclusively on regurgitated vegetable matter. Birds I have bred in captivity have totally ignored insect food and to my knowledge there are no records of birds taking insects as food in captivity.

MOVEMENTS It is normally resident subject to seasonal movements (Ali & Ripley 1987). It is sedentary in southern China according to Riley (1938).

There are indications that it might be migratory altitudinally, moving up to the higher levels when both the food supply is plentiful and the weather is favourable, when it then breeds, retreating to the lower levels when conditions become less favourable. It may be found from sea level up to 2,000m (in the Himalayas) breeding up to 1,500m in Thailand and Burma (Smythies 1986), and 1,500m in China (Meyer de Schauensee 1984), but it is uncommon above 1,000m.

CALL The contact notes are variations on *prsit prsit*. There are differences between the call notes of the sexes, as in most munias, more noticeable in the loud call. The note of adult males is a single note, while that of females is a double or rolling note. The call of males is relatively deep *quoi quoi*, that of females is a higher pitched and rattling or churring *terr terr* (Immelmann *et al.* 1968-72) or *peep* for male and *trrrt* for female (Baptista 1995). In the case of the domesticated Bengalese, there is a clear distinction between the voice of the adult male and female. Goodwin (1982) described the distinction between the voices of male and female Bengalese as the female having a definite 'r-sound', a short rolling 'r', while that of the male is a more flowing *quoee quoee*, with no 'r-sound'. According to Yoneda and Okanoya (1991) young birds have the ability to give both male and female notes until the age of 55 days. In my own experience with Bengalese bought in southern China, young birds up to as late as six months old may have the same rolling female call note, regardless of sex. With these birds I found that young males tried to sing quite early on. Those that accomplished this ceased to make the rolling call note.

SONG The song of *L. s. striata* males from Sri Lanka that I kept for study was either *pit pit pit spee boyee* or *prt prt prt spee boyee*. The last *boyee* had a distinctive downturn. This song sounds different from that of Malaysian *L. s. subsquamicollis* which in turn differs from Chinese *L. s. swinhoei*. The *boyee* is homologous to the 'legato' note described by Guttinger (1970) for 'munia' (*L. atricapilla* group) mannikins.

COURTSHIP AND DISPLAY In the normal courtship display the male usually begins with a nod or bow. The throat and crown feathers are flattened, but the nape and belly feathers are fluffed out. The legs are bent and the tail is slightly raised. The bill is held horizontal and opens and shuts rapidly in an exaggerated manner during the song.

High intensity display

In high intensity display the male exhibits all the elements of the straw display. The straw carrying itself is not common, and I have not seen it personally, but it has been observed by both Slater (1970) and Baptista and Horblit (1990). When the female is alongside and possibly interested in mating, the feathers of the male are all much more erect, and the crown is also fluffed up. The neck is stretched, holding the head higher but still horizontal, and the tail is held horizontally. The male pivots towards the female, swinging from side to side, and bobbing upwards in an inverted curtsey (Morris 1958), singing all the time.

High intensity display

In high intensity display, during which copulation takes place, the male may raise the tail above the horizontal to the extent that the tips of the tail are the same height as the head. He swings from side to side fully facing the female sideways on, bouncing up and down at the end before swinging back. The receptive female crouches absolutely horizontally across the perch, with the tail rapidly vibrating up and down.

White-rumped Munia tail-flicking

BREEDING The nest is a strong ovoid of grasses, coarse on the outside, finer in the lining. Occasional nests incorporate pliable bents, small twiglets, root fibres, etc., lined with softer finer strands and panicules. The entrance is low down on one side, and the lengths used to line the roof of the nest project out to form a porch and may effectively conceal the entrance hole. It may be located in a bush, shrub, cactus, conifer or other tree and the site may well be close to human habitation. In Sri Lanka, Phillips (1948) says it is usually in a tall bush or sapling 2–3m from the ground, on occasion however he found a nest as low as half a metre from the ground, or at the other extreme, 8m up in a Jak tree in a garden. In China, Schafer (1988) found it nested most commonly in conifers. In India the nest is usually placed in a small tree in the upper or outer branches, between 2 and 6m from the ground (Ali & Ripley 1987).

Judging from the willingness with which the species will accept a half-open nest box or basket in captivity, I would be surprised if it did not also build in used weaver nests, or take to suitable niches in trees and houses.

The male, showing a preference for fresh growing green stems, collects most of the nesting material but the female does most of the building, waiting at the nest for the male to deliver. He collects broad-leaved grass and bamboo leaves and the nest is lined with finer stems and inflorescences which can form a porch or short entrance funnel. It is a solitary nester, never breeding in colonies or in close proximity to other munias (Phillips 1948).

The clutch may be anything from 3–8 with 5 the average, variation no doubt being a function of the age of the female and available food supplies. The eggs are white, somewhat ovoid, being wider towards one end. The average from 100 *L. s. striata* eggs in the collection of Baker (1934) averaged 15.3 x 10.7mm. Those that I measured of the Sri Lankan *L. s. striata* that bred in my study collection measured from 15.9 x 11.75mm to 16.0 long x 12.5mm across at the widest part. This compares to a series of *L. s. subsquamicollis* collected by Stevens in northern Tonkin (Kinnear 1929) which ranged from 15.8 x 11.25mm to 16.7 x 11.75mm. Eggs of *L. s. fumigata* measured about 15.5 x 11.4mm (Baker 1926).

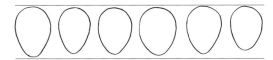

Comparison of egg sizes of White-rumped Munia *L. striata*.

White-rumped Munia is multiple-brooded and will effectively breed all year round, assuming ample food, favourable weather and the absence of inhibiting factors such as moulting. Incubation lasts 14 days, though in the domesticated Bengalese it may be longer. Both sexes brood. The brooding bird leaves the nest after its partner has entered. It is recorded by Spavin and Spavin (1991) that 2 pairs of captive *L. s. acuticauda* both covered the eggs and nestlings when leaving the nest unattended. This was not observed in the case of the 2 pairs of *L. s. striata* that bred to second generation in my collection. Caldwell (1931) found what is described as a communal nest, with two females incubating, but did not record the number of eggs in the nest. It apparently deserts the nest readily, although personal experience in breeding wild-caught birds in captivity suggests quite the opposite. Both sexes

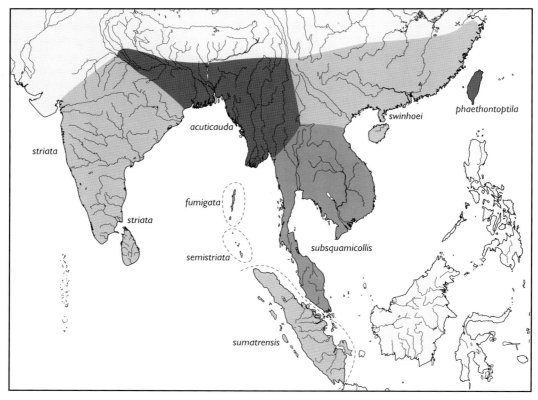

Distribution of White-rumped Munia.

share the incubation and brooding during the day, and both birds spend the night in the nest.

The young fledge in 3 weeks and are independent within 2 weeks of leaving the nest. The family will continue to use the nest as a roosing place after they have fledged. "Often ten or more birds may be trapped in a nest by stealthily approaching and closing the entrance" (Caldwell 1931).

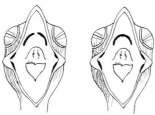

Palate markings of nestling White-rumped Munia from Sri Lanka bred by the author, left, and after Eisner (1960).

DISTRIBUTION As can be seen from the map, this is a widespread species. I have indicated distribution by race but must stress that the boundaries are approximate. This is because all contiguous races intergrade. Beware of this if you are attempting to identify a race that does not clearly fit any of those illustrated.

The nominate race *L. s. striata* occurs in Sri Lanka and ranges north through India to a line that runs roughly from Baroda to Jamshadphur and the Subaranekhar

Valley. *L. s. acuticauda* ranges from Garwhal in Nepal eastwards in a wedge-shaped territory bordered by a line across the Brahmaputra to the Mishmi Hills and on to the Yunnan hills where it intergrades with *L. s. swinhoei* in the east. To the south *L. s. acuticauda* ranges into northwestern Vietnam, Laos, Thailand and Burma where it intergrades with *L. s. subsquamicollis* around a line roughly from Hanoi westwards through Chiang Mai and Pegu. There is uncertainty and some confusion in identification of races in northern Indochina. The Chinese race *L. s. swinhoei* ranges from northwestern Vietnam and across China to north of Shanghai. There is a distinct race, *L. s. phaethontoptila* that is endemic to Taiwan. Stevens (Kinnear 1929) referred to the birds he found in northern Tonkin as *L. st. subsquamicollis* but they could have been a form of *swinhoei*.

The Andaman White-backed Munia *L. s. fumigata* is found in the central and south Andaman Islands. The Nicobar White-backed Munia *L. s. semistriata* is resident in the central Nicobars and Car Nicobar (Ali & Ripley 1987). *L.. s. subsquamicollis* ranges from a line roughly drawn from Pegu in Burma across to Hanoi in Vietnam intergrading with *L. s. acuticauda* in the west and *L. s. swinhoei* in the east, down to Singapore, where it is now scarce and northern Sumatra where it is also scarce. *L. s. explita* intergrades from northern Sumatra and populations that occur to the southern end of the island are clearly distinct.

DESCRIPTION   **Plates 23–26**

When museum specimens are laid out on a bench in a pattern following their geographical distribution, there is a very clear and noticeable triangular cline from west to east and from the middle of this line to the south. Birds from the west are more sharply contrasted in their colouring. They have the dark brown uniform, and the rumps and underparts are white; from the south they become more spotted and marked, from the east paler and more fawn and tawny. The extremes of east, west and south are dramatic. All the races intergrade and virtually none of the recognised subspecies are clearly delineated. In preparing the identification plate and the following descriptions, I studied specimens in the collection of the Natural History Museum at Tring, the birds in the collection of the University of Singapore, and those in the AMNH in New York. I have also kept live birds from several countries.

Goodwin (1982) follows Paynter (1968) and orders *L. striata* into six distinct races. In addition to these six I have restored two forms dropped by Paynter. The first is the Sumatran form which seems to me to be genuinely distinct. Paynter points out that the populations in the eastern range have been inadequately studied. I have responded to this by recognising the Taiwanese population described by Oberholser (1926). It is not only distinct but, by being recognised, does help to reduce the confusion of the Chinese populations. I have painted *L. s. swinhoei* from three areas in the main plate, and another from Hong Kong in a measured drawing. The variety within what is currently regarded as one race illustrates the opportunity for a full study both in the field and under controlled conditions. I suspect that more detailed study could well result in more subdivisions if these were useful.

The eight subspecies of White-rumped Munia can be separated as follows; the Indian race has the breast, flanks and rump white, the ear-coverts are unmarked. The Burmese race is variable, forming a cline from the Indian to the Indochinese races. It ranges from being a little duller on the white with slight greyish lines on the flanks in the western end of its range to a richer cream with lines on both flanks and belly. There are whitish tips to the outer ear-coverts. The birds in northern Indochina have pale edges to the breast feathers. The Nicobar race is like the Indian but has pale edges to the lower breast feathers. The belly and flanks are warmer cream-coloured. The ear-coverts are unmarked. The Andaman race is similar but the underparts are a warm cream and the pale edges to the breast are restricted to the few feathers at the sides of the breast only. It is the only race without any striations on the back. The birds from Indochina seem to be variable from population to population, though not as much as those in China. The underparts are light cream and lined. The breast has pale edges to all the feathers and the ear-coverts are well spotted with white. The Sumatran race is similar but has the rump more prominently streaked and the underparts are dull greyish with brownish-grey lines. The ear-coverts are greyer than on the previous race and have whitish spots. The striations on the back are less prominent than on the Indochinese birds. The Chinese populations are the most varied of all and a detailed and comprehensive study could well result in racial divisions. Generally the birds are a lighter and warmer brown above than the other races. The rufous of the ear-coverts merges into the brown of the breast, which has all the feathers with pale edges. The rump and underparts are creamy-buff, darkest on northern birds, lined with brownish or dark grey. Birds from eastern China are distinctive in having the brown of the breast graduating into the buff of the belly, rather than the clear division

that is usual. Birds from Hainan have the ear-coverts markedly paler than do mainland birds. The centre of the belly is unlined but the flanks are clearly lined. The Taiwanese race has the fuscous of the face mask continuing down to the breast which has pale-edged feathers only at the sides. In this it is similar to the Andaman birds.

Sri Lankan White-rumped Munia, left, with Chinese White-rumped Munia.

INDIAN WHITE-RUMPED MUNIA
L. striata striata
Former scientific name: *Loxia striata*, Linnaeus, 1766, *Syst. Nat.*, ed. 12, 1, p.306. *Loxia striata estriata*, Koelz, 1939.

Other common names: White-rumped Munia, Striated Munia, Striated Finch and Southern White-backed Munia (Ali and Ripley 1987).

Adult male 105–110mm depending on the length of the central rectrices. Wing length 50–52mm, culmen 10–11mm, tarsus 10mm. Above, it is fuscous from forehead to lower back, short uppertail- and undertail-coverts. The long uppertail-coverts on birds from southern India and Sri Lanka are almost black. The lores, sides of face, wings and tail are darker brown, throat and upper breast blackish. There are striations caused by the quill shafts being pale to whitish on the entire back and wing-coverts, and on the short uppertail- and undertail-coverts. The sides of the neck, between the blackish-brown of the face and throat and the dark brown of the nape, is a lighter brown on birds from northern India. The rump is white, without any spots or flecking. The sides of the breast, flanks and belly are creamy-buff or creamy-white, whitish on the breast. The underwing-coverts are pale buff. The thighs are the same brown as the undertail-coverts. The irides are dark brown or ruby, the mandibles are black above and pale blue-grey below, the legs and feet are grey. The sexes are visually similar. Intermediates between this race and *L. s. acuticauda* have pale grey lines on the flanks.

Adult female 100–105mm. Wing length 48–50mm, culmen 9–10mm, tarsus 10mm. It is visually indistinguishable from the male.

Juvenile Slightly paler and less clearly marked, somewhat cinnamon version of the adult, lacking or faintly showing the striations. The lower mandible of newly-fledged birds is dark but it soon lightens.

BURMESE WHITE-RUMPED MUNIA
L. striata acuticauda
Former scientific name: *Munia acuticauda* Hodgson, 1836, Asiatic Researchers, 19, p.153.
Other common names: Sharp-tailed Finch, Striated

Munia and White-backed Munia (Ali and Ripley 1987).

Adult *c*.120mm depending on the length of the tail which is longer on second-year birds. Wing length *c*.52mm, culmen 10–11mm, tarsus 10–11mm. The forehead to lower back and wing-coverts are earth-brown with pale striations on the nape, back and wing-coverts. The rump is usually buffish with slight brownish flecking, but birds from north-east India have a white rump. The upper- and undertail-coverts are a warmer brown with both striations and pale edgings to the feathers. The wings are dark brown. The tail, which is slightly longer and more pointed than that of the preceding race (but the same as *L. s. swinhoei*) is blackish. The face, lores, mesial and bib are blackish; sides of face, neck and upper breast reddish-brown with pale shafts and pale edges to the breast feathers. The patch at the side of the neck has pale spots. The sides of the breast, flanks and belly are greyish-buff or greyish-white with light brown lines on the lower breast and grey lining on the flanks and this is the main distinction between this race and *L. s. striata*. The underwing-coverts are buff. The undertail-coverts are reddish-brown usually with pale shafts and pale edges. The irides are chestnut or ruby-red, the bill is black on the upper mandible and pale blue-grey on the lower. The legs and feet are greyish or vinous.

Juvenile Similar to the adult but duller and paler, with some fine barring on the underparts.

NICOBAR WHITE-RUMPED MUNIA
L. striata semistriata
Former scientific name: *Munia semistriata*, Hume, 1874, Stray Feathers, 2, p.257.
Other common names: Nicobar Munia, Nicobar White-backed Munia.
Adult Similar to *L. s. striata* above but with the striations on the back restricted to the mantle. The throat is dark brown and the upper breast has a gradation in irregular scalloping from dark brown to light brown. The uppertail- and undertail-coverts are verona-brown, edged with a paler shade. The lower breast, flanks and belly are cream with the thighs barred cream and brown.

ANDAMAN WHITE-RUMPED MUNIA
L. striata fumigata
Former scientific name: *Munia fumigata*, Walden, 1873, *Ann. Mag. Nat. Hist.*, Ser.4, 12, p.488.
Adult *c*.115mm. It is dark brown above, virtually or totally devoid of any striations on the back. The rump is white. The underparts are distinctly creamy to warm buff. The upper- and undertail-coverts are barred brown.
Female Has the reddish-brown edging to the breast feathers more noticeable (Goodwin 1982) and there are white edges to the sides of the breast.
Juvenile Distinctly buffish on the throat.

INDOCHINESE WHITE-RUMPED MUNIA
L. striata subsquamicollis   Plates 23–25
Former scientific name: *Uroloncha striata subsquamicollis*, Baker 1925, *Bull. Brit. Ornith. Club*, 45, p.59, *Uroloncha acuticauda lepidota* Oberholser, 1926
Other common name: Striated Munia
Adult male Varies from 105–115mm, depending on the length of the tail. Wing length 49–52mm, the

culmen 10–11mm, tarsus 10–11mm. It has the forehead, face and throat dark brown. The patch on the side of the neck is slightly orange-brown with white terminal spots. The crown to lower back, the scapulars, and the uppertail-coverts are mid-brown with white striations. The rump is cream and is lined with brown on the more southern birds but unmarked on birds from the north. The wings and tail are dark brown. The breast is dark reddish-brown with pale shafts and pale edges to the feathers, the sides of the breast, flanks and belly are buff to cream with slightly curved lines, rather like an elongated U with the centre of the bottom missing. In birds from Singapore, the belly is distinctly yellowish in tone. The undertail-coverts are light brown with pale shafts and edgings on birds from the southern end of the range, but on birds from the north the undertail-coverts are clay-coloured without any pale edges. The irides are ruby red. The mandibles are black above and pale blue-grey below. The legs and feet are grey.
Female 105–110mm. Wing length 48–50mm, culmen *c*.10mm, tarsus 10mm. There is no plumage difference that I could detect.
In Kuala Lumpur I was able to inspect two different batches of *L. s. subsquamicollis*, one trapped locally, the other from the north of Malaysia. I bought some examples from each batch and painted them carefully that day, before giving them to a colleague to release out of town. They were sufficiently distinct for me to include both birds in the plate on this species to show how the race intergrades within a comparatively small area.

SUMATRAN WHITE-RUMPED MUNIA
L. striata sumatrensis
Described as *L. striata sumatrensis* Chasen
Adult Differs from *L. s. subsquamicollis* by being richer brown above, and more heavily streaked below, with a more noticeable grey to the belly and flanks. The ear-coverts are paler, and the breast is a brighter brown.

CHINESE WHITE-RUMPED MUNIA
L striata swinhoei   Plate 26
Former scientific names: *Uroloncha swinhoei* Cabanis, 1882. *Journ. Ornith.*, 30. p. 462. *Uroloncha squamicollis* Sharpe, 1890.
Other common names: Chinese Striated Munia, Swinhoe's Sharp-tailed Munia, White-rumped Munia.
Adult *c*.115mm, depending on the length of the central tail feathers. Wing length *c*.50mm, culmen 10.5mm, tarsus 11–12mm. The typical bird from Hong Kong is raw umber-brown with cream striations from forehead to lower back and wing-coverts. The rump is buff with brown flecks. The wings and tail are dark brown. The uppertail-coverts, undertail-coverts and the thighs are tawny brown with pale shafts and pale edges to the feathers. The lores, around the eyes, base of the mesial and bib are fuscous. The ear-coverts, sides of neck and throat are tawny with white shafts on the ear-coverts, white terminal spots on the sides of the neck, and pale edges to the feathers at the sides of the throat. The feathers of the centre of the throat have dark brown centres. The underwing-coverts are warm buff to tawny. The breast, flanks and belly are drab buff with lines of brown on the breast and whitish on the flanks. The irides are chestnut to red. The

bill is black above and pale bluish below, legs and feet vinous to pink. It is distinguished from *L. s. acuticauda* by Riley (1938) as having the chest feathers much lighter brown, with broader and lighter edges.

I have found this to be a most variable race. Birds from Sichuan have a clearly-defined throat patch, and the breast is a lighter brown with pale striations. The breast is lined with grey. Birds from Zhejiang have the ear-coverts and uppertail-coverts paler, and the lines on the breast are even greyer. From eastern China the face and throat mask is very clearly defined but the brown of the breast graduates into the cream of the belly. Birds from Hainan resemble the race from Taiwan but have the ear-coverts markedly paler than any other form.

Juvenile Paler and more buffish bird than the adult with much weaker striations on the back and tail coverts.

Taiwan White-rumped Munia in undirected song.

TAIWAN WHITE-RUMPED MUNIA
L. striata phaethontoptila
Former scientific name: *L. acuticauda phaethontoptila*, Oberholser, 1926, *Journ. Washington Acad. Sci.*, 16: p521.

Adult *c.*115mm. Wing length 48–50mm, culmen 10.5mm, tarsus 13mm. It is raw umber-brown with cream striations above. The rump is buff with brown flecks. The wings and tail are dark brown. The uppertail-coverts, undertail-coverts and thighs are tawny-brown with pale shafts and paler edges to the feathers. The face, throat and breast are fuscous, darker than birds from China, with only a trace of pale edging, this being only noticeable at the sides of the breast. The ear-coverts are tawny with small white shafts. The belly and flanks are drab creamy-buff with greyish lines. The underwing-coverts are warm buff. The irides are chestnut to ruby. The upper mandible is blackish, the lower is grey. The legs and feet are grey.

THE BENGALESE

Introduction This is a domesticated variety of the Striated Munia, almost certainly the Chinese race *L. s. swinhoei*. There is a popular belief among cage bird keepers that the Bengalese is a fertile hybrid, produced hundreds of years ago by the Chinese, using a mixture of various species, details of which are lost in antiquity. The irony of this is that the activities of modern bird breeders in cross-breeding the Bengalese with various other munias, in an ongoing effort to produce novel types, are producing strains that are reluctant to breed, particularly F2 birds, and are turning the Bengalese into the hybrid it never was. The double irony is that some strains of these new types may only be produced with the aid of pure Bengalese

to act as foster parents.

Description It is distinguished from the wild White-rumped Munia by being to some extent piebald. The amount of white varies from almost none, to completely white. The brown is usually of a dark brown or a fawn. Rarely do birds carry both types of brown. Those that look remarkably like wild White-rumped Munias almost invariably show a pair of white 'pince nez' spots on the forehead, and usually a few white feathers in the wings. In recent years there has been much cross-breeding with other species of munia, in particular Black Mannikin *L. stygia* (see plate 41). These have been stabilised in various types and now breed true. They have been accepted by the avicultural communities as new varieties of Bengalese.

As a domesticated bird, the Bengalese has a devoted following of its own. There are specialist societies and clubs devoted to the Bengalese and several publications dealing exclusively with it.

To the munia enthusiast the original Bengalese has genuine utility, for it normally breeds very readily and can be used to foster eggs or nestlings of other munias. Indeed, in my own experience, even two males or two females may be placed in a suitable cage together with a nest and eggs and will brood and rear the resulting young (this is not a guarantee, but there is a high probability it will happen). The significance of this for the munia breeder is that the Bengalese is an excellent and inexpensive insurance against natural parents deserting their young. Care must be taken to obtain quality pure-bred domestic birds. The cheap, mixed types produced in considerable quantity in Taiwan and southern China for the international bird market are short-lived birds that do not breed well. This is also true of the expensive 'New Variety' types that are essentially F2 and F3 hybrids bred in The Netherlands and Germany.

The Bengalese, fawn pied above, normal pied below.

Calls Calls are virtually the same as those of White-rumped Munia. However there is much variation and dialect, no doubt brought about by the unintentional teaching effect of other munias that have been kept with the young Bengalese. It should also be noted that juvenile males call with the same loud call as adult females, sometimes up to six months old. It is only after they have begun to sing with any frequency that they utter the male call note exclusively.

Song The natural song of the Bengalese is similar to that of White-rumped Munia, although a comparison between the sonograms of the songs of a Chinese Bengalese and a

Chinese White-rumped Munia in my possession show the wild bird's song to be more complex. In general both song and display are similar to that of *L. striata* but there is much individual variation, particularly in the song. One male I studied had a clear descending warble or trill quite unlike any the song of any *L. striata*. The song is usually given only by the male. The sight and sound of a crowing bird satisfies most observers that the bird in question is male. However, more attention must be paid to the call note distinctions as females are known to sing. Christa Powers in England (*in litt.*) had a breeding pair in which both birds sang, and I too have had this experience. Luis Baptista in California (*in litt.*) had a female *L. striata* that sang and successfully raised five chicks, leaving no doubt of its sex.

Male Bengalese in directed song display.

Courtship and display The undirected song is given by the male sitting across the perch, head raised, bill pointing forward and held open. More often it is directed at another bird, when the male will twist to face the other, nape fluffed slightly, flanks and belly feathers erected. In high intensity the bird will bob and bow, often beginning the display with a deep bow. Eisner (1963) conjectured that if kept in near natural conditions, the Bengalese would use a straw in its display. I have not personally noticed the use of a straw held in the bill while displaying but it has been confirmed by Baptista and Horblit (1990).

Breeding Bengalese will nest in any suitable receptacle, though obviously a box with a removable lid to facilitate easy access to the eggs and nestlings is the most suitable. The birds are unwittingly most cooperative in this as they are poor nest-builders, so much so that human access to the central cavity of the nest is usually an easy matter. Bengalese are used as foster parents for a wide variety of species (not only estrildids) and many experiments have taken place over the years. It must be recognised, however, that they naturally feed only regurgitated vegetable matter to the young, usually simply seed. Some Bengalese will take only the usual seedeater fare and greens but others will take a variety of soft food and this should be encouraged if the species likely to be fostered are naturally raised with a high percentage of animal protein in the diet. The formula of the soft food can be as varied as the resources or imagination of the keeper and can include all the animal protein or fresh green food necessary. Some domestic strains will feed the nestlings on mealworms.

The palate markings of the nestling Bengalese are similar if not identical in birds that are plumaged like the wild *L. striata*, but as the Bengalese becomes more pied, with increasing amounts of white feathering in the plumage, so the palate markings become less, with the upper palate horseshoe disappearing altogether in near-white birds.

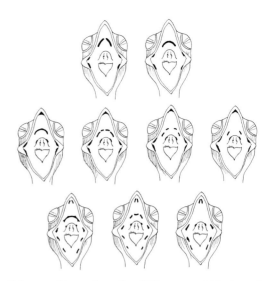

Palate markings of nestling White-rumped Munia and Bengalese. Upper row, left, a Sri Lankan White-rumped Munia bred by the author. Right a Chinese Bengalese bred by the author. Middle row, showing how the palate markings vary according to the amount of white in the plumage, as found by Eisner (1960). The bird on the left is a dark *striata* type, the bird on the far right is largely white. Bottom row, a similar decline in the amount of palate markings found by Immelmann *et al.* (1968-72).

Bengalese feed nestlings in response to begging calls, which is one reason why breeders using Bengalese prefer to use them as fosters in small cages, so that the adults are never out of earshot of hungry nestlings. A full brood of four or five is usually reared more efficiently than a small brood, for the same reason. Professional breeders will take chicks from a small brood of mannikins or grass-finches and add them to another small brood that is being fostered by Bengalese, thus leaving the original parents relieved and able to begin another brood. Mixing the species does not deter the Bengalese from their duties.

Bengalese eggs usually hatch in 15 or 16 days and the nestlings fledge a few days later than other species. Parent Bengalese are no different from other parent birds in that they tend to ignore smaller chicks - it is probably more accurate to say that smaller chicks compete less successfully for food. However, the parents are so tolerant of interference that chicks may be moved around from nest to nest to ensure evenly-sized broods. It is more important to have nestlings of the same size in the nest than of the same age.

Imprinting Much has been written about the dangers of imprinting when using foster parents. The most relevant studies are those of Klaus Immelmann (1962, 1969), using the Bengalese as a foster for the domesticated Zebra Finch *Poephila guttata*. Immelmann demonstrated that young Zebra Finches will become irreversibly imprinted upon the Bengalese if kept in their company past weaning. His conclusions about imprinting in Zebra Finches, combined with lesser and less detailed experiences with other estrildids, were taken as applying to all Estrildidae. This is quite unproven and in my opinion and experience does not apply to the genus *Lonchura* .

HYBRIDS No hybrids have been recorded in the wild, but both the wild *L. striata* and the domesticated Bengalese have been hybridised with many species in captivity. Gray (1958) lists 18 cross-breedings of *L. s. striata* or *L. s. acuticauda* with other *Lonchura* spp., plus cross-breedings with three species of *Poephila*. The Bengalese is listed by Gray as having crossed with about 16 species of *Lonchura* and with aviculturists having access to species from New Guinea in more recent years this list would now be much longer. In addition, Gray lists Bengalese crosses with the Cut-throat *Amadina amadina*, the Red-faced Parrotfinch *Erythrura psittacea*, the Red-cheeked Cordon-bleu *Uraeginthus bengala* and several *Poephila* spp.

CONSERVATION In Singapore the White-rumped Munia was formerly common and widespread (Gibson-Hill 1950) but is now listed as Threatened by Lim (1992), being reduced to occurring in only a few wooded areas, old plantations and cultivation. The only protected area where it is found is the central water catchment area. The only locations in Singapore where it is considered secure are the islands of Ubin, with a maximum population of 20 birds, and Tekong, where the population is put at a maximum of 15 birds by Lim.

The species is potentially vulnerable, at least in suburban areas and in places where man's activity can cause continual disturbance, which seems to be the case in Singapore. It seems as if escapes from the bird trade in Singapore are augmenting and reinforcing the population, so that numbers might have declined more dramatically without this. The escapes incidentally are invariably Malaysian birds, *L. s. subsquamicollis*. On Hong Kong island, the species was a regular visitor to my garden overlooking Repulse Bay in 1989 and 1990, but by the end of 1994 I had not seen it for three years. In those 6 years the local urban development had been extraordinary, the traffic on the road had quintupled, and the amount of disturbance to the wildlife due to construction, never-ending road works and noise pollution over several years was significant.

It is regularly trapped for the bird trade, mostly and illegally, from the Malay Peninsula. Significantly, the species is not listed in Strange and Jeyarajasingam (1993), and Tweedie (1960) said of it, "...rather less common than any of the (other munias) ..."

The trade in common birds in Thailand has reduced in recent years, and it is noted by Philip Round (Lekagul and Round 1991) as being a "...very common resident." It simply does not occur in shipments of birds trapped in Sumatra, which reflects the scarcity of the species there rather than trade preference, since Scaly-breasted Munia and White-headed Munia are regularly trapped in considerable numbers in Sumatra.

REFERENCES Ali & Ripley (1987), Avery (1978), Baker (1926 and 1934), Baptista (1995), Baptista & Horblit, (1990), Burton (1993), Caldwell & Caldwell (1931), Eisner (1960 & 1963), Gibson-Hill (1950), Goodwin (1982), Gray (1958), Immelmann (1962 & 1969), Immelmann *et al.* (1968-72), Kinnear (1929), Lekagul & Round (1991), Lim Kim Seng (1992), Meyer de Schauensee (1984), McClure (1993), Mitra & Nayar (1972), Morris (1958), Oberholser (1926), Paynter (1968), Phillips (1948), Riley (1938), Schafer (1938), Slater (1970), Smythies (1986), Spavin & Spavin (1991), Strange & Jeyarajasingam (1993), Tewari (1993), Tweedie (1960), Van Marle & Voous (1988), Viney *et al.* (1994), Yoneda & Okanoyo (1991).

9 JAVAN MUNIA
Lonchura leucogastroides   Plate 4

Described as *Lonchura leucogastroides* Horsfield and Moore
Former scientific names: *Munia leugastroides*, Horsfield and Moore, 1856, *Cat. Birds Mus. East India Co.*, 2, P.510.
Other common names: Black-rumped Munia, Javanese Mannikin, Black-beaked Bronze Mannikin (Lodge 1991), Javanese White-bellied Munia (Clement *et al.* 1993).

Javan Munia

FIELD CHARACTERS This is a small munia, dark brown above with a black face, breast, rump and undertail, with white belly and flanks. It is unlikely to be confused with any other species in the field except in southern Sumatra where White-rumped Munia *L. striata* and White-bellied Munia *L. leucogastra* occur. All three are scarce and local there. White-rumped Munia is distinguished by having a white rump. Javan Munia differs in having the white restricted to the belly; it reaches the sides of the breast and flanks in White-bellied Munia which also has yellow edges to the tail feathers, but when feeding on the ground the species appear to be identical, and it is only when White-rumped Munia flies up that the white rump identifies it. The three juveniles are similar, but Javan Munia is more buffy, and more likely to be confused with juvenile Scaly-breasted Munia *L. punctulata*. The other two are duller versions of the adults, but juvenile White-bellied Munia lacks any yellow on the tail.

Javan Munia

STATUS Common and widespread but never numerous except when flocks form to feed in the rice paddies.

HABITAT It is a bird of grassy areas, scrub and land that has been cleared for arable use and particularly areas developed by man, such as parkland and hotel developments, golf courses, etc. I found it widespread in the hills of western Java up to 1,750m, and it probably occurs higher.

HABITS AND BEHAVIOUR When I have seen the species in the wild in Singapore and Bali I have usually only seen it in pairs. In Mega Mendung in Java I watched a single bird attempt to join a pair in a tall fir tree and be repulsed by one of them. The interaction lasted about 10 minutes before the interloper gave up and flew off. On another occasion in the vicinity of Borobudur in Java, I watched while a male in a tall pine interspersed bouts of singing with an interesting searching behaviour, peering into and beneath clumps of pine leaves. Occasionally it would tug at a leaf but never dislodged one. It seemed at times to be foraging and at others to be engaged in nesting activity.

Peering has been observed in Javan Munia and a female has been observed peering at a male singing (Baptista *in litt.*).

It is usually found in pairs or small groups, up to a dozen birds. It joins feeding flocks of Scaly-breasted Munias in the paddyfields but otherwise tends to keep to itself.

FOOD AND FEEDING The secret of its success in Singapore is attributed by Hails and Jarvis (1987) to its habit of feeding on lawn grasses, Bermuda Grass, Buffalo Grass, etc., where the seed heads are found close to the ground. It is widespread, being found on lawns, open parkland, grassland and open scrub. However, it is not exclusively a ground feeder, and may be found feeding in tall grasses or trees and shrubs. In Indonesia I have seen it feeding on paddy fields, and high among the branches of tall trees. On one occasion a small group of up to a dozen birds visited a large bank of *Saccharum arundinaceum* each morning about 15 minutes after dawn.

Mason (1989 and pers. comm.) describes it as a serious crop pest, "a rice ravager" that feeds in mixed flocks on the paddyfields. Children are encouraged to destroy the nests wherever they may be found which, says Mason, is sad but understandable.

MOVEMENTS Fairly sedentary, but there is some wandering of small groups of young birds. It is likely that the extension of range into southern Sumatra is by natural colonisation.

CALL The soft contact call is a short *tit*. There are two loud contact calls, one the *peteet*! of Hoogerwerf (1949) is actually the call of the female. This can even sound like a *chirrup* at times. The loud call of the male is a simpler *p'tit*!. When disturbed they fly off with an alarm note *zitt*!

SONG The advertisement song is complex, particularly when compared to the longer directed courtship display song. This latter is a series of light but complex phrases that may continue for 10 or 12 seconds.

Male Javan Munia in courtship display.

COURTSHIP AND DISPLAY The display and song is very similar to that of Moluccan Munia *L. molucca*, and includes most of the elements of the straw display (Baptista and

Horblit 1990), but I have not observed straw carrying as the prelude to displaying. The male in undirected song sits at an angle and broadcasts forward. When a female is nearby, howeve,r he fans his tail and leans forward, tail almost horizontal, but does not raise the tail quite as high as White-bellied Munia does. He edges towards the female, feathers of the belly erected and flanks filled out, singing with the bill open and mandibulating slightly, and swaying from side to side. If the female stays and seems receptive, the male's posture will become more erect, he will stop singing and attempt copulation.

BREEDING The nest is a loose hollow sphere (MacKinnon 1988) of grasses and soft bents, fibres, etc, and is built in shrubs and bushes. It may also be found in thick foliage or in epiphytes at the ends of branches of trees. Mason and Jarvis (1989) say that in Bali it may often nest in loose colonies, "seeming to favour ornamental palms planted near restaurants and pools in hotel gardens." I have found it several times nesting in what might be taken for loose colonies in the grounds of hotels in Bali but I think the birds might have been taking advantage of benign areas full of suitable nesting sites rather than responding to a colonial instinct. The nest itself varied according to the location, ranging from being a fairly loose sphere to a comparatively compact oval. When it was built in the crown of a palm it usually had no regular outside shape at all, being essentially a filling of the wedge between palm stems.

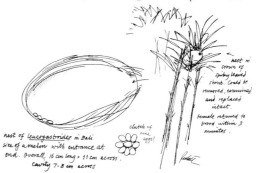

nest in crown of spiky leaved shrub. Comb to removed, examined and replaced intact. female returned to brood within 3 minutes.

clutch of nine eggs!

nest of *leucogastroides* in Bali size of a melon with entrance at end. Overall 16 cm long x 11 cm across. cavity 7-8 cm across.

Field sketch of the nest of Javan Munia in a garden palm in Bali, with cross section of the nest to show location of the eggs. There were 9 eggs in this nest, which was tended by one pair of birds.

Javan Munias favoured ornamental plants in the small gardens around the chalets of the Hotel Oberoi in Bali. One pair nested in a spiky shrub, the nest was about 1.8m from the ground, melon-shaped, measuring 16cm long and 11cm across. It was resting in the hand of leaves and seemed quite secure. Nonetheless I was able to remove it whole and examine the inside. The cavity measured about 7 or 8cm across and the whole was made of dry grasses and straws. The clutch was of nine eggs. The nest was set at an angle of about 30° up from the horizontal with the entrance hole at one end higher than the clutch, as shown in the sketch. After the examination I replaced the nest and stood nearby and watched while the female returned to brood and the male sat guard nearby. When another Javan Munia entered the garden it was chased away, but a pair of Scaly-breasted Munias came to drink and bathe and were ignored.

The clutch is recorded as normally being 5 to 6 but

smaller and larger clutches are produced and I am sure my own record of 9 is no exception. The egg is white and typically 14mm long x 10mm wide at the broadest part. Incubation is shared alternately, but in Bali I only ever saw the female brood. She left the eggs unattended when she left to feed. The male would be in evidence, and would fly off with her. As the air temperature was 32°C there was obviously no danger of the eggs going cold. Incubation is about 13 days and the nestlings fledge in 18 to 20 days. They are fed on regurgitated seed, more soft ripening seeds than hard dry seed and green food. It seems they rear the young entirely on vegetable matter (Restall 1987), but while it is entirely possible they take some insect matter they have reared young on se   and greens in captivity.

Palate marking of nestling Javan Munia.

It seems to be an opportunistic breeder, breeding all year round in west Java where there is lush grass growing at all times, but in the dryer parts of east Java it breeds only in the wet season (Hoogerwerf 1949 and Immelmann *et al.* 1968-72). I get the impression it breeds during most of the year in Bali, but only in the wetter part of the year in Lombok which is a more arid island.

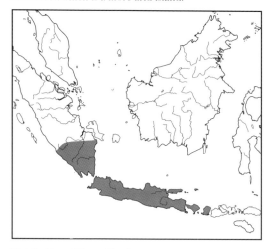

Distribution of Javan Munia.

DISTRIBUTION Southern Sumatra, Java, Bali and crossing Wallace's Line to Lombok. It was introduced into Singapore in 1922 where it is now considered to be the most abundant munia.

DESCRIPTION Plate 27
Monotypic.
Adult male 102–106mm. Wing length 49–52mm, culmen 9.5mm, tarsus 10mm. It is dark brown from crown to lower back, wings and tail also dark brown; there are no striations on the back. The forehead, face, bib to breast, rump and undertail-coverts are apparently black (actually very dark brown) with a purple sheen on the breast in certain light. The belly, flanks and vent are white. The underwing-coverts and trailing edges of the flight feathers on the underwing are creamy-buff, the thighs are similar with slight barring of black and brown. At the side of the neck is a patch of slightly paler brown which is brighter, tending to tawny in older males. The upper mandible is black, the lower pale grey becoming very pale blue at the base. The irides are dark brown. The legs and feet are vinous-grey with dark nails.

Adult female 99–102mm. Wing length 47–50mm, culmen 9–9.5mm, tarsus 10mm. The sexes appear to be alike but the pale patch at the side of the neck is slightly duller and less noticeable in the female. In a true pair side by side this distinction is clear. The male also has a larger bill with a more pronounced base to the culmen.

First-year Striations on the mantle and scapulars. The belly, flanks and vent are cream or whitish-cream and there are some brown flecks on the lower breast becoming short lines on the flanks. In my experience there is a difference between the sexes in these flank markings, those of the female being U-shaped, those of the male being more linear, as illustrated. I have not been able to confirm this with data from elsewhere.

Juvenile Dark sepia above, darker on wings and tail, light buffy below, darker on the breast. It is lightly or slightly barred on the upper- and undertail-coverts and the latter may be dark brown with pale spots instead of barred. I do not know if this difference is sex-related. The thighs are dark, like the back. The underwing-coverts are creamy-buff. The bill of the newly fledged bird is all dark grey-horn but the lower mandible becomes paler before the bird moults, and the upper mandible gradually darkens. This colour change is complete before the bird moults. The legs and feet are horn-grey.

HYBRIDS No natural hybrids have been recorded from the wild, although it has produced fertile young in cross-breedings with both White-rumped Munia and the Bengalese in captivity.

CONSERVATION Javan Munias are regularly caught in small numbers in Java where it occurs among flocks of Scaly-breasted Munias. The absolute quantities are very small and pose no threat to the species. I have seen it included in large shipments (several thousands) of munias for the bird trade from Indonesia, but there have only ever been a few Javan Munias for every hundred or so White-headed and Scaly-breasted Munias. The ubiquitous nature of the species ensures that changes to habitat are not an issue.

REFERENCES Baptista & Horblit (1990), Clement *et al.* (1993), Goodwin (1982), Hails & Jarvis (1987), Hoogerwerf (1949), Immelmann *et al.* (1968-72), Lodge (1991), MacKinnon (1988), Mason & Jarvis (1989), Restall (1987).

10 DUSKY MUNIA
Lonchura fuscans   Plate 5

Described as *Lonchura fuscans* Cassin.
Former scientific names: *Spermestes fuscans*, Cassin, 1852, *Proc. Philadelphia Acad.*, 6, p.185. *Uroloncha fuscans*.
Other common names: Black Borneo Mannikin, Black Mannikin, Brown Munia, Borneo Munia, or Mannikin, Bornean Munia or Mannikin, Dusky Mannikin.

Dusky Munia

INTRODUCTION For a common and widespread bird that ventures into gardens in towns and cities with little fear of man, it is remarkable how little is known about this species. Its behaviour suggests an atypical munia that would be worthy of dedicated study.

FIELD CHARACTERS This is a medium-sized robust-looking munia, dark brown all over with blackish edges to the feathers, darker above. It is unlikely to be confused with any other munia when seen clearly, though when seen at a distance it might be confused with Chestnut Munia *L. atricapilla*, particularly the dark race in the south-central part of Kalimantan *L. a. minuta*. It may be found in the company of Chestnut Munias, with the latter feeding high in the reeds while Dusky Munias occupy the lower levels. Fluffy-backed Tit-babbler *Macronous ptilosus* may be confused with Dusky Munia if seen in shrubs or undergrowth at the forest edge or in forest clearings as it is a dark, skulking bird of similar size though of different form and character once seen clearly.

The juvenile is similar to the adult, but is more drab and paler below. It could be confused with juvenile Chestnut or Scaly-breasted Munias.

STATUS Common and locally abundant.

HABITAT It is widespread throughout lowland Borneo, occurring up to only 500m or so. It can be found in grassy open country and cultivated land, secondary woodland, scrub, clearings, and cleared land. It may be found in gardens and around human habitation, even in towns and cities "wherever suitable food is available" (Clement *et al.* 1993). It was a common garden bird in Kuching (Harrison 1950) and is frequently seen in the gardens in Pontianak (Linda Santosa pers. comm.). It also favours reedbeds and can be found along river banks far inland (MacKinnon and Phillipps 1993). It is commonly found in paddyfields when the rice is growing.

HABITS AND BEHAVIOUR The Dusky Munia is a little different from the other munias within its range. It is a bird of somewhat skulking habits described by several sources as 'mouse-like', keeping low in vegetation, and feeding on the ground much of the time. Its distinctive behavioural characteristic is that it has great curiosity combined with little fear of man. When alarmed or frightened it sits quite still, in contrast to other species that will fly off in a twittering flock (Smythies 1981). This behaviour confounds the local rice farmers, who take much trouble to construct bangers and rattling scarecrows to frighten birds away from the seeding crops.

Smythies (1981) says it has the tactics of a rodent, nipping about and running much like a mouse. It has a habit of entering and exploring things, and this frequently leads to its getting caught in hung-up fish traps, rice bins, and dwellings.

Dusky Munias roost communally, and will roost in the disused nests of other species. Apparently, nests are built for roosting (Clement *et al.* 1993).

FOOD AND FEEDING It feeds both on the ground and in vegetation, climbing up stems to reach the seeding heads with great agility. It has been observed feeding on the surface of roads, but it is not recorded what the birds actually eat there. In my personal observations of Scaly-breasted Munias foraging on roadway surfaces, the birds have been feeding on flattened road kills. It is possible this is what has attracted Dusky Munias. It certainly takes all kinds of grass seeds and the seeds of weeds and shrubs. It has a particular liking for growing rice. In captivity it thrives and breeds well on an all-seed diet, and is especially partial to ripening wheat.

MOVEMENTS Apparently sedentary.

CALL Williams (in Smythies 1981) describes the call note as a shrill *pee pee*. Harrison (in Smythies 1981) mentions a thin *chirrup*, and a quick low *teck teck* in flight.

SONG Nothing recorded.

COURTSHIP AND DISPLAY Nothing recorded.

BREEDING Batchelor (1959) records nests in the Kimanis area in northern Borneo being mostly situated in holes in (presumably river) banks, or among exposed roots just below the lip, or roadside banks, at a height of 1–2m. Other nests were located in holes in trees, in the roots of fallen trees, and occasionally in low bushes under the eaves of houses. Nests were also found in the terminal leaf clusters of sena and mango trees 3–8m from the ground. Motley and Dillwyn (1855) said it often nested in hollow trees and Whitehead (1893) records it nesting in fruit trees. In contrast, Harrisson (1950) says it is a bird that nests far from the ground, preferring a height of 4.5–6m. He found nests commonly between 8–15m from the ground in fruit trees in the Kelabit uplands and between 5–10m around Kuching. He also records nests in the Niah Caves some 77m from the ground.

Breeding seems to be a function of food supply, occurring more or less at any time of the year but apparently stimulated by the availability of ripening rice more than anything.

The nest is a more or less spherical bundle of grasses and similar material with the entrance at the side. The entrance is protected by a projecting dense porch of stems and blades.

The size of the brood is variable and, like the breeding season itself, is probably a response to food availability. 2–8 white eggs are laid, usually 3 form a clutch in upland areas, but in captivity 3–6 are usual.

The species was first bred in captivity by Langberg (1955). Four youngsters fledged from the first brood. They resembled the parents but for the bill being entirely black. They began to feed themselves within three or four days and were independent two weeks later. Within a month the lower mandible had become pale grey.

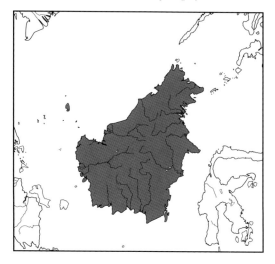

Distribution of Dusky Munia.

DISTRIBUTION Borneo and the outlying islands of Natuna and Banggi, and Cagayan Sulu in the south-west Philippines.

DESCRIPTION
Monotypic.
Adult male *c.*120mm. Wing length 57–58mm, culmen 12–13mm, tarsus 14mm. It is burnt umber all over. This is not the lustrous chestnut of Chestnut Munia, but is a deeper rich earthy colour. It is darker above and on the lower breast and belly. The feathers of the head have the terminal shaft and centre of the edges of the feathers paler, giving a slight speckled appearance and there may be a purple gloss to the head and throat. The rump and uppertail-coverts are even dark brown. The feathers of the breast, flanks and belly have black edges giving a somewhat scaled appearance, and this may be noticeable on the wings also. The bill is black above, pale bluish-grey below, palest at the base. The bill of the male may be more noticeably ridged at the forehead and the curve of the culmen more pronounced than in the female.The irides are chestnut brown. The feet and legs are bluish-grey. Albino or leucistic birds have been found in the highlands of Borneo (Clement *et al.* 1993).
Adult female *c.*115mm. Wing length 54–57mm, culmen 12mm, tarsus 13mm. I have been unable to distinguish the sexes visually. There is considerable variation in size and it is worth noting that there is considerable variation in coloration between individuals, some being more speckled or scaled than others. This could be a matter of wear, abrasion and age. Known pairs should be compared carefully when both are in fresh plumage and the details recorded, especially if the age is known.
First-year Plumage is slightly lighter than on an adult, and the flight feathers are noticeably darker than the

wing-coverts.
Juvenile Dark drab to burnt umber above, slightly darker on wings and tail. Below it is dark drab. The bill is black upon fledging, but the lower mandible gradually becomes paler before the bird moults into first-year adult plumage.

CONSERVATION There is very little bird trade from Kalimantan, compared to the rest of Indonesia, and the Dusky Munia is very rare in dealers' holding farms. I found it in one dealer's stock in Jakarta only once in five years, and then only twenty birds. Nothing is known of population densities, and its status is largely assumed. Nontheless there seems to be no cause for concern.

REFERENCES Batchelor (1959), Clement *et al.* (1993), Harrisson (1950), Langberg (1955), MacKinnon & Phillipps (1993), Motley & Dillwyn (1855), Smythies (1981), Whitehead (1893).

11   MOLUCCAN MUNIA
Lonchura molucca   Plate 4

Described as *Lonchura molucca* Linnaeus
Other common names: Black-faced Munia.

INTRODUCTION The races of this somewhat variable species are poorly delineated, and the species invites detailed field study (See comments under Description and Distribution, below).

Moluccan Munia

FIELD CHARACTERS This is an average-sized munia with a black face and breast, brown on the upperparts. The white belly, flanks and rump are finely flecked with black but often appear white in the field. On the island of Lombok, where Javan Munia *L. leucogastroides* and Moluccan Munia both occcur, the latter may be distinguished by the white rump. The juveniles would be very hard to separate. I have seen it accompanied by Five-coloured Munia *L. quinticolor* on several islands when, at a distance, the white of the belly of both species is obvious. In the event of the white rump of Moluccan Munia not being seen, the black of the face reaching down to cover the breast distinguishes it.

STATUS Common or locally common.

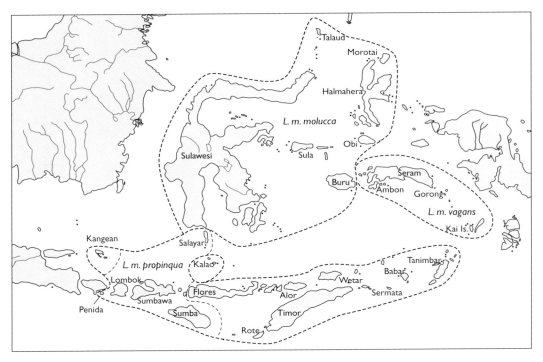

Distribution of Moluccan Munia, based on analysis of the origins of specimens in the AMNH collection. The Kalao population matches the characteristics of *L. m. molucca*. The populations that form *L. m. propinqua* fall into three groups, based primarily on the density of the breast patterns: Kangean; Lombok, Sumba and Sumbawa; and Flores to Tanimbar.

HABITAT It is a bird of grassy and bushy areas at forest edges and clearings in open forests. It is found also in areas overgrown with the cotton grass *Imperata arundinacea*, known in Indonesia as alang-alang, and also regions cultivated by man.

HABITS AND BEHAVIOUR It shows no fear of man, ignoring the alarms and rattles to frighten it away from crops, and this equanimity has earned it the sobriquet of 'Deaf Munia' in Sulawesi and probably elsewhere. It travels in pairs and small groups. I have seen it in flocks of up to several dozen birds. Watling (1983) found it to be the least abundant munia on Sulawesi but still relatively common. It often joins other munias in rice growing areas but is also frequently seen in small family parties at the forest edge, and in forest openings not far inside.

I first saw Moluccan Munia in a mixed flock with some Zebra Finches *Poephila guttata* on the island of Sawu. They had been feeding in long grass along the side of a dried-up river bed and were disturbed by some goats and a goat herder who inadvertently drove the birds towards me as he drove the goats in my direction. The white rump was obvious when the birds turned and flew away, and clearly separated it from the retreating Zebra Finches with their boldly barred black-and-white uppertails.

They were working the stems with considerable agility and, while the little flock of a dozen or so birds kept close together, each bird worked its own branch or stem. There was none of the two or three to a stem behaviour I noted with Scaly-breasted Munias *L. punctulata* and Pale-headed Munias *L. pallida* in the same area. I also saw it in long grass and in rice paddies with Five-coloured Munias. The

black face and breast contrasted brilliantly and was quite different from the similar front view of the other bird.

FOOD AND FEEDING It feeds on the seeds of grasses of all kinds, weeds and small shrubs, both from growing plants and those that have fallen to the ground. It normally alights on the stems and works its way to the inflorescences or buds. From observations of birds in captivity it will also eat small amounts of tender green leaves such as lettuce, and may take small insects.

MOVEMENTS It seems to be more or less sedentary.

CALL The contact note is a buzzy *tissip* or *t'sip*, similar in character to that of White-spotted Mannikin *L. leucosticta*. Immelmann *et al.* (1968-72) recorded a call note as *tr, tr*, but I have not heard this from captive birds.

SONG The song is a continual run of wheezing *peeps* and *wheees*.

Directed advertisement song.

COURTSHIP AND DISPLAY In undirected advertisement display the male appears to lean forward very slightly, the

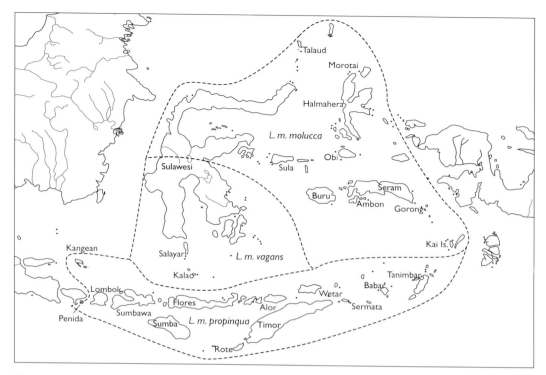

Distribution of Moluccan Munia following Paynter (1968).

tail almost horizontal, singing. The bill is open all the time. When directed, the bird swivels from side to side. In full intensity, when a female is nearby or alongside, she becomes the focus of attention and he hops towards her, still swaying from side to side but more twisted in her direction. After bowing deeply he performs a deep inverted curtsey; his bill is open all the time, with only slight mandibulatory movements, and the tail is fanned as he continues singing. His swivelling from side to side is quite pronounced. The female usually regards this in a fairly upright posture, thereby ensuring that the performance will cease. If she lowers her body at all this encourages the male to higher intensity, he becomes more upright and hops closer leading to attempted copulation.

High intensity display showing swivelling.

BREEDING Whilst I visited 10 islands around Timor, Sumba and Flores, the only places I saw Moluccan Munia were Timor, Flores, Sawu and Roti. At the edge of the town of Aileu, at about 1,400m in northern East Timor, by the Japanese memorial overlooking rich grassland, I could see the grasses growing up to 2m high or more. Next to the grassland were extensive paddyfields. It was comparatively easy to find munias in the grass because there was invariably a solitary Moluccan Munia perched high on a tall stem keeping lookout, the white belly show in clear contrast to the green of the grass. I watched the two resident species, Moluccan and Five-coloured Munias flying out from the grass into the paddies to feed.

Close to where I was standing, village boys had collected some nests of the munias and thrown them down; the eggs, typical small white oval munia eggs, had spilled out and broken. There were ten nests in all and they were of two types, both perfectly round with a side entrance without a porch. In one kind of nest the walls were thick and densely packed, with much use of soft fluffy grass panicles. The other kind were more loosely made with less of the fluffy grassheads. They were about 16cm round, with a cavity of about 8cm across. There was no way for me to identify which of the two species had produced which nest.

There is no qualitative field information in the literature about this species but it seems to be fairly typical in breeding behaviour. The nest may be placed among twigs in a tree (Goodwin 1982) but cicumstantial evidence at Aileu suggests the nests are built among the long dense grasses as well.

The clutch consists of 4 or 5 eggs, and up to 7 are recorded in captivity. The incubation is 15-16 days. The young nestlings have white down on their backs. They appear to be quite precocious and may fledge in 18 days, but 20 to 21 days has also been recorded. Stresemann (1939) records it as breeding at the end of the rainy season

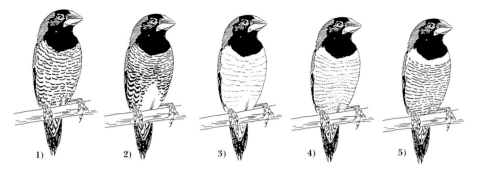

Typical breast patterns of Moluccan Munia. From the left, 1) *L. m. molucca*; **2)** *L. m. vagans*; **3, 4, and 5)** *L. m. propinqua*. Generally, *L. m. propinqua* is distiguished by lighter barring and a white space between the black throat and the barring. **3) From Kangean:** This population is extremely lightly marked, and merits careful study. **4) From Lombok, Sumbawa and Sumba:** These populations vary one from another but all more or less resemble the bird illustrated. **5) From Flores to Tanimbar:** The populations tend to be darker and more densely marked.

and the beginning of the dry season, precisely when the grasses are at their most lush and heavy with rich, milky ripening and soft seeds. Watling (1983) found it breeding at 500m in Lore Lindu in July, August, September and January. The nests with eggs I saw in East Timor were at the beginning of June.

Various reports in *Die Gefiederte Welt* (Deckert 1980) and Faulkener (1986) in the UK, indicate that while live food is not essential to successful rearing, most times the parents will take small chopped mealworms and wood ant pupae ('ants eggs') and some parents take mealworms freely. They also take plenty of green food when rearing.

DISTRIBUTION Because of the variability in plumage characteristics and the difficulty in defining the precise range of each subspecies, it is not possible to draw a truly accurate map of distribution. I have drawn two distribution maps, the first shows the distribution of the three subspecies following Paynter (1968). The second is based on the locations of origin of the specimens in the AMNH New York. By matching these museum specimens to the map one can place *L. m. molucca* on Sulawesi, the Sangihe Islands, Talaud, the Sula Islands, Morotai, Halmahera, Ternate, Bacan, Obi and Buru and no doubt many small islands within the parameters of this area.

L. m. propinqua is from Kangean, north of Bali, and Penida south of Bali (but not on Bali). The birds from Salayar, south of south-east Sulawesi appear to be of this race, but the birds from the islands between Salayar and Flores, Kalao and Kalao Tolea are more boldly barred and look like *L. m. vagans* which clearly they cannot be. From Lombok, Sumbawa, and Sumba the race is clearly defined but from Flores, Lomblen, Pantar, Alor, Timor, Roti, Wetar, Sermata and Babar to Tanimbar the black barring is bolder and is almost intermediate with *L. m. vagans*. These eastern populations are grouped within *L. m. vagans* in Paynter (1968).

L. m. vagans occurs on Ceram, Ambon, Gorong, Manawoka and the Lesser and Greater Key Islands and no doubt some of the other islands within these parameters.

DESCRIPTION   **Plates 28–29**

Goodwin (1982) recognises the three races of Paynter (1968), but observes they are not very well defined. White and Bruce (1986) take a more extreme point of view and suggest there is not good enough reason for recognising

any subspecies, because the variation is geographically inconsistent and there is little constant difference visible in the field. In making the colour plates and reference drawings for the three races recognised here, I have drawn upon the collection of skins in the collection of the Natural History Museum at Tring, and the AMNH in New York, using individuals most typical of each race. I also referred to detailed drawings of several live birds that I have kept and studied.

L. m. propinqua is the distinctive and comparatively easy to identify race, having a white area between the black of the breast and the fine barring on the breast. Those markings on the breast, belly and flanks are noticably finer than on the other two races. The birds from Kangean are particularly finely marked, with the bars more widely spaced, and the six specimens in the AMNH collection numbered 721185 to 721190 are labelled *L. m. kangeanensis*. Only one of these is a full adult. They have been included within *L. m. propinqua*, but invite further field study.

The distinction between *L. m. molucca* and *L. m. vagans* is less easy. As a generalisation, *L. m. vagans* has the barring on the breast bolder and more densely black, and the black V-markings on the short uppertail-coverts are bolder than on *L. m. molucca*. In many of the specimens I studied, but not all, *L. m. vagans* was much paler on the vent and lower belly.

The common names I have given to each race are to help enhance the distinctions, the common name for the nominate being obviously appropriate. This species would undoubtedly benefit from being studied in greater detail, with careful comparative notes made of every island population.

MOLUCCAN MUNIA
L. molucca molucca   **Plates 28–29**

Former scientific names: *Loxia molucca* Linnaeus, 1766, Syst. Nat., ed. 12, 1, p. 302.

Other common names: Moluccan Mannikin, Celebes Munia or Mannikin.

Adult male 109–112mm, but the central rectrices varies and fine extended tips could add another 2–4mm. Wing length 50–52mm, culmen 9.5–10mm, tarsus 10mm. It has the head from the crown down behind the eyes to the ear-coverts, throat and upper breast, and the long uppertail-coverts black. The nape, outermost ear-coverts and sides of neck, mantle and lower back dark earth-brown; the wing-coverts are darker brown, as are the tertials. There is a fine, slightly blackish barring from the rear crown to the lower back and tertials, but not on the wings. The flight feathers are blackish-brown and contrast with the lighter brown of the greater wing-coverts. The lower breast, belly, flanks and undertail-coverts, rump and shorter uppertail-coverts are white, barred with flecking that forms wavy and dotted bars. These become V-markings on the undertail-coverts. This patterning is quite dense. The underwing-coverts are buffish, barred black-and-white along the wing edge. The irides are brown. The upper mandible is dark grey to blackish, the lower mandible pale bluish-grey. The feet and legs are dark grey.

Female 107–110mm. Wing length 48–50mm, culmen 9.5mm, tarsus 10mm. The sexes appear to be similar but in careful comparison it can be seen that there is a paler, tan-coloured patch on the sides of the neck which is lighter and brighter on the male birds.

Juvenile Warm brown above, darker on the forehead, crown and lores, with a little dark barring or flecking on the face and bib. The rump is paler, similar to the underparts, with a tendency to some barring where the rump meets the uppertail-coverts and on the undertail-coverts. The tertials, uppertail-coverts and flight feathers are dark brown.

CERAM BLACK-FACED MUNIA
L. molucca vagans
Former scientific name: *Munia molucca vagans* Meise, 1929, *Journ. Ornith.* 77, p. 440
Adult Rear crown, nape and outer ear-coverts dark earth-brown. The wing-coverts, tertials, mantle and lower back are medium earth-brown lightly barred with dark brown. The wings and tail are dark brown. The long uppertail-coverts are black. The rump continues the earth-brown of the back but has fine white barring. The short uppertail-coverts are white, initially with earth-brown barring with bolder black scallops on the lower feathers. The belly, flanks and undertail-coverts are white, but the belly definitely tends to cream or buffish and the black flecking-barring is less dense and more clearly defined and becomes brown, not black, on the flanks. The irides are brown. The bill is dark grey to blackish above, pale blue-grey below. The legs and feet are pale grey.
The sexes are fairly easy to identify once the lighter patch on the side of the neck is noticed. It is brighter on males tending to being almost orange.
Juvenile A little paler than the juvenile *L. m. molucca*.

LESSER SUNDAS BLACK-FACED MUNIA
L. molucca propinqua
Former scientific name: *Uroloncha propinqua* Sharpe, 1890, *Cat. Birds Brit. Mus.*, 13, p. 368.
Adult Has the head from the crown down behind the eyes to the ear-coverts, throat and breast black. The nape, outermost ear-coverts and sides of the neck, mantle and lower back light earth-brown to tan, the wings being a little darker. The distinguishing feature of this race is that it lacks any barring on the brown upperparts, and is entirely cream below (*L. m. molucca* being entirely white with a dirty-looking belly patch, while *L. m. vagans* is white with cream at the centre of the belly). The barring on the underparts is noticeably greyer and paler on the flanks. The irides are

brown. The bill is dark grey to blackish above, pale blue-grey below. The legs and feet are light grey.

HYBRIDS Nothing recorded in the literature.

CONSERVATION Insufficient information. The species appears irregularly in the bird trade and in small numbers, but demand is not great enough to encourage deliberate specific trapping and there appears to be no threat to the species from this.

REFERENCES Deckert (1980), Faulkener (1986), Goodwin (1982), Immelmann *et al.* (1968-72), Paynter (1968), Stresemann (1939), Watling (1983), White & Bruce (1986).

12   SPOT-SIDED MUNIA
Lonchura sp.   Plate 5

An undescribed taxon.

INTRODUCTION This species is known only from a single specimen brought to me in Jakarta in 1990, said to be from Bandjarmasin. A second bird was reported to be in the hands of an importer in Singapore but I was unable to see or obtain it to verify its identity. I am loath to publish the formal description of a single specimen that might turn out to be a hybrid bred in captivity, but in the event that other workers should find a similar bird in unforseen circumstances, I am recording it here.

FIELD CHARACTERS A medium-sized munia, mainly brown with a white belly white spots on dark flanks.

HABITAT Not known.

HABITS Only known from a single bird in captivity. Nothing exceptional recorded.

CALL The bird that I kept was a female. The only vocalisations I noted were a small range of buzzing *tzit!* sounds.

SONG AND DISPLAY None.

DISTRIBUTION Unknown. It is apparently from southwest Kalimantan, an area where there appears to be very little information about the local grassland birds.

DESCRIPTION   Plate 30
A brown munia with a white belly, dotted with black and white on the flanks.
First-year female 110mm. Wing length 51mm, culmen 12mm, tarsus 11mm. It is fuscous on the forehead, lores, base of mesial and bib. This quickly graduates into cinnamon on the crown, ear-coverts, sides of neck and nape. The mantle, scapulars and wing-coverts are chestnut, slightly darker on the flight feathers and tail. The chestnut continues onto the rump, becoming a little richer. The uppertail-coverts are dark brown with clear reddish-chestnut edges. The tail is dark brown. The fuscous of the bib graduates into reddish-chestnut on the upper breast which in turn becomes dark greyish-brown. This breaks up into irregular spots across the lower breast, flanks and vent, surrounding a white belly. The flanks covered by the wing have some white shaft lines with double white crosses. The underwing-coverts are buffy-salmon. The reddish-chestnut of the rump continues round the lower flanks to merge into dark greyish-brown to black undertail-coverts.

The thighs are brown, barred and spotted with white. The bill is pale blue-grey, violaceous on the upper mandible, palest at the base of the lower mandible. The irides are dark brown. The legs and feet are bluish-grey.

Second-year female From crown to lower back and wings is brown. The rump, uppertail-coverts and edges of the deep brown tail are a deep brick-red. The forehead, face, bib, throat and breast are a deep warm brown, almost purplish. At the side of the neck is an area of cinnamon. The belly is white with a touch of cream where it meets the sides of the breast. The flanks are brownish under the wings but all the visible part is the same deep purplish warm brown. The feathers nearer the breast are white with dark spots but these change until at the rear of the flanks they are blackish with white spots. The white belly is thus surrounded by irregular spots. The underwing-coverts are pale buffy-salmon. The undertail-coverts are black. The irides are dark brown. The bill is pale blue with blackish at the base of the upper mandible.

This bird is now in the collection of the American Museum of Natural History and is catalogued without name as No. 831289.

BEHAVIOUR IN CAPTIVITY The bird I have described died in my collection in Hong-Kong in mid 1993. It was normally a quiet and peaceful bird. In a large cage with two Cream-bellied Munias *L. pallidiventer* each bird established its own territory and a favourite perch, and this bird was mildly aggressive if disturbed. It took all the seeds in my eclectic mixture of grasses, weeds, herbs, canary and millets, and was fond of fresh green seeding grass.

Over three years, I tried keeping it with White-bellied Munias *L.leucogastra* and others but it never bonded nor showed any interest in any other munia.

13   HILL MUNIA
Lonchura kelaarti   Plate 16

Described as *Lonchura kelaarti* Jerdon.
Other common names: Rufous-bellied Munia, Rufous-breasted Munia, Black-throated Munia (not advisable because of confusion with *L. ferruginosa*).

Sri Lankan Hill Munia.

FIELD CHARACTERS This is an above average-sized munia, brown above with yellowish uppertail-coverts or completely brown above, pinkish-tan flush to sides of neck and part or all of underparts which are patterned with distinctive dark brown spotting. It is superficially similar to Scaly-breasted Munia *L. punctulata* which occurs throughout the range of Hill Munia. The two species may be found feeding together. They are not easy to separate at a distance without careful comparison, when Hill Munia can be seen to be larger and the pale patch on the sides of the neck distinctive. In addition, the fuscous of the face is darker than the face of Scaly-breasted Munia, is more clearly defined and extends to the centre of the breast.

The birds I found at Pattipola in Sri Lanka were more richly coloured than I recalled from museum specimens. The pinkish patch on the side of the neck is very noticeable and provides an efficient diagnostic when birds are seen in flight in poor light. I particularly noticed and made sketches of the undertail-coverts, these were well-defined on some birds, and almost black on others. In one pair, presumed to be mated, it was the presumed male that had the near-black undertail. It has not been possible to confirm this feature as sexually diagnostic feature in museum specimens through lack of sufficient comparative material.

The notes on the Indian birds here only apply to the race *L. k. jerdoni*. I am unaware of any field notes on the behaviour of the race *L. k. vernayi*. It is worth noting that there may be significant differences between the Indian and Sri Lankan birds and further study could indicate that they are sibling species rather than conspecific. They have been separated by Wijesinghe (1994) but I would like to see some comparative behavioural data before accepting this treatment.

STATUS Locally common or scarce.

HABITAT It inhabits forest edges and grassy clearings, *Lantana* scrub, tea and coffee plantations and similar cultivations, and gardens. It is more inclined to forest habitat than most munias. It is frequently found in the interior of the gloomiest forests (Legge 1880) but when I was seeking the bird in the highlands of Sri Lanka, whenever we found our path leading into gloomy forest my guide turned back insisting we would not find it there.

With regard to the species in India I have to rely on Ali and Ripley (1987) who describe it as a fairly common resident, subject to local movements, in the hills of south-western India. It occurs 'from the foothills' (no lower altitude is given) up to 2,100m or even higher in the summer in the Nilgiris where it breeds. In India it is a bird of scrub, grassland, fallow fields in forest clearings, and the neighbourhood of settlements and cultivations.

HABITS AND BEHAVIOUR Legge (1880) describes it as being an unsociable bird, living for the most part in pairs or in very small parties of three or four, except at night when it comes together at night to roost. I saw two parties of twenty or more birds flying overhead, calling, an hour or two after dawn in Sri Lanka. Steitz (in Nachrichten 1978) found that his captive birds built roosting nests. Legge (1880) gives no details of roosting but seems to suggest they roost communally in tall trees.

It is shy and restless, and is a bird of rapid and fairly direct flight, the group undulating a little as it goes. It flies high, and may often be detected first by the contact calls of the flying birds.

FOOD AND FEEDING It may be seen flying over patna grass and will gorge itself on the seeds when they are ripe. The bill of the bird is comparatively straight and sharp for a munia, not curved and stout like Tricoloured Munia *L. malacca*. This suggests a modified feeding behaviour but there are little or no clues as to what it might be. Legge (1880) says it feeds on small seeds.

It feeds on the ground, may be seen on the road, or on freshly turned soil, such as potato plantations, and perhaps the sharper bill is an adaptation for picking out tiny seeds from the grit and soil. Legge (1880) mentions watching it on dunghills and rubbish heaps, when maybe it was taking small insects. Henry (1955) mentions watching a bird at Opanake (alt. 215m) searching among the leaves of a creeper growing on a tall stump which suggests the bird might have been feeding on small insects of some kind. In my limited observations of feeding behaviour it was on the ground in a truck farm and was in the company of Scaly-breasted Munias that were taking the flowering and seeding heads of chickweed and groundsel. Ali and Ripley (1974) list its food as simply grass seeds, weed seeds and grain. It takes cultivated rice where available (Goodwin 1982). Deepal Wakaragoda, a professional bird guide in Sri Lanka, has watched Hill Munias feeding in rice paddies at both Sinharaja and Kitulgala in November, but says it is not considered to be a pest (Warakagoda pers. comm.).

In Germany, it is known to take mealworms when rearing young in captivity (Siegfried Kirschke *in litt.*) but is also recorded to rear young without live food.

MOVEMENTS Some seasonal movements, with altitudinal migration in the summer to over 2,150m recorded in the Nilgiris in India (Ali and Ripley 1987). In winter in India it is only found as high as 1,250m (Baker 1926). There are no specific records of altitudinal movements from Sri Lanka.

CALL The contact call is a high pitched nasal or metallic toot, similar in tone and timbre to the calls of Streaked-headed Mannikin *L. tristissima* and White-spotted Mannikin *L. leucosticta*, but much louder and as such more reminiscent of Zebra Finch *Poephila guttata* in the field.

SONG Nothing has been recorded.

COURTSHIP AND DISPLAY The display of the male appears to be similar to that of other munias. It "jerks up and down in a quaint manner" (Henry 1955).

BREEDING Details of the nest and nest habits are recorded in exquisite detail by Phillips (1948). Warakagoda and I found four nests in the Botanical Gardens in Nurawa Eliya and whilst we did not remove them for detailed examination (they were extremely well embedded in shrubby trees) they confirmed Phillips' and other descriptions. The typical nest is a compact ovoid, variable in size but generally about 25cm from front to rear, maybe 25cm high but only 20cm wide. The walls are more densly packed than those of a typical *L. punctulata* or *L. malacca*, both of which make larger and more loosly constructed nests. It is lined with finer threads, filaments and grasses. The entrance hole is a neat 3cm and might have a vestigial porch. The whole is well insulated against cold wind and rain. Bligh (in Legge 1880) records a pair taking over a bulbul's nest and using it as a base for their own construction.

The nest may be placed under the eaves of a house, in a creeper on the wall of a building, in a cavity in a tree trunk, in a shrub, such as a coffee or tea bush, high in a tall umbrageous tree (Legge 1880) or in bushes, hedges or even a topiarised garden cupressus (pers. obs.). Both sexes build the nest, although the male is usually occupied flying back and forth with material. A typical nest may take six days to complete. Phillips (1948) found it

common in his garden and around the Mousakande Estate at about 1,000m in Gammaduwa in the East Matale Hills. It breeds all year round but there are two peak seasons, the main one being from March to May and again August to November. Three or four broods a year are produced with an average clutch size of 5 in Sri Lanka. Average measurements given by Phillips (1948) are 16.1mm x 11.3mm. Incubation lasts 16 days and the young fledge in 15–17 days (Phillips 1948).

In India the nest is described as being indistinguishable from that of *L. striata* and built in similar situations (Ali and Ripley 1987). Nests are apparently used for roosting purposes as groups of 8–10 birds have been flushed out of nests which showed no signs of having been used for breeding. The clutch of the Indian bird ranges from 6–8. The incubation and nidification appears not to be recorded in India.

Kirschke's birds were reared successfully on sprouted millet, canary seed, oats, wheat, 'well nourished' mealworms of his own breeding, egg food, and cottage cheese. At all times of the year they took chickweed, groundsel, various salad greens and the seed heads of garden flowers. Subsequently he told me he found it bred well once established, but never as freely and easily as other munias. He remarks that they are among the largest of the munias and he found them to be rather quarrelsome, especially in the breeding season.

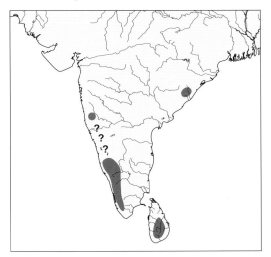

Distribution of Hill Munia

DISTRIBUTION The nominate race *L. k. kelaarti* is found in suitable habitat in Sri Lanka. The south-western third of Sri Lanka is known as the wet zone, the rest of the country is known as the dry zone. It is in the hill country, which forms the north-east corner of the wet zone where *L. k. kelaarti* is found. It is recorded as occurring from 500m upwards (to over 2,100m) but is very uncommon at these extremes. Most of the population seems to occur between 1,000m and 2,000m. However, it has recently been recorded at 500m and below by Warakagoda (pers. comm.) who twice saw birds flying with nesting material at Singharaja in January 1993 and later the same month saw two adults with a juvenile at Kitulgala, at 60m.

Of the two Indian races, *L. k. visnayi* is known only

95

from specimens collected around Somkramatha at 1,000m in Andhra Pradesh. *L. k. jerdoni* is found in the hills of south-western India south from Coorg and southern Karnataka (Ali and Ripley 1987) and rarely in the jungles west of Belgaum (Barnes 1897) although this northern extreme of distribution is not recognised by Ali and Ripley.

DESCRIPTION

Three subspecies are recognised (Paynter 1968), but one of them is virtually unknown. Ceylon Hill Munia is heavily marked on the breast and underparts, the little-known Eastern Ghats Hill Munia is only lightly marked, while Kerala Hill Munia has these markings restricted to the undertail-coverts.

SRI LANKAN HILL MUNIA
L. kelaarti kelaarti

Former scientific name: *Munia kelaarti* Jerdon (ex Blyth MS), 1863, *Birds of India*, 2, p.356 - Ceylon. *Uroloncha kelaarti kelaarti* Whistler, *Avi, Sur.* 1944.p.187.
Adult male *c*.120mm. Wing length 56–57mm, culmen 10.5–11.5mm long with a height at the base of 8 or 9mm and the lower mandible 12.5mm, tarsus 13mm. It has the forehead blackish-brown shading to earth-brown on back, wing-coverts and lower back and may have pale shaft striations on the nape and back. The wings and the tail are dark brown. The rump is darker brown and has slight cross-shaped white spots. The uppertail-coverts are olivaceous-yellow to gold. Most of the face, throat and central breast is fuscous. From the sides of the neck to lower flanks it is flesh-coloured (pinkish-tan), belly to undertail-coverts white. The underparts have dark brown dots and streaks on either side of a central white line to each feather that form unusual and elegant V-marks on the flanks. These may become so dense on the undertail-coverts as to appear almost black. The bill is flattish on the culmen, not curved as with most munias. It is blackish, dark grey or dark horn, bluish-grey at the base of the lower mandible. The irides are brown. The legs and feet are dark grey, with a greenish tinge in some birds (Legge 1880).
Adult female Similar to the male with the same range of measurements in the few specimens I handled. There is a tendency for the undertail-coverts to have broader pale centres. Males have a tendency for double cruciform spots on the upper rump, while those of females are only single-barred crosses.
First-year Plumage is distinctive. The facial bib is flecked with pale to whitish and the belly and flanks are spotted with brown. The rump has white striations, the uppertail-coverts are brown. The rufous patch that runs from outer ear-coverts down the side of the neck to the sides of the breast is emergent but flecked with brownish crescents. From crown to lower back, wings and tail it is the earth-brown of the adult. The undertail-coverts are less heavily marked than on the adult in second-year plumage. Sexual distinctions are not known.
Juvenile Uniform warm brown from crown to uppertail-coverts. The throat is greyish with slight barring, and from lower face to undertail-coverts is warm buffish with pale shaft lines on the ear-coverts, breast and flanks, the undertail-coverts having slight irregular dark barring.
From my observations in the field at Pattipola in Sri Lanka, I am concerned that my colour plate for *L. k.*

kelaarti shows birds that are too pale below, and not densely streaked enough. These birds were drawn from museum specimens in England (Tring) and New York (AMNH). I suspect they may be birds in first-year plumage. I was able to examine the specimens in the National Museum in Colombo, but they did not include a complete bird in adult plumage. It should be noted that Keulemann's plate in Legge (1880) shows a bird as dark as the one drawn at the beginning of this chapter, which is like the live birds I saw at Pattipola.

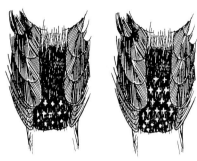

There is a tendency for females of the Sri Lankan race (right) to be more spotted on the rump than males.

KERALA HILL MUNIA
L. kelaarti jerdoni

Former scientific names: *Amadina pectoralis* Gould, 1841; Blyth (ex Jerdon MS), 1844, *Journ. Asiat. Soc. Bengal*, 13,p.949. Not *Amadina pectoralis* Gould, 1841. *Munia jerdoni* Hume, 1873, *Nests, Eggs Indian Birds*, 2, p.448. *Uroloncha rufiventris* Baker, 1925, *Bull. Brit. Ornth. Club*, 45, p.84. New name for *Amadina pectoralis*, Blyth, preoccupied.
Other common name: Jerdon's Rufous-bellied Munia.
Adult male Same measurments as *L. k. kelaarti* and is similar above to the female *L. k. kelaarti* but lacks the white spotting on the rump, this being uniform dark chocolate-brown. The uppertail-coverts have no yellow, and instead are dark glistening rufous. The forehead, face, throat and central breast are dark brown with pale striations. The entire underparts are pinkish-tan (between light russet-vinaceous and beige) with only a little brown crescent marking on the breast, each having a pale central shaft forming a cruciform. The undertail-coverts are streaked with brown.
Adult female Similar to the male but in the one individual I was able to handle the wing was only 53mm and the tarsus 12mm. I have been unable to distinguish any sexual dichromatism and conclude the sexes of this race are visually similar.
Juvenile Little paler than that of the the other races, is a little darker on the breast and the sides of the neck. It has whitish cruciform spots on the throat and the pale striations are more noticeable.

EASTERN GHATS HILL MUNIA
L. kelaarti vernayi

Former scientific name: *Uroloncha kelaarti vernayi* Whistler and Kinnear, 1933, *Journ. Bombay Nat. Hist. Soc.*, 36, p.835.
Little is known of this race. It was mistakenly described

by Whistler and Kinnear (1933) from three specimens of *L. k. jerdoni* in immature plumage, and subsequently treated as a synonym by Ali and Ripley (1987). Majumdar (1978) subsequently reinstated the race with a description that I draw upon below. The birds featured in my colour plate are taken from specimens in the collection of the AMNH. It is similar to *L. k. kelaarti* but has a paler breast, between cinnamon-pink and cinnamon drab, rather than pinkish-brown. The dark chocolate brown of the forehead stops at the middle of the head. The rump is dark brown with several conspicuous pinkish-white, cruciform markings. The uppertail-coverts are light yellowish-brown. The whole of the lower abdomen has pearly-pink, cruciform markings.

HYBRIDS Nothing has been recorded from the wild. The Kerala race has hybridised with the Bengalese in captivity (Kirschke *in litt.*).

CONSERVATION I feel there is cause for concern. Reports of distribution in the late nineteenth century (viz. Barnes 1897) compared to the late twentieth century suggest a dramatic reduction in the range of the Kerala population in India.

In Sri Lanka there is no similar evidence but still possible cause for concern. It is described as common in the highlands (Legge 1880, Phillips 1948 and Ali and Ripley 1987) but from personal observations in 1994 it appears to be only locally abundant at best and cannot be found with ease and certainty. Deepal Warakagoda told me he had accompanied Ben King for 3 days in search of the Hill Munia before they found a small family group of 5 birds. Around Nuwara Eliya, where the bird was said to be common, freely nesting among human dwellings, in 2 days we saw only a single Hill Munia feeding with a flock of Scaly-breasted Munias late in the afternoon. Warakagoda told me he had recorded it on the Horton Plains. In trying to ascertain whether the population had declined I was told that it had and that the clearance of forests for the creation of potato fields and the widespread and very heavy use of insecticides was the main reason. Ironically, it was in precisely these conditions that we found the bird at Pattipola. This is the highest railway station in Sri Lanka (1,980m) and is a scattered village where considerable areas of forest have been cleared. The countryside was bleak, dotted with burned and charred tree stumps. The ground everywhere was freshly tilled and in many fields small potato plants were growing. Men spraying the plants with insecticide could be seen in several fields.

We observed the bird at close range, several times between 6.30am and 8.30am, but by 9am they had all gone and there was no further sight of them. They sat up in shrubs on either side of a cutting of the railway line where we had close view several times, sheltered from the wind. There is virtually no trade in wild birds in Sri Lanka and while I was able to trace a few locally-caught White-rumped Munias and Tricoloured Munias in pet shops, there was no interest in Hill Munia. The danger to the species seems to be an extravagant use of pestcides.

There is an active bird trade in India, but it is not widespread nor of a broad nature. The Hill Munia has occasionally been trapped in Kerala State, but apparently in insignificant numbers and probably to order.

REFERENCES Ali & Ripley (1987), Baker (1926), Barnes (1897), Goodwin (1982), Henry (1955), Legge (1880), Majumdar (1978), Nachrichten (1978), Paynter (1968), Phillips (1948), Whistler & Kinnear (1933), Wijesinghe (1994).

14   SCALY-BREASTED MUNIA
Lonchura punctulata   Plate 6

Described as *Lonchura punctulata* Linnaeus
Other common names: Scaly-breasted Mannikin or Finch. Usually referred to as the Spotted Munia, which is inappropriate because the bird is not spotted. In avicultural literature it is invariably called the Spice Bird, Spice Finch or Nutmeg Finch.

Scaly-breasted Munia.

FIELD CHARACTERS A medium-sized munia, brown on the head and upperparts with a scaled patterning on the underparts, it may be confused with other munias at a distance. The juvenile is virtually the same as those of other congeners in the field and may only be told with certainty if it is with adult Scaly-breasted Munias. It is difficult to confuse this species with any other once the breast patterning is seen clearly. In parts of India and Sri Lanka it could be confused with Hill Munia *L. kelaarti*. The juvenile flocks with the juveniles of other munias, especially White-headed Munia *L. maja* in Sumatra and Java and is indistinguishable from them in the field. In those races of Scaly-breasted Munia where the bill is black, this character will enable identification of older juveniles from the juveniles of other munias where the bill is either all pale, or darker above and paler below.

Scaly-breasted Munia.

STATUS Common and widespread, it is undoubtedly the commonest munia in Asia.

HABITAT It is essentially a bird of open or semi-open country with bushes, trees and scrub, and secondary forest with grassy clearings. But it is ubiquitous and very adaptable to man-made environments. I have observed it

97

in cultivated land, wasteland covered with weeds and grasses, parkland and gardens, golf courses and construction sites, and even urban areas.

It is primarily a bird of lower elevations, but is found in or around cultivated areas up to 2,000m in the Himalayas and along the Burma-China border also up to 3,000m in southern China (Caldwell 1931). It is highly tolerant of man, often nesting readily among human habitation. Immelmann (1965) describes it nest building in the middle of a busy shopping centre in Townsville, Australia. Catherine Levy in Jamaica (pers. comm.) described a pair nesting in a hanging plant basket over the front door of her house. In contrast to this picture of ubiquity Clive Viney (*in litt.*) says that it was once abundant in Hong Kong but has declined notably in recent years and is now difficult to find, apparently coinciding with the demise of rice-growing.

HABITS AND BEHAVIOUR It is a highly sociable bird and may be found in flocks of a few individuals, to several hundred birds. That the juveniles leave their parents to form wandering flocks, or mixed flocks of munias, is evidenced by the fact that trappers in Indonesia and Vietnam may have holding cages full of juveniles with no adult bird present. Shipments I have intercepted and examined in Jakarta and Singapore have consisted entirely of immature Scaly-breasted Munias with perhaps 10% White-headed Munias, and in Ho Chi Minh City to be 95% with the remainder being White-rumped Munias *L. striata*.

On the island of Liran in the Lesser Sundas near Wetar, I spent an afternoon studying a flock of about 50 Scaly-breasted Munias feeding on *Cyperus* grass, probably *C. distans*. One or two birds at the edge of the flock would fly forward a metre or so to fresh grass, then some others would fly to fill the gap and then others and so on, the process being a series of waves or undulations. They worked a patch for about 20 minutes whereupon the entire flock would fly to another area several metres away. I saw the same pattern in grassland in Malaysia. I have watched it feeding on recently cleared open ground in Singapore, the flock moving forward by birds at the rear flying over the mass of feeding birds and alighting in front. In contrast, small groups of from five to a dozen birds I watched in Queensland, Australia would feed haphazardly with no group cohesion at all.

When a feeding flock takes off to fly a distance, the flock as a whole flies direct, with little or no undulation. Within the flock, each bird has its own erratic corkscrewing line of flight. The effect on a raptor attempting to catch a bird in such a flock must be visual confusion. When a small group takes off in alarm or in determined flight the entire body can be seen to be corkscrewing. During the breeding season and often when not breeding, pairs will roost at night in their nests which may be distributed hundreds of yards apart, and fly to areas where they may be found feeding all the year round. The pairs fly to the feeding areas about half an hour after dawn and may be seen returning to their respective roosts up to an hour before dark. In these circumstances small feeding groups of four, six or eight may form, giving the impression of family groups since some of the birds may be in only partial adult plumage. They pair up between three and six months old, during which time males commence advertisement singing and both sexes begin to moult. A pair disturbed while feeding in long grass will fly in a hesitating and nervous manner over the grass, calling all the time, flushing other

pairs they pass over until several birds have been raised and then the small flock will soon settle back out of sight.

Scaly-breasted Munias like to gather in a tree, preferably the topmost branches of a bare or open tree, in the twenty minutes or so before flying off to roost in the evening. This appears to be a social gathering, with a variety of contact and call notes being uttered but with little or no advertisement singing.

I have twice observed and made sketches of a wing-raising behaviour by birds in captivity. In both instances the wing-raising bird was a first-year male of the Philippine race *S. p. cabanisi* that shared an enclosure with a White-bellied Munia *L. leucogastra*. The White-bellied Munia had approached the Scaly-breasted Munia along the perch whereupon the latter appeared to perceive a threat. It reacted to the approaching bird by lowering itself slightly, leaning away slightly, and raising the far-side wing vertically in a sail position. This is a behaviour hitherto only recorded for African mannikins but I have also recorded it for the Chestnut Munia *L. atricapilla*.

Wing-raising defence display by a young Philippine Scaly-breasted Munia in response to a perceived threat from a White-bellied Munia *L. leucogastra*.

In a flock or group situation, a male engaged in undirected singing may well stimulate other males to sing. The singer might attract the attention of another male Scaly-breasted Munia which will perch close to the performer, lean forward and appear to be totally engrossed in listening attentively to the song. He also appears to be peering intently at the bill of the performer and this has given the term 'peering' to this phenomenon. On occasions two, three or even more birds will crowd round, attempting to peer together. For those seeing this behaviour and thinking the peering bird may be an admiring female paired to the songster, it is highly unlikely to be so for peering birds are almost invariably males. Luis Baptista (*in litt.*) tells me he has recorded cases when a peering bird is a known female. A lengthy paper by Moynihan and Hall (1954) describes this and other behaviour of Scaly-breasted Munia in considerable detail and Morris (1972) summarises it well.

Outside the breeding season Scaly-breasted Munias will build nests to roost in, and these will be used communally at night; up to a dozen or more birds may squeeze into a single nest.

FOOD AND FEEDING The favourite food of Scaly-breasted Munias is seeding grasses and seeding weeds. It climbs grasses to reach the seeding heads with great agility, but it will feed almost as readily on the ground, taking seeds that have ripened and fallen from their pods. I studied it in Saraburi outside the Khao Yai National Park in northeast Thailand where it is common in areas covered in tall grasses, up to two metres high. Despite there being several species of tall grass in full seed, including *Panicum maximum*, *Sorghum bicolor* and *Pennisetum* spp., they were feeding low down on smaller grasses such as *Paspalum* and *Digitaria*. In direct contrast, I have often watched it in the area of Ubud in Bali, feeding on the tall seeding plumes of *Saccharum arundinaceum*.

Like many munias it will flock to the paddyfields when the rice is ripening, feeding busily from the laden panicles. In Australia and maybe elsewhere, it has developed habits similar to those of the sparrows *P. domesticus* and *Passer montanus* in Asia, of taking human waste food including breadcrumbs, potatoes, etc. It feeds extensively on cultivated cereal grains when available, and small berries, particularly the fruits of *Ziziphus mauritania* and *Z. nummularia*, berberis berries and *Carissa opaca* berries (Roberts 1992), and the berries of the lantana *Lantana camera* (Clement *et al.* 1993). It will visit rubbish dumps in towns and villages. I have twice seen it feeding on flattened road kills in Bali, and there are other reports of this behaviour (Immelmann 1965).

Birds have apparently been observed carrying small caterpillars to their nestlings (Mason and Le Froy 1912), an unusual incident and possibly incorrect, because munias normally ingest their food and regurgitate it into the open gapes of the young. Most reports of Scaly-breasted Munias breeding in captivity affirm that the nestlings are reared entirely on vegetable matter.

Breeding birds will join other pairs of Scaly-breasted Munia at regular feeding areas forming small or loose flocks or fly to join foraging flocks of mixed munias when seeking food.

In India it is often seen in the company of White-rumped Munias and will roost with other species, not only other munias, but also with weavers (Ali and Ripley 1987). In Indonesia, on smaller islands in the Lesser Sundas, I have seen it in groups of several dozen birds when it was often accompanied by Five-coloured Munia *L. quinticolor* and Pale-headed Munia *L. pallida*. In Sri Lanka I have found it feeding with Hill Munia *L. kelaarti*. De Zylva (1984) says of it in Sri Lanka that in addition to being a pest to the rice farmers it also causes considerable damage to kurakkan crops and green-gram.

MOVEMENTS It is sedentary but there is some wandering, especially by flocks of young birds, no doubt influenced by food supplies, particularly grain crops.

CALL The quiet contact note between birds that are close together is an often-repeated *Tit -ti Tit-ti*. The loud contact call, uttered when a bird is separated from the others is *kit-teee kit-teee* with the second syllable pitched higher than the first. There is a sharp alarm note *tchp*! Only the female is recorded as giving a particular alarm note, described as a sharp, creaking *tret-tret* by Moynihan and Hall (1954), but Immelmann (1965) and Guttinger (1970) apparently failed to note any sexual differences. Over a period of 5 years I kept 8 different races in Hong Kong and in every case found there to be a clear tonal difference in the loud contact note when calling between the sexes.

The call when a group or flock is in a determined, prolonged or alarmed flight is a *sieuw*! *sieuw*! rising slightly in the middle and very penetrating. When a small family group flies up from feeding the contact call is *psitt*! Feeding pairs that are flushed when in long grass will loudly call *sieuw*! *sieuw*! as they fly, drawing other pairs or small groups up to join them before they drop back into the grass. A single bird in flight will call loudly and continually.

SONG The typical song is a series of *klik-klik-klik* or *tit-tit-tit* that continues for a few seconds, is followed by a short series of whistles and churrs ending with a longer *weee*. I managed to listen carefully to one male from Ho Chi Minh City. The song began with a series of soft *tik tik tik* that changed to a stronger *trik trik trik* seeming to gain speed whereupon it switched to the legato *wwhheeeeeeeeee* and ended with a short tumbling of notes. The whole song lasted about 10 seconds. There is considerable variation of song pattern from male to male. Males may sing out of apparent *joie de vivre* and for no other reason. Males indulge in advertisement singing continually whether alone or in company and will approach and display to any opportune female, and often to another male. I have frequently seen a male alight on a vertical stem beneath its mate and sing directly upwards to her.

Indian Scaly-breasted Munia in undirected advertisement song, left, and high intensity display, right.

COURTSHIP AND DISPLAY The male usually initiates courtship by flying about with a length of grass in his bill, flicking his wings and tail intermittently. (Scaly-breasted Munia flicks its tail from side to side whether engaged in courtship or not). If the female is sexually stimulated by the grass-toting and tail-flicking display she will also fly about with wing-flicking, and may well carry a straw or grass. If she alights near the male he will drop the grass, bend forward a little and begin singing, turning from side to side as he does so. The female solicits by crouching and quivering her tail. The male will stop singing before mounting.

BREEDING Scaly-breasted Munia usually breeds colonially but it is always possible to find solitary nests. The nests are usually placed quite close together and may be even touching. They are frequently well hidden. The colony may be in a tree, in bushes, creepers or in fact anywhere the birds may find suitable. Breeding birds may be seen trailing long lengths of straw or a tangle of grass as they fly to the tree in which the nests are being built. Rather like House Sparrows *Passer domesticus*, they do not seem to know when to stop and often a nest may grow to the size of a water melon. Nests have been found in the niches of tree trunks, bases of palm leaves, holes in buildings, or in among the thatch or eaves of houses. Whatever site is chosen it tends to be 4 or 5m from the ground.

In Nurawa Eliya, Sri Lanka, I found five nests within centimetres of each other in the centre of a dense topiaried cupressus that measured about two metres across. They would have been impossible to find had I not spotted a bird entering with a length of grass trailing behind it. I found a solitary pair nesting in a *Pandanus* palm on a golf course in Port Douglas, Australia, and in Sri Lanka I found two pairs with nests in a solitary mangrove tree, standing in water some 15m from the edge of the grove. De Zylva (1984) says they will often nest in trees that have plenty of red ants *Oecophylla smaragdina* on them, suggesting this is no coincidence. I often came across small groups of breeding birds during visits to Sri Lanka and Australia and several tours of various Indonesian islands, but was unable to find any colonial nesting of the enormity reported by Clement *et al.* (1993) of several hundred nests together. In the vicinity of Ubud in Bali I noticed that all the nests were in the crowns of tall palms. I discussed this with Victor Mason and we concluded this was probably an adaptive behaviour, providing the birds with protection from the never-ending destruction of munia and parrotfinch nests by the rice farmers and their children.

Nest built in a shrub about 1.5m from the ground on Bali.

While the location and siting of a nest may be varied, the nest itself is usually a flattened globular structure constructed of both green pliable grasses, dry and dead grasses and long leaves, strips of other vegetation, bits of bark, etc., and is remarkably well made. The bird often shows a distinct preference for fresh green grasses when building, although several pairs I watched nest building both in Bali and near Kuala Lumpur were choosing bulky lengths of dead grasses and weeds in preference to green grass. The entrance hole is at one end, tending to be higher rather than lower on the side and it usually has a short porch-like projection over it which serves both to conceal the entrance and possibly to protect it from inclement weather. The lining is of softer materials, seed panicles, finer strands and maybe feathers. The whole thing is very robust, well able to withstand strong wind and heavy rain. The male collects the nest material while the female waits at the site, often working inside the nest. Both sexes are said to share in nest building, but in my observations only the female does this.

There is no weaving in the nest construction, the structure is formed by the birds pushing the material into place. In this way it tends to work around branches and stems and becomes quite well anchored. However, it is often comparatively easy to actually remove a nest whole, study it and replace it undamaged.

Clutches are recorded as being from 3–10, but considering the colonial nesting propensity of the species it seems unlikely that one female alone would lay 10 eggs, perhaps two females had contributed eggs in such cases. A normal clutch is 5 or 6 white, oval eggs. Incubation is by both sexes and both birds spend the night in the nest together.

Incubation lasts about 14 days and the young fledge in 18 or 19 days.

The fledglings continue to roost in the nest for a few days and nights more. Breeding is known to take place all year round, but is normally triggered by the end of the rainy season and continues into the dry season. The species is certainly double-brooded and pairs may well produce a third or even a fourth brood if conditions are favourable.

DISTRIBUTION As with other species of *Lonchura* that are divided into several races, the distribution map places the range and location of the races into perspective. *L. p. punctulata* ranges from northeastern Pakistan (Roberts 1974) and the Punjab through the Indian subcontinent to Sri Lanka and eastwards to Bhutan and Sikkim. *L. p. subundulata* ranges from Assam through Bangladesh and north-east India to Burma. *L. p. yunnanensis* ranges from south and west Burma to Yunnan. *L. p. topela* ranges through Thailand across Indochina and southern China as far as Shanghai and the island of Taiwan. In the Philippines *L. p. cabanisi* occurs on the northern island of Luzon and the adjacent southerly islands to Panay and Mindoro. *L. p. fretensis* ranges from southern Thailand and peninsular Malaysia through Sumatra and Nias Island. *L. p. baweana* is restricted to the island of Bawean. *L. p. nisoria* is found on Java, Bali, and Lombok. *L. p. fortior* occurs only on Sumbawa. *L. p. holmesi* is found in southern Kalimantan. *L. p. sumbae* occurs only on Sumba. *L. p. blasii* ranges from Flores across the archipelago through Timor to Tanimbar. *L. p. particeps* is restricted to Sulawesi.

The species is presumed to have been introduced into Singapore (Ward 1968), despite occurring naturally on the Malaysian peninsula and in Sumatra, it is not listed by Robinson and Chasen (1927-29). I incline to Lever's (1987) opinion that it could well be a recent arrival from across the Strait. It has been introduced into Australia, the Hawaiian Islands, Mauritius and Réunion, in each case the race concerned is *L. p. topela*. However, the race *L. p. cabanisi* occurs on Babelthuap and Koror in the Palau Islands in the Pacific, due east of the Philippines, along with another Philippine munia, the Chestnut Munia *L. atricapilla jagori*. It is not certain whether these are natural colonists or introductions by man. When visiting Port Moresby, Papua New Guinea, I was told of a single report of a sighting of the species locally but I was unable to trace the observer or the record and regard it as highly doubtful. Catherine Levy tells me it is now established in Jamaica.

DESCRIPTION   **Plates 31–40**
There is no universal agreement about the number of races and identifying a specimen of unknown origin can be extremely difficult. But after studying the skins in the collection of the Natural History Museum at Tring, the American Museum of Natural History in New York, covering most of the literature and having kept live birds from most of the races to study over many years, I recognise 13 races including the usually overlooked *L. p. baweana*, and a recently described race from Borneo *L. p. holmesi*. I feel there is still room for careful study of the forms occurring on the small islands in Indonesia.

There is usually a gradual enriching of colour from a first-year to an older bird and there is often variation within a population. There is gradation from race to race where the distribution is contiguous and racial separations can only be made with certainty in the island populations. Bill

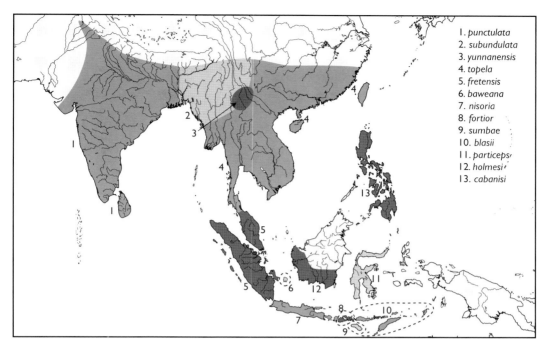

Distribution of Scaly-breasted Munia.

1. punctulata
2. subundulata
3. yunnanensis
4. topela
5. fretensis
6. baweana
7. nisoria
8. fortior
9. sumbae
10. blasii
11. particeps
12. holmesi
13. cabanisi

colour is a partial discriminator. Five races, *L. p. punctulata*, *L. p. subundulata*, *L. p. fretensis* in Thailand, *L. p. yunnanensis* and *L. p. topela* have black bills, and the bill of the Philippine *L. p. cabanisi* is variable and may be all-grey or black above with grey below, depending on the age of the bird. The other races usually have the upper mandible black and the lower grey. The colour of the uppertail-coverts is also important but is most helpful in side-by-side comparison. The colour and shape of the scaling on the flanks can be helpful in identifying races, but I have found there to be too much variation for this to be diagnostic. The chart shows these features in a comparative manner.

INDIAN SCALY-BREASTED MUNIA

L. punctulata punctulata   Plates 31–32

Former scientific names: *Loxia punctulata* Linnaeus, 1758, *Syst. Nat.*, ed. 10, p. 173. *Munia lineoventer* Hodgson, 1836.

Other common name: Indian Spotted Munia.

Adult 107–120mm, depending on age and sex although most of the live adults I measured in both India and Sri Lanka were *c.*112mm. Wing length 52–54mm, culmen 11–12mm, tarsus 11–12mm. There seems to be no significant difference in the measurements of the sexes.

The full adult has the forehead, supercilium, lores, base of mesial, throat and centre of the upper breast reddish-brown. The ear-coverts and sides of the upper breast are brown with a few spots of white edged with black on the sides of the upper breast that may even reach the sides of the neck. From the crown to the lower back and wings it is uniform, warm earth-brown. Older birds from the north-western part of India have very few striations on the mantle and none on the nape. The rump, uppertail-coverts and tail are brown with orange-straw edgings, and this may form

barring on the rump. There is large orange-straw spotting on the uppertail-coverts and orange-edging to the tail feathers. The underwing-coverts are buffish. The lower breast, and flanks are white with black edgings that form strongly contrasting scaling. The belly and undertail-coverts are cream. This becomes richer and warmer on the undertail-coverts which have black V-marks. The irides are usually red but I have seen birds where they have been chestnut. The bill is large, dark greyish-horn to black. The legs and feet are leaden.

There is no apparent difference between the appearance of the sexes. Males may have larger bills, and the culmen is generally more pronounced. This may be felt with the fingernail if birds can be handled. In two certain pairs I studied, the females were distinguished by having clear undertail-coverts with no flecking. In several adults I examined in Sri Lanka the females had some striations on the mantle, wing-coverts and tertials. In a given series of birds, males tend to be larger and slightly longer in length of body, wing and tail, but it would not be possible to predict sex accurately this way.

In my experience with live birds from Bombay and Colombo, the Sri Lankan birds are different from those collected in Maharashtra State in being more clearly striated on the mantle, having the lower rump only flecked with black and white compared to the entire rump of the Indian birds being barred with whitish, and the underwing-coverts of the northern birds were flecked instead of having white circles in brownish feathers. The measured drawings of this race (plates 31–32) show the differences.

Juvenile I have painted a juvenile typical of the nominate race *L. p. punctulata* in the identification plate,

101

which serves to indicate the specific characteristics. It is brown above, paler below but a little darker perhaps on the breast and flanks. There is some variation of individuals within a given race, as with all immature *Lonchura*, and a tendency to greyish tones of the browns. The tail of young birds is rounded to square cut with no point. When mixed with juveniles of other species of munia it is at first difficult to separate them. In flocks of White-headed Munias in Indonesia the young Scaly-breasted Munias may first separated by their slightly smaller size, being up to 10mm shorter, and usually seeming to be a tone greyer. On examination in the hand it is usually possible to find an odd scalloped feather on the flanks or belly that confirms the identification. In my experience, when moulting into first-year plumage the head is the last to show full colour. I have also shown a juvenile of the very distinct Philippine race, which is paler and more barred or scalloped above than the nominate.

BURMESE SCALY-BREASTED MUNIA
L. punctulata subundulata

Former scientific names: *Munia subundulata* Godwin-Austen, 1872, *Proc. Zool. Soc. London*, P.48. *Lonchura punctulata catervaria* Koelz, 1954.

Other common name: Burmese Spotted Munia

Adult *c.*115mm. Wing length 55mm, culmen 11mm, tarsus 11mm. It has the forehead, lores, and base of mesial a reddish-brown which extends to cover the chin and throat. Above, from crown to upper rump and the wings is earth-brown with some paler edges to the wing-coverts and flight feathers. There are pale quill shaft striations that run from the rear crown and extend to the lower back and the wing-coverts. The edging to the lower rump, uppertail-coverts and tail may be a clear and noticeable yellow or olivaceous. The entire breast, sides of the neck and flanks are white, double-scaled with brown. This brown becomes darker on the flanks and may become black on birds from some localities, and the second or inner scallop becomes broken and forms two curved lines that disappear as the scalings on the lower flanks become blackish. The barring on the thighs is white and dark brown. The belly and undertail-coverts are cream with brown V-marks on the undertail-coverts. The bill is dark greyish-horn to black.

This race is rather variable and inconsistent. It can be regarded as a morphographic bridge between the distinct Indian *L. p. punctulata* and the *yunnanensis/topela* group to the east (Parkes 1958).

YUNNAN SCALY-BREASTED MUNIA
L. punctulata yunnanensis

Parkes, 1958, Proc. U.S. Nat. Mus., 108, p. 285

Adult *c.*120mm, females being a little shorter than males. Wing length *c.*55mm, culmen 11mm, tarsus 11mm. The lores and bib are rich reddish-brown. The lower edge of the throat is somewhat diffuse, edging into the scaling of the breast. From forehead to lower back and wings it is cinnamon with white shaft lines or striations. The rump, uppertail-coverts and tail are olive-brown edged with yellow-straw, more warmly yellow than on *L. p. topela*. The breast and flanks are whitish, double-scaled with dark brown. There is some pencilling on the centre of the belly. The belly, ventral region and undertail-coverts are pale cream with

some light flecking. The bill is all black. The legs and feet are grey.

CHINESE SCALY-BREASTED MUNIA
L. punctulata topela   Plates 33–35

Former scientific name: *Munia topela* Swinhoe, 1863, *Ibis*, P. 380.

Other common name: Topela Finch.

Adult male 115–120mm. Wing length 56–57mm, culmen 11–12mm, tarsus 11–12mm. The lores, most of the ear-coverts and the full bib are reddish-brown. From forehead to lower back and wings it is earth-brown, the centre of the mantle may be darker. In birds I collected near Ho Chi Minh City the centres to the feathers on top of the head were darker, giving a heavily spotted effect. These spots became dark barring from the nape, over the back and wing coverts. There are no striations as a rule, but if the quill shafts are pale it will only show on the mantle. The rump, uppertail-coverts and tail are brown, edged with a yellow-straw similar to that on *L. p. subundulata*, but the entire rump has yellow edging and appears barred yellow and brown. Birds I collected from Kanchanaburi in west-central Thailand had the uppertail-coverts salmon-ochre. The lower throat, entire breast and flanks are whitish, double-scaled with brown. The flanks are also double-scaled but the scales tend to break into lines at the edge of the belly. The belly, thighs and undertail-coverts are cream, barred heavily on the thighs, with very light flecking on the undertail-coverts.

The bird illustrated in the main colour plate is from northern Thailand and has the flanks warm. However, birds from Taiwan are greyish on the flanks, while those from southern China are pale grey. There is an outstanding colour photograph of this race in the *Readers Digest Book of Australian Birds* (1976), it shows only too well how poorly defined the yellow of the rump and uppertail-coverts may be. This is almost certainly a bird in its first-year plumage (note the bill is blackish).

Adult female 110–115mm (though one live adult female I kept for painting measured only 100mm). Wing length 54–56mm, culmen 10–11mm, tarsus 11mm.

Juvenile Birds collected in Kanchanaburi had bills entirely black, but birds from southern China had the upper mandible black and the lower grey.

PHILIPPINE SCALY-BREASTED MUNIA
L. punctulata cabanisi   Plate 36

Former scientific names: *Oxycera (Uroloncha) jagori* Cabanis,1872, *Journ. Ornith.*, 20, P.317 *Munia cabanisi* Sharpe, 1890.

Adult 97–105mm. Wing length 48–50mm, culmen 10–11mm, tarsus 10–11mm. The forehead, lores and bib are rich brown, the remainder of the upperparts are earth-brown with pale quill-shaft striations over the entire upper surface, including the ear-coverts which are a paler brown than the neck and back. The throat and sides of neck, breast and flanks and thighs are cream with greyish-brown edgings to the feathers, with converging curved lines inside distinctively narrow scallops. The undertail-coverts are a richer cream and this colour edges the uppertail-coverts and tail slightly. There are brown V-marks on the undertail-coverts. The scaling on the breast and undertail-coverts becomes

	bill all black	bill black above and grey below	bill dark grey above and pale grey below	bill all grey	uppertail-coverts orange	uppertail-coverts salmon-ochre	uppertail-coverts warm olive	uppertail-coverts olive-yellow	uppertail-coverts yellow	uppertail-coverts yellow-straw	uppertail-coverts warm straw	uppertail-coverts pale straw	uppertail-coverts pale olive-grey	striations on nape and back	striations on back only	no striations	underparts all cream	underparts with white belly and flanks	underparts white with cream belly	underparts all white
L. p. punctulata	●				●									●	●			●	●	
L.p. subundulata	●							●	●					●				●	●	
L. p. yunnanensis	●										●			●				●	●	
L. p. topela	●					●[1]		●[2]	●[3]					●					●	
L. p. cabanisi		●[4]		●[5]					●						●		●			
L. p. baweana		●									●				●					●
L. p. fretensis	●[6]	●[7]									●			●[8]	●[9]	●[10]		●	●	
L. p. holmesi			●										●	●				●	●	
L. p. nisoria		●									●						●	●	●	
L. p. fortior		●									●			●			●			
L. p. sumbae		●					●								●			●	●	
L. p. particeps		●						●						●			●			
L. p. blasii		●							●									●	●	

Guide to the identification of Scaly-breasted Munia by subspecific differences. Key to notes: 1) Western end of the range. 2) Vietnam. 3) China. 4) Second-year. 5) First-year. 6) Thailand. 7) Malaysia and Sumatra. 8) Thailand. 9) Malaysia. 10) Sumatra.

darker and bolder with age. The bill is all grey in first-year plumage but the upper mandible darkens to become blackish as the bird ages.

Juvenile 95–99mm. Wing length 48–49mm, culmen 10mm, tarsus 10mm. The edges to the drab upperparts are buffish, giving a soft scaling effect. From chin to undertail-coverts it is light creamy-buff, flushed with drab on the chin, throat, sides of breast and flanks. The bill is grey, slightly violaceous on the upper mandible. The legs and feet are pale grey.

SUMATRAN SCALY-BREASTED MUNIA
L. punctulata fretensis   Plate 37
Kloss, 1931, *Treubia*, 13, p. 363.
Adult male 112–115mm. Wing length 53–54mm, culmen 10–11mm, tarsus 11mm. It has the forehead, lores, foreparts of the ear-coverts, base of the mesial and the bib reddish-brown. The outer ear-coverts, sides of neck round to the throat orange-brown. The crown and nape are dark brown. The mantle, wings and tail are warm earth-brown with some pale striations on the mantle. The rump and uppertail-coverts have very slight straw edgings. The breast and flanks are white with a distinct pattern of dark reddish-brown double scaling. The belly, thighs and undertail-coverts are cream with the same distinctive scaling on

the thighs and undertail-coverts. The bill is all black in birds from Thailand, but black above and grey below in birds from Malaysia and Sumatra. The legs and feet are violaceous grey.

Adult female 110–113mm. Wing length 52–53mm, culmen 10mm, tarsus 11mm. It is similar in plumage to the male.

BORNEAN SCALY-BREASTED MUNIA
L. punctulata holmesi   Plate 38
Restall, 1995, *Bull. Brit. Orn. Club.*, 115(3), 140-157.
Adult male 105–115mm. Wing length 49–52mm, culmen 11mm, tarsus 11–12mm. It is dark cinnamon-brown above with the edges of the wing-coverts broadly fringed with light cinnamon-brown. From nape to lower back and on the wings, but not the paler edgings, it is finely barred with darker wavy lines similar to the upperparts of African Silverbill *L. cantans*. There are fine striations from the nape to lower back. The lower back is olive-brown graduating to brownish olive-grey on the uppertail-coverts and tail, which are barred and edged with very pale straw. The visual effect is of a pale grey. The face is dark reddish-umber, becoming hazel on the outer ear-coverts and side of the neck where there are a few pinky-white dots. The breast and sides of breast and

flanks are white with the characterisitc scaly markings in dark umber. The thighs are umber, spotted and barred with off-white. The underwing-coverts are pale cinnamon with some darker centres to the feathers and some dark edging. The centre of the belly is pale cream, this graduates to very pale straw on the undertail-coverts. There is a variable amount, but always very little, brownish flecking on the undertail-coverts. The irides are dark ruby. The bill is bluish-grey, tending to blackish on the upper mandible. The legs and feet are dark grey.

Adult female 103–108mm. Wing length 48–50mm, culmen 10–11mm, tarsus 10–11mm. Sexes appear to be alike with most if not all of the male's additional length due to the longer tail.

Juvenile Not described.

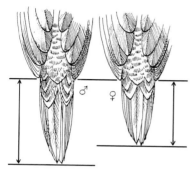

Comparison between length of the tail of male, left, and female, right, of Bornean Scaly-breasted Munia.

JAVAN SCALY-BREASTED MUNIA
L. punctulata nisoria   **Plate 39**
Former scientific name: *Fringilla nisoria* Temminck, 1830, Pl. Col., Livr. 84, Pl. 500, fig.2.
Adult male 115–120mm. Wing length 52–54mm, culmen 11–12mm, tarsus 11–12mm. It has the entire head except the nape deep reddish-brown, a little paler on the ear-coverts, darkest on the forehead, lores and base of the mesial. The nape and rest of the upperparts are dark earth-brown with some irregular scalloping of deep reddish-brown on the mantle. There are no striations on the back. There is a little pale straw edging to the rump, uppertail-coverts and tail feathers. Birds that I observed in Bali seemed to be paler on the lower rump and uppertail-coverts. The sides of the breast and flanks are white, with some white extending up to the sides of the neck, heavily scaled with deep reddish-brown, and slightly suffused with reddish-brown on the upper breast. The centre of the breast, belly, thighs and undertail-coverts are cream, barred on the thighs and undertail-coverts with reddish-brown suffused with cream. The bill is blackish above, grey below.
Adult female 104–114mm. Wing length 50–52mm, culmen 11–12mm, tarsus 11mm. It is similar in plumage to the male.

BAWEAN SCALY-BREASTED MUNIA
L. punctulata baweana
Hoogerwerf, 1963, *Bull. Brit. Orn. Club*, 83, p.38.
Adult *c*.105mm. Wing length 50–52mm, culmen 10–11mm, tarsus 11mm. The face, forehead, ear-coverts,

mesial and chin and bib are reddish-brown, but this does not extend as far down towards the breast as it does on other Indonesian races. From crown to tail it is earth-brown above, darker on the wings and tail, striated on the mantle and wing-coverts and having the edges of the lower rump and uppertail-coverts straw. The scale markings on the whitish flanks are brown and the white belly appears to be more extensive. The bill is blackish above, grey below. There appears to be no clear difference between the sexes.
Juvenile Similar to, but paler than that of the other Indonesian races.

SUMBAWA SCALY-BREASTED MUNIA
L. punctulata fortior
Former scientific name: *Munia punctulata fortior* Rensch, 1928, *Ornith. Monatsb.*, 36, p.7.
Adult *c*.110–115mm. Wing length 49–52mm, culmen 10–11mm. The entire head and upperparts are warm earth-brown, reddish-brown on the forehead, lores and chin, but not a clear mask as in some races. There are pale striations from the rear crown to the rump and straw edgings to the feathers of the lower rump and uppertail-coverts. The breast, belly and flanks are creamy with brown scalings, darker on the flanks. The belly and undertail-coverts are cream, and apparently may be marked on the undertail but not on specimens I have examined. The bill is blackish above, grey below.
Juvenile Not described.

SUMBA SCALY-BREASTED MUNIA
L. punctulata sumbae
Mayr, 1944, *Bull. Amer. Mus. Nat. Hist.*, 83, p.169.
Adult *c*.110mm. Wing length *c*.50mm, culmen *c*.11mm. It is very similar to *L. p. nisoria* and *L. p. blasii* but may be distinguished by having noticeably paler ear-coverts, the colour of which extends to the sides of the neck. The breast and flanks are white with black scallopings; on the other two races the scallopings on the breast are the same colour as the throat and only become black on the flanks. The edges of the uppertail-coverts and edges of the tail are a warm olive. The bill is blackish above, grey below. The sexes are similar.
Juvenile Not described.

SULAWESI SCALY-BREASTED MUNIA
L. punctulata particeps
Former scientific name: *Munia punctulata particeps* Riley, 1920, *Proc. Biol. Soc.* Washington, 33, p.57.
Adult *c*.110mm. Wing length 48–51mm, culmen 10–11mm, tarsus 11mm.. The entire face is dark reddish-brown becoming earth-brown from rear-crown to tail and wings. Pale striations run from the rear crown to the rump where they become pale edgings to the feathers forming irregular bars. The uppertail-coverts are broadly edged olivaceous-yellow. Below it is cream, with dark brown scaling on the breast and flanks. The undertail-coverts are cream with light flecking. The bill is blackish above, grey below.

TIMOR SCALY-BREASTED MUNIA
L. punctulata blasii   **Plate 40**
Former scientific name: *Munia punctulata blasii* Stresemann, 1912, *Novit. Zool.*, 19, p.317.
Adult male 110–115mm. Wing length 52mm, culmen 10–11mm, tarsus 11–12mm. The old bird has the

entire face, including ear-coverts and throat, clear reddish-brown, becoming rufous on the supercilium and ear-coverts, and maybe lightly barred with brown on the ear-coverts. The crown to the lower back, including the wings, brown, barred from crown to lower back, scapulars and upper tertials with darker reddish-brown. There are no striations on the back.There may be pale edges on the scapulars and tertials. The entire underparts are light cream, the upper breast being scaled with the same brown of the throat, becoming darker on the middle-lower breast, and black scaling on the flanks. There are brown broken U-lines on the thighs and undertail-coverts. The rump, uppertail-coverts and tail are edged with yellow similar to those of *topela*. The bill is blackish above, grey below.

Adult female 100–105mm. Wing length 48–50mm, culmen 10mm, tarsus 11mm. Of two I examined, the undertail-coverts were clear buff and the edges to the rump and uppertail-coverts were far less noticeable than on the males.

First-year Duller version of the adult, and the belly and flank markings are more generic, less clearly characteristic of the particular race.

HYBRIDS Scaly-breasted Munia is recorded as having hybridised naturally with Chestnut-breasted Mannikin *L. castaneothorax* in Australia (Immelmann 1965). Gray (1958) lists many cross-breedings produced in captivity. These include Bronze Mannikin *L. cucullata*, White-headed Munia *L. maja*, both African Silverbill *L. cantans* and Indian Silverbill *L. malabarica*, White-rumped Munia *L. striata* (several races) and Madagascar Mannikin *L. nana*. Two hybrids with Java Sparrow *L. oryzivora* were produced in California (Brooksbank 1949). Outside the genus, it has hybridised with Long-tailed Grassfinch *Poephila acuticauda* on several occasions (Gray 1958).

CONSERVATION This is perhaps the most frequently caught munia for the international bird trade with single shipments of up to at least 7,000 birds at a time (frequent personal observations in Jakarta and Singapore). This appears to have no effect whatsoever on the wild populations. The main souces of supply are Java, Sumatra, southern China and India, with Vietnam following closely behind and emerging as possibly the biggest supplier. I fear for the population of Scaly-breasted Munia in Vietnam, for not only is the export trade in small birds recklessly uncontrolled, but the birds are being eaten in large numbers as well. In Ho Chi Minh City there are several locations where bird vendors, sitting with cages literally packed with live munias, buntings and swallows, take one bird at a time, pluck it naked, and toss the corpse into a bowl to be cooked later. The birds are caught as they leave their feeding grounds to roost in the evening and taken to market the next morning. They never receive food nor water.

REFERENCES Ali & Ripley (1987), Brooksbank (1949), Caldwell & Caldwell (1931), Clement *et al.* (1993), De Zylva (1984), Gray (1958), Harvey & Holmes (1976), Immelmann (1965), Lever (1987), Mason & Le Froy (1912), Morris (1972), Moynihan & Hall (1954), Parkes (1958), Restall (1995b), Roberts (1974 & 1992), Robinson & Chasen (1927-29), Ward (1968).

15 WHITE-BELLIED MUNIA
Lonchura leucogastra   Plate 5

Described as *Lonchura leucogaster* Blyth
Other common names: White-breasted Munia or Mannikin, White-bellied Mannikin.

White-bellied Munia in full song display.

FIELD CHARACTERS An average-sized munia. It is dark brown all over except for a white or creamy belly patch. There are six races, comparatively similar and difficult to separate without reference to colour plates or specimens. It may be told from White-rumped Munia *L. striata*, with which it overlaps in peninsular Burma, Thailand and Malaysia, by having a dark rump and uppertail-coverts, with yellow edges to the tail feathers. The juveniles are similar and would be difficult to tell apart in the field.

STATUS Locally common (western and north-eastern Borneo and Palawan), uncommon (Malaysian peninsula), scarce (Luzon), rare (Sumatra) and very rare (west Java). Its status in central and southern Kalimantan is unknown.

HABITAT It is a bird of woodlands, evergreen forest clearings and edges, secondary growth, cultivation and gardens but most of all appears to be that rare bird, a woodland munia.

HABITS AND BEHAVIOUR It is recorded in pairs or small groups, possibly family parties. They are extremely sociable. The members of a flock or group keep close together. This urge is so strong that escaped birds in a trappers farm will often attempt to rejoin the flock in the holding cages rather than fly away. They like to roost in nests during the day, and a community will all try to roost in the same nest. Linda Santosa (pers. comm.) reports that in Pontianak, small groups would keep close together when coming into the open to feed on grass seeds in the garden, and all fled at the same instant if alarmed. When the alarm note is given, the birds will quickly dive for cover. They will disappear into a nest or other place of concealment and sit still and silent. Harrisson (in Smythies 1981) says it is not only shy, but he often found it solitary.

From observations of birds in captivity I would say they are perfectly equable and sociable, without any form of aggression towards each other or any other species. When kept in a group, a single bird that begins to feed is sufficient stimulous to attract the others to join it and within moments they will all be feeding from the same pot. They will usually feed from one pot exclusively, until it is exhausted, before moving to another even if it is quite close by. Their behaviour feeding on lawns in Pontianak echoes this. They clump and allopreen freely. I find it very similar to White-rumped Munia in all aspects of its behaviour.

A singing male will attract admirers who will gather round and peer closely. I have never seen a female peer. With peering I found that a solitary male that began a spontaneous undirected advertisement song would almost invariably attract a peerer. When he had finished singing, and flew off, the watcher in turn became a performer, but I never saw the original songster return to peer in turn. Often an advertisement-singing male would be approached by one of the females whereupon he would subside and begin to preen himself. I never saw a conversion from advertisement song to sexual display.

FOOD AND FEEDING There is some variation in bill size between the races, which might suggest a regional adaptation to differing local food sources, but there are no data to support this. Despite being a bird of wooded areas and woodland verges it appears to be unremarkable in its food preferences. It certainly takes seeds from growing grasses and weeds. Harrisson (in Smythies 1981) found it to be "always skulking in rice", which is the only reference I have to rice, although it would be remarkable if it did not take rice. Bartlett (1896) in contrast, and in agreement with Santosa, found it would come close to human dwellings foraging for food, especially in the vicinity of stables and outhouses. In captivity, I found it would take all kinds of seeds and some green food, chewing the stems of grass stalks as well.

MOVEMENTS There appears to be some altitudinal movement in eastern Kalimantan. Smythies (1981) records birds migrating to the Kelabit uplands in January, where they do not breed, but does not say how long they stay before returning to breed in the lowlands. It is recorded as breeding in Sumatra and west Java. It is rare in both places, but it is not known whether the species in either place is a vagrant, migrant or a colonist from Malaysia.

CALL The male's contact call is a clear and strong *twyrt* or *twyert* and the female will respond with *tee tee tee*. If the male calls *twet!* the female will respond with *tit*, and if the male utters the querulous *twyert?* the female will respond *weet* or *wit*. The alarm note is a stong *tik!* or *tchek!*

SONG The song is a *di-di-ptcheee-pti-pti-pti-pteep!* which is repeated without pause several times.

COURTSHIP AND DISPLAY In a typical undirected song sequence the male grasps a length of grass and hops about calling excitedly. The grass is dropped and the advertisement song is begun. The head is raised, and the neck stretched but held horizontal, as is the tail. Only the white belly feathers are erected and held away from the body. The head turns from side to side and sometimes with, but not always, a little wing flicking. The bill opens and closes continually and the head moves up and down a little.

Carrying a stem is often a preliminary to displaying but not always, and the grass or stem is always dropped once singing begins.

In direct courtship the male incorporates all the elements of the full straw display (Baptista and Horblit 1990). He has his throat and crown feathers flattened and his nape feathers slightly erect. His belly feathers are fluffed out. The legs are bent, the tail is slightly raised. The bill is held horizontal and opens and shuts rapidly during the song. There is a little bobbing in the inverted curtsey (Morris 1958) and the display concludes with a

deep bow with tail raised and fanned wide to show the yellow tail-edges.

Bowing display of male White-bellied Munia showing yellow edges of the tail, before beginning the full song and dance.

At the start of a high intensity courtship display the male will bow low, to the level of the perch, raising his tail thereby displaying the yellow edges of the rectrices which contrast with the black uppertail-coverts. If the female stays nearby the male returns to a normal angle. The tail is raised slightly above the horizontal. The feathers are all more ruffled, and the crown is also erect. The head nods up and down and is also turned from side to side. The bird swings from side to side, pivoting towards the female, and bobs upwards in an inverted curtsey. In this display I have seen vigorous bobbing up and down, with the male jumping well clear of the perch. In this degree of intensity, the male is clearly directing his performance at a particular female, pointing his head at her and, if the perch ran roughly in her direction, he might edge along the perch towards her. Usually this happens when the female is nearby on the ground feeding. If she is alongside the male she will turn towards him and they will touch bills, tip to tip. This stops the male in mid performance, but he usually recovers and repeats the routine.

The male intent on breeding will sing in the nest. He will also lean out of the entrance hole directing his song at the female as if to entice her in. I have never seen a female respond to this display.

'Kissing'. At the end of a courtship sequence the birds will touch bills in a ritualised bill-fencing display.

BREEDING Smythies (1981) says it is common in the Kuching area (Sarawak) during the breeding season. He found a colony of six nests that was active from February to May and mentions another small colony active in June. All breeding colonies recorded were in trees. He mentions an unusual behavioural characteristic of the birds of hovering in front of the nests as hummingbirds hover over flowers. Several broods of newly hatched young were found in Borneo in October (Pfeiffer, in Goodwin 1982) but the reference does not say where in Borneo. Another note I have, without source but also in Borneo, mentions it breeding in dense forest nearly 10km from the nearest open space.

Nesting material seems to be carried exclusively by the male. The nest is a typical spheroid of grasses, bamboo leaves and fibres, or maybe made entirely of grasses lined with finer parts and soft panicles. One nest collected by Bartlett (1876) was made entirely of bamboo leaves. That report says the nest is placed one to two metres from the ground. In captivity it shows a remarkable propensity to bulk out and line the nest with strips of soft paper, feathers and any pliable detritus (pers. obs.) very much like House Sparrow *Passer domesticus*. Baker (1926) says the nest is "the usual type of munia nest" but it sometimes employs bamboo leaves in its construction.

Siegfried Kirschke in Germany (*in litt.*) found them easy to breed in captivity. The clutch would always be from 4–6 eggs. They feed the young well, and are conscientious and satisfactory parents. He found the young would take 3 months to attain adult plumage and become sexually mature at 5 months. He warns at the willingness with which it will hybridise with other *Lonchura* species and so should not be mixed when breeding. From some excellent photographs he sent me, Kirschke's birds were apparently of the race *L. l. everetti* from the Philippines.

Palate markings of nestling White-bellied Munia.

DISTRIBUTION This is a widely ranging species but with a somewhat fragmented and poorly detailed distribution. The nominate race *L. l. leucogastra* is said to range from Tavoy in southern Burma (Baker 1926) south through peninsular Thailand and peninsular Malaysia. It is generally presumed to be absent from Singapore, but I have been told locally that it appears to have colonised or been introduced fairly recently. It is rare, presumed a vagrant in Sumatra (van Marle and Voous 1988) and a nest with eggs was found in west Java (MacKinnon 1988), not far from Bogor. But the species has not been studied on either island and it is unknown whether the birds recorded are vagrants, migrants or the extent to which it is actually established. It would be remarkable if the Sumatran and Javan records are all of vagrants for this is a sedentary woodland species, not a nomadic savanna bird.

One race, *L. l. everetti*, is found in the northern Philippines, most of Luzon and the islands to Cantanduanes, including Mindoro and Polillo. The race found in the central and southern Philippines, *L. l. manueli* has been recorded on Mindanao and Tawi Tawi. The race *L. l. palawana* is known from Calamianes, Balabac, Palawan, Culion, Busuanga and Calauit to the north, also Bongao. In south-western Sarawak and north-west Kalimantan the race *L. l. smythiesi* may be found. The race *L. l. castananota* is known from the area around Riam and the junction of the Sampit and Tjempaga Rivers (Mayr 1938). It is recorded in the Barito Ulu region in central Kalimantan (Wilkinson *et al.* 1991) but the bird is not described, and it is not known whether this is an extension of a known race or a new one. It is probably more widespread in Borneo than hitherto recorded, and a comprehensive field study of the distribution and full descriptions of the

populations on that island is indicated. Certainly an effort should be made to describe the Barito Ulu population.

Distribution of White-bellied Munia.

DESCRIPTION   **Plate 42**
There are six recognised races. The subspecific differences are subtle and it is not easy to identify a race in isolation. The chart shows the key differences.

MALAYSIAN WHITE-BELLIED MUNIA
L. leucogastra leucogastra
Former scientific name: *Amadina leucogastra* Blyth, 1846. *Journ. Asiat. Soc. Bengal*, 15 p.286.
Adult male 110–115mm. Wing length 51–53mm, culmen 10mm, tarsus 11mm. It has the entire face, throat, breast, flanks and thighs, and undertail-coverts deep raw umber. The belly is cream and joins the flanks in an irregular broken line. There may be a few cream or white spots on the brown flanks. The underwing-coverts are pale buffy-salmon. Above, from crown and rear ear-coverts, sides of neck and wings to the lower back it is dark olive-brown. There are clear white striations on the mantle, wing coverts, tertials and lower back. The uppertail-coverts are black. The tail is blackish with ochreous to orange-straw edgings. The irides may range from brown (museum specimen labels) to ruby (pers. obs.). The bill of this race is smaller than usual for the species, the culmen being *c.*10mm. The bill is blackish on the upper mandible, pale bluish-grey on the lower mandible, and whitish at the base. The legs and feet are bluish-grey.
Adult female 105–110mm. Wing length 50mm, culmen 10mm, tarsus 11mm. In other respects there appears to be no difference.
Juvenile Duller version of the adult, and is more buffish-coloured on the belly.

PALAWAN WHITE-BELLIED MUNIA
L. leucogastra palawana
Ripley and Rabor, 1962, *Postilla*, Yale Univ., No. 13, p.11.
Adult male *c.*115mm. Wing length 52mm, culmen 11mm, tarsus 11mm. It has the forehead, sides of face

	striations back to rump	striations nape to lower back	striations crown to lower back	striations crown to rump	striations on sides of neck	striations on flanks	back dark brown	back earth-brown	back chestnut-brown	uppertail-coverts black	uppertail-coverts brown	tail edged orange-yellow	tail edged yellow	tail edged cream	tail edged straw
L. l. leucogastra	●						●			●		●			
L. l. palawana			●	●				●			●		●		
L. l. everetti		●	●		●			●			●				●
L. l. manueli		●						●			●		●		
L. l. smythiesi	●							●			●		●		
L. l. castanonota		●							●	●				●	

Guide to the identification of White-bellied Munia by subspecific differences.

and entire underparts (except the belly) and the uppertail-coverts rich raw umber. The belly patch is white and where it joins the flanks is broadly scalloped. From crown to rump, wing-coverts and tertials it is earth-brown with noticeable white striations from nape to rump, on the ear-coverts and usually on the edges of the upper breast. The flight feathers are dark brown with a little yellow-straw edgings to the tail. In other respects it resembles *L. l. leucogastra*.

LUZON WHITE-BELLIED MUNIA
L. leucogastra everetti
Former scientific name: *Orycerca everetti*, Tweeddale, 1877, *Ann. Mag. Nat. Hist., Ser.* 4, 20, p.96
Other common names: Everett's White-bellied Munia.
Adult male *c.*115mm long. Wing length 53mm, culmen 12–13mm, tarsus *c.*11mm. The brown of the face and underparts is not so rich nor as intense as in the former two races, the burnt umber becoming russet to hazel on the edges of the ear-coverts, sides of breast and flanks. The white belly patch is edged with spots and irregularities and there are usually some striations on the flanks. The underwing-coverts are white. It is dark cinnamon-olive above, with strong white striations from forecrown to the lower back. The rump and uppertail-covers are burnt umber, without striations. The tail is brown with yellow-straw edgings. The thighs are hazel, the undertail-coverts burnt umber. The irides are ruby. The bill is slightly heavier in the male, being deeper and broader. It is dark grey on the upper mandible and pale bluish-grey on the lower, white at the base. The legs and feet are pale grey.
Female *c.*112mm. Wing length 51mm, culmen 11–11.5mm, tarsus 11mm. Plumage resembles the male.

MINDANAO WHITE-BELLIED MUNIA
L. leucogastra manueli
Parkes, 1958, *Proc. U.S. Nat. Mus.*, 108, P.280.
Adult male *c.*115mm. Wing length 53mm, culmen 12–13mm, tarsus 12mm. From the forehead and forecrown to a line ending midway above the eye, the

entire ear-coverts, bib, throat and centre of the breast and the uppertail-coverts are rich burnt umber. However, the sides of the breast and upper flanks are noticeably paler, being the same russet as *L. l. everetti* and there may be black scallops or spots on the sides of the breast. The upper flanks are barred with dark brown. The white belly has small brown patches where the breast joins the belly and the white lower flanks are spotted or barred with brown and black. Above the rear crown to rump is dark earth-brown. The white striations extend from the nape to the lower back and also on the wing-coverts and tertials. The uppertail-coverts are burnt umber. There is yellow edging to the tail. The thighs, vent and undertail-coverts are burnt umber.
Female *c.*110mm. Wing length 51mm, culmen 11mm, tarsus 11mm. There is no visible difference in the plumage to that of the male.

SMYTHIES' WHITE-BELLIED MUNIA
L. leucogastra smythiesi   **Plate 42**
Parkes, 1958, Proc. U.S. Nat. Mus., 108, p.282
Adult male 112–115mm. Wing length 51–53mm, culmen 11–13mm, tarsus 11mm. It is natal brown from forehead to the short uppertail-coverts, a little darker on wings and tail. There are striations on the mantle, wing-coverts and tertials, and rump, but not on the short uppertail-coverts. The long uppertail-coverts are brown. The tail is dark with pale olivaceous-straw edging. The face, ear-coverts, chin to breast, flanks and thighs and undertail-coverts are russet to tawny, darkest on the centre of the breast and the undertail-coverts. The sides of the neck and breast, running along the part of the flanks covered by the closed wings, is a rich brown. The belly and ventral area is pure white, with perhaps a little spotting at the edge of the breast.
Female *c.*107–111mm long. Wing length 49– 51mm, culmen 10–11mm, tarsus 11mm. Otherwise similar to the male.

REFERENCES Bartlett (1896), Baker (1926), Baptista & Horblit (1990), Goodwin (1982), Lekagul & Round (1991), MacKinnon (1988), MacKinnon & Phillipps (1993), Mayr (1938), Morris (1958), Smythies (1981), van Marle & Voous (1988), Wilkinson *et al.* (1991).

Comparison between the bill size of female *L. l. smythiesi*, left, and male, right.

MAYR'S WHITE-BELLIED MUNIA
L. leucogastra castanonota
Mayr. 1938, *Bull. Raffles Mus.*, 14, p.45
Adult *c.*112mm long. Wing length 51mm, culmen 11mm, tarsus 11mm. It has the face, to breast, flanks and thighs rich burnt umber, very deep on the front. The undertail-coverts are also darker. From top of head to rump and wings it is warm sepia. There are slight striations on the nape, and these become the typical strong white striations on the back and wings. The lower rump and uppertail-coverts are blackish. The tail is dark with warm straw edging. The belly is white.
Female Similar but males tend to be bigger and bolder as with the species typically.
Juvenile Warm sepia with a cream belly and flanks, the latter being spotted or marked with sepia. There are faint striations on the lower mantle and wings. The irides are dark brown. The upper mandible is grey, the lower mandible pale bluish-grey.

HYBRIDS No hybrids have been reported in the wild. I successfully produced two hybrid young from a male White-bellied Munia crossed with a female (dark brown-and-white) Bengalese. The young resembled wild White-bellied Munia.

CONSERVATION Anecdotal evidence suggests there is cause for concern for the species in the Philippines and possibly in peninsular Malaysia. In the Philippines the destruction of forest is out of control and the essential habitat of this species has all but disappeared. I failed to find it during my own visits to the Philippines. An experienced bird trapper/dealer, now out of the business, was able to obtain a few pairs for me on Luzon in 1989. By 1994 he found it impossible to find the bird and said there were none in the trade at all. In 1990–91 small numbers were found on Luzon and Mindanao and reasonable numbers on Palawan (Nigel Redman pers. comm.). Forest destruction in Malaysia is also a concern, but virtually nothing is known of the bird there and I have been quite unable to find it in the trade at all. It was recorded from Tavoy in Southern Burma by Baker (1926), but Philip Round (in Legakul and Round 1991) shows it to be irregular and uncommon at best. Undoubtedly forest destruction in Thailand has resulted in a drop in population levels there as well. It is possible that the extensive forest fires in southern Kalimantan in recent years have caused irreparable damage to the habitat of the virtually unknown race *L. l. castanonota.* On the other hand it seems probable that White-bellied Munia is more widespread on Kalimantan than hitherto recorded. Wikinson *et al.* (1991) recorded it, without comment, in the Barito Ulu region.

Throughout its range, the species is virtually unknown to the bird trade and any trapping of it, legal or otherwise, is absolutely minimal.

INTRODUCTION TO STREAK-HEADED AND WHITE-SPOTTED MANNIKINS

An introduction to these two species is necessary because of the confusion surrounding their identity in the literature which, by and large, is not helpful. There is an unfortunate tendency for modern authors to regard them as conspecific. My introduction to them was in Goodwin (1982) and my interest was sparked when I was able to acquire two live White-spotted Mannikins for study a few years later. I subsequently saw a pair of Streak-headed Mannikins in Singapore and I realised that these two species are not only closely related, but offer a perfect opportunity for a comparative study. This I was able to do while living in Hong Kong, and my conclusion was that there is no doubt that these are two perfectly valid species. There is still plenty of opportunity for a thorough and formally structured comparative study.

Streak-headed Mannikin ranges around the island of New Guinea from the Noord River area and the town of Agats in Irian Barat westwards to the Vogelkop and eastwards across the northern part of the island as far as Popondetta in Papua New Guinea and then up the south-eastern coast as far as Hall Sound. White-spotted Mannikin is found in the southern part of the island, mainly from the Noord River to the Gulf of Papua.

There is some overlap in the Noord River area (Junge 1939), the Port Moresby area, and apparently in the Kiunga area north of Lake Murray (Hicks pers. comm.). The existence of sympatric or parapatric populations is sufficient reason to accept the birds as distinct species as proposed by Delacour (1943) and Sibley and Monroe (1990) and in my opinion that is the only way to regard them. In this way, data relating to one form or another is kept discrete and comparative analyses can be attempted. By lumping the two forms into a single species as Coates (1990) has done the distinctions become blurred and possible discriminating distinctions are lost.

An apparent hybrid was collected by Junge in the Noord River area and described by Mees (1958) in detail. Normally the occurrence of natural hybrids in the wild is enough to question the integrity of the two species involved. However, with most *Lonchura* this is not so simple. If hybridisation in the wild were sufficient evidence for conspecificity then Chestnut-breasted Mannikin *L. castaneothorax* would be conspecific with Yellow-rumped Mannikin *L flaviprymna*, Grey-headed Mannikin *L. caniceps* and Scaly-breasted Munia *L. punctulata*. The genus is notoriously promiscuous and aviculturists and researchers alike must always take care to avoid unwanted and unexpected hybrids appearing when more than one species is kept in the same enclosure.

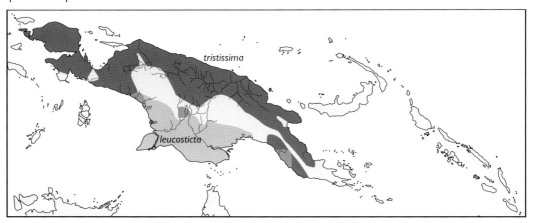

tristissima

leucosticta

Map showing the comparative distribution of the two species, and areas where they are known to overlap.

Coates (1990) refers to 'a stable hybrid population' of *L. tristissima* x *L. leucosticta* along the coastal area of the Central Province of Papua New Guinea, but a close examination of the excellent quality series of skins of these birds in the collection of the National Museum in Port Moresby led me to the conclusion that they are a perfectly viable and distinct race of *L. tristissima*. The single skin of *L. leucosticta* taken in the Moresby area is marginally distinct from the type of the main population and to ensure that future behavioural observations are kept discrete I have treated it as a valid subspecies (Restall 1995b). By no stretch of the imagination could it be taken for a hybrid. In fact the aforementioned data reinforces that the two are distinct species, being both sympatric and parapatric.

In behavioural terms there is little comparative information in the literature. While Streak-headed Mannikin is a bird of secondary growth and forest edge, White-spotted Mannikin is a bird of reedbeds and more open habitat. That is also the observation of Roger Hicks (pers. comm.). Sibley and Monroe (1990) contrast them as: Steak-headed Mannikin is a bird of "grassy edge near water, towns" and White-spotted Mannikin is a bird of "savanna, riparian grass, bamboo."

The voice of each species is similar but not identical, and both are different from any other *Lonchura*. It was remarks by Oreste Piotto (pers. comm.) who kept and bred White-spotted Mannikins in England, that its voice reminded him a great deal of Double-barred Finch *Poephila bichenovii* that started me thinking about this. In my own notes I have recorded that the song of White-spotted Mannikin is reminiscent of Timor Zebra Finch *Poephila guttata guttata* while the call of Steak-headed Mannikin is like that of Timor Zebra Finch. It has made me wonder at times if these two *Lonchura* species might be genetically close to the *Poephila* grassfinches or even form a genetic bridge between the mannikins and the grassfinches. Piotto managed to breed a hybrid between White-spotted Mannikin and a female domesticated Australian Zebra Finch *P. guttata castanotis*, in England. This in itself does not prove anything, but it does illustrate there is much opportunity for detailed comparative study.

REFERENCES Coates (1990), Delacour (1943), Goodwin (1984), Junge (1939), Mees (1958), Restall (1994b & 1995b), Sibley & Monroe (1990).

---

16   STREAK-HEADED MANNIKIN
Lonchura tristissima   Plate 7

Described as *Lonchura tristissima* Wallace.
Other common name: Streak-headed Munia.

TAXONOMY This is a rather variable species and there has been some doubt about the validity of the race *L. t. calaminoros*, which is sometimes considered synonymous with *L. t. tristissima*. Mees (1958) reviewed all the literature and original descriptions and could not justify the difference, concluding that Reichenow's *L. t. calaminoros* was Wallace's *L. t. tristissima*. This does not explain the population of *L. t. hypomelaena* that occurs in the region between *L. t. tristissima* and *L. t. calaminoros*. I have studied the specimens in the Natural History Museum at Tring, the National Museum in Port Moresby and the American Museum of Natural History in New York and have concluded that while the species is undeniably variable, there are four quite distinct types. Three of these fit comfortably into the existing taxonomy and I therefore retain all the subspecies hitherto described. They are each described below and illustrated in colour together with a new race *L. t. bigilalei* (Restall 1995b).

I have reservations about the Karkar (formerly Dampier) Island population being considered synonymous with *L. t. calaminoros*. It is a very distinctive form in which the birds have prominent white wing bars. This population was recorded as feeding on insects (Diamond and LeCroy 1979) and deserves further study. It could well merit subspecific recognition. It should be mentioned here that in a comparison of this kind it is appropriate to compare males in second year plumage. To the best of my judgement my descriptions reflect these.

A further complication with this species is that it is mistakenly regarded by some writers as being conspecific with White-spotted Mannikin *L. leucosticta*. This results in both original observations and received wisdom being combined and attributes of one being assumed to apply to the whole. They are distinct species, and with somewhat different habits, and must be treated as such. Sadly any observations that fail to enable accurate identification may be useless.

FIELD CHARACTERS This is a small, dark brown munia with a violaceous bill, small pale streaks around the eyes

and a patch of straw colour on the lower rump. It is much darker than White-spotted Mannikin, which is noticeably more cinnamon but can be distinguished in all plumages by its pale throat. The ranges of the two species overlap in the Noord River area, possibly north of Lake Murray and presumably in the Port Moresby area. More detailed field records are needed.

STATUS It is locally or sporadically common.

HABITAT It is a bird of grassy areas in or near forest, and alongside mountain streams. It may be found on floating mats of grass and vegetation in rivers and in grassland bordering the rivers but seldom in open grassland. Lindgren (1975) only records it in small grassy clearings within forests, usually near streams of rivers. It is distributed unevenly and information on populations is not helpful. It normally keeps to the lowlands, occurring up to 1,000m but on occasions, and presumably in the absence of congeners, may be found up to 1,600m on the northern slopes of the Snow Mountains (Rand 1942) and up to 1,700m on Karkar Island (Diamond and LeCroy 1979).

HABITS AND BEHAVIOUR It usually occurs in small parties of about four to eight birds, occasionally in flocks of up to twenty (Coates 1990), or "fairly large flocks which occur in grass patches in open river-edge forest, and forest edge" (Gilliard and LeCroy 1966). In the northern part of New Guinea it appears to be fairly common in and around gardens near Lae and Madang. It occurs in the Port Moresby area but is rarely recorded as it appears to be an uncommon bird (Hicks pers. comm.).

It is undoubtedly adapted for life at the forest edges and forest clearings. Like other munias of this kind it tends to be shy and will quickly retire to cover in the forest undergrowth if disturbed. In my experience with four pairs in captivity, it is very shy and will dive for cover in the nest baskets when disturbed, noticeably preferring the one they roost in, lying still for a long time before one bird will venture out to see if the coast is clear. This apprehensive behaviour is far more extreme than in any other munia I have kept, including White-spotted Mannikin which will usually drop to the ground and sit still, or even flee rather than actually hide. Virtually nothing is recorded of the species' behaviour in the wild.

FOOD AND FEEDING Baptista (1990) recorded it several times one January in an open field about half a hectare in size in the company of a few hundred other mannikins, mostly Grand Mannikins *L. grandis* with some Chestnut-breasted Mannikins *L. castaneothorax*. It was observed feeding on the seeds of the introduced *Rottboellia exaltata* grass. This grass grows up to 2m tall and although the stems and leaves looked dead and dry, in fact the seeds, which are as large as rice grains, were green and milky. Immelmann *et al.* (1977) reported Streak-headed Mannikins feeding on bamboo seeds. Birds I have kept in captivity have eagerly fed on freshly picked seeding grasses of a wide variety of types.

Stomachs of birds taken on Karkar Island contained mostly insects (Diamond and LeCroy 1979) and the report suggested that this is a natural food for the species, having been forced to a graminivorous diet elsewhere by competition from *Cisticola* warblers. Cisticolas are common throughout the grasslands frequented by *Lonchura* mannikins in Africa and Asia, but are largely absent from Karkar. Rather than agree with Diamond and LeCroy's interesting hypothesis, I have the feeling the reverse is true, that the naturally graminivorous mannikins on Karkar have adapted to take insects. It might be that the species everywhere takes insects, but I am unaware of any records in support of this.

MOVEMENTS Not known.

CALL At dawn the birds converse in a series of soft buzzy notes, together with a song-like twittering. There are two distinct contact notes uttered during the day. The call of Streak-headed Mannikin is described as a short buzzy note (Coates 1990) and flowerpecker-like *jjbb* (Beehler *et al.* 1986). In fact the vocabulary is rich and varied. The contact call is a short *tzip! tzip!* from the male and longer, more complex *tzeep! tzeep!* from the female. The female's note sounds one tone lower than the male's. Either bird

Short song of Streak-headed Mannikin.

Antiphonal calls of bonded pair of Streak-headed Mannikins, recorded at dawn.

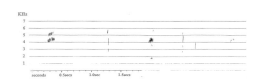

Call of female Streak-headed Mannikin.

will call the *jib!*, sometimes a rapid series which is rather scolding in tone. When a separated pair is reunited, even from a distance of a metre, the male will utter a series of intimate-sounding churring buzzes on a descending scale. There is also a sharp *tchek!* almost like a sneeze. It is usually uttered singly, but I have heard a series of three or four, when it sounds like a scold or admonition. I have only heard this from bird that was solitary but which was within earshot of other Streak-headed Mannikins.

SONG The advertisement song begins with a couple of trumpets, *bzeet bzeet squeek-bdiddly-wee squeek-bdiddly-wee bzeet bdiddly-wee beer-beer*, reminiscent of Timor Zebra Finch *Poephila guttata guttata* but more complex and seemingly twice as fast. The entire double phrase, occasionally triple, lasts barely 3 seconds. The directed song begins in the same way but has the middle phrase extended by repetition, and ends with two stronger notes. It lasts 7 or 8 seconds.

COURTSHIP AND DISPLAY In advertisement song the male stretches up and leans forward slightly. When the female is present he hops towards her and begins to perform when a few centimetres away, leaning and turning towards her slightly. I have not observed any straw display.

Streak-headed Mannikin in undirected song display.

BREEDING The nest is "spherical" (Beehler *et al.* 1986), and appears to be a ball of grasses with a side entrance, but reports in the literature are too confusing to be able to elaborate further. One nest recorded by Clapp (in Coates 1990) was located in forest about 70m in from the edge and was placed in rattan. A nest attributed to the species is described in Gilliard and LeCroy (1966). It was 3m above ground, ball-like with a side entrance, in a forest-edge tree bordering a wide stream near the Sepik River. The report in Beehler of the nest being "suspended" gives an erroneous impression of something like a weaver's nest. Breeding details are not known.

There is no record of the species occurring in captivity. I was fortunate to be given four birds by Herwin Purwahariyanto in 1994. They had apparently come to him from somewhere near Wamena and were taken to Jayapura. These proved to be 2 males and 2 females that formed into 2 pairs. I placed them in a large wire-fronted breeding cage with a nest at either end. All four birds roosted together in one nest. Within a few days they had stuffed it full with every blade of grass, fibre and strips of newspaper neatly torn from the cage floor covering. The entrance hole was about 3cm across, and the cavity inside about 7cm in diameter. Subsequently one pair took an interest in the other nest and visited it during the day,

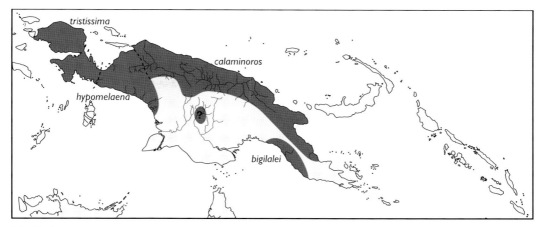

Distribution of Streak-headed Mannikin.

occasionally taking a stem or other scrap, but continuing to roost in the main nest with the other pair. Throughout the day they alternated periods of considerable activity with long periods of resting in the nest. When caged separately, the males were very vocal, singing often. When together they called a lot but either male only sang when it was alone, when the others remained in the nest.

DISTRIBUTION It is a bird of lowlands and hills up to at least 1,700m, ranging over much of New Guinea. The various subspecies are distributed as follows. *L. t. tristissima* is found in the Vogelkop of north-western Irian Jaya. *L. t. hypomelaena* is found around the Wissel Lakes in Irian Jaya and ranges far down the south-western coast to the Noord River and along the north-western coast to somewhere west of the Mamberamo River. There is undoubtedly some irregular intergrading between it and the next race to the east. *L. t. calaminoros* is found across the whole of northern New Guinea from west of the Mamberamo River to Cape Nelson. *L. t. bigilalei* occurs in the coastal Central Province of Papua New Guinea. Further information and descriptions are needed of populations and distribution in the Kiunga and Lake Murray region.

DESCRIPTION   **Plates 43–44**
There are four described subspecies. The illustration of wing and rump differences is a good basis for separating them.

VOGELKOP STREAK-HEADED MANNIKIN
L. tristissima tristissima
Former scientific name: *Munia tristissima* Wallace, 1865, *Proc. zool. Soc. London*, p.479.
Adult male 105–110mm. Wing length 52–55mm, culmen 10–11mm, tarsus 15mm. It is burnt umber above, from forehead to lower back, wings and tail There are whitish lines on the feather shafts of the forehead, crown, supercilium, lores and ear-coverts. There are faint streaks on the mantle and scapular, whitish terminal spots on the median and greater wing-coverts, and pairs of subterminal spots on the tertials. On most birds that I have examined, the edges of the median and greater wing-coverts were broadly marked with brown. The rump is mainly brown, with a narrow bar of black immediately adjoining the uppertail-coverts. The short uppertail-coverts are straw-yellow, the long uppertail-coverts are black. The

tail is fuscous. From chin to belly and flanks it is sepia which becomes black on the thighs, ventral region and undertail-coverts. The underwing-coverts are creamy-salmon. The bill is steel-blue or violaceous blue-grey. The irides are dark brown. The legs and feet are grey.
Adult female 104–106mm. Wing length 50–52mm, culmen 10mm, tarsus 14mm. I found it very difficult to distinguish any plumage characteristics, but Clement (*et al.* 1993) says the female is slightly paler with the buff streaks on the crown and ear-coverts being wider. The pale streaks on the head may be a little paler, and the straw of the short uppertail-coverts may be paler but it would be unwise to determine sex on this basis.
Juvenile Slightly smaller and duller version of the adult, with the streaks on the head much paler, finer and restricted to the head. The ends of the body feathers are edged with darker brown, giving a faintly scaled appearance. There is no straw on the uppertail-coverts, the brown of the back becomeing warmer brown on the lower rump and short uppertail-coverts.

WESTERN STREAK-HEADED MANNIKIN
L. tristissima hypomelaena   **Plate 43**
Stresseman and Paludan, 1934, *Ornith. Monatsb.*, 42. p.43.
Adult male Face blackish. It is hair brown above, from forehead to the lower back and wing-coverts. The flight feathers are darker brown, being more sepia, with browner edges to the tertials. The tail is dull, brownish-black. The rump is black, forming a broad bar. The short uppertail-coverts are bright straw-yellow, or cream. The long uppertail-coverts are black. Below, from bib and throat to the undertail-coverts it is dark greyish-brown in younger birds to black in second year birds. There are pale shaft streaks on the upper head, and outer ear-coverts, and in younger birds the sides of the upper breast where they may form a slight barring pattern (Rand 1967). There may be faint streaks on the mantle and subterminal spots on the lesser and median wing-coverts. The centres of these feathers may be paler, giving a distinct wing-bar effect. The edges to the tips of the median and greater wing-coverts are black, forming two black bars. There are pairs of subterminal pale spots on the out-

113

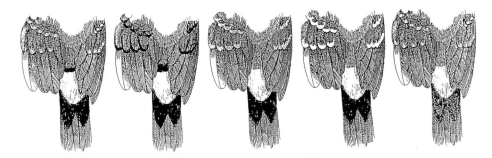

Comparison between the wing-coverts, rump and uppertail-coverts of the four subspecies of Streak-headed Mannikin. 1) *L. t. tristissima* 2) *L. t. hypomelaena*, 3) *L. t. calaminoros*, 4) *L. t. calaminoros* from Karkar Island, and 5) *L. t. bigilalei*.

tertials, which also have dark edges.

Adult female Similar, but has more pale streaking on the head, ear-coverts and sides of breast. The wings are not so dark and the contrast between the wing-coverts and flight feathers is not so noticeable. The edges to the median and greater wing-coverts are dark brown and not black. On the females of two pairs that I kept, there were slight patches of black in the uppertail-coverts, which were a slightly richer or warmer shade than on the males.

Juvenile Not described, but presumably is similar to that of the nominate race, also lacking the straw short uppertail-coverts.

NORTHERN STREAK-HEADED MANNIKIN
L. tristissima calaminoros   **Plate 44**
Former scientific name: *Munia calaminores* Reichenow, 1916, *Ornith. Monatsb.*, 24, p.169.

Adult Head and back brown, the wings tending to fuscous. There are whitish streaks from the forehead to the nape, and the outermost ear-coverts, but none on the mantle or scapulars. There are buffish subterminal spots on the lesser and median wing-coverts. The edges and tips of the greater wing-coverts are white or creamy, forming a bar across the wing. There were no spots on the tertials of any of the birds I examined. From chin to undertail-coverts the body is sepia with some brownish spotting on the sides of the breast. There is no black on the lower rump. The short uppertail-coverts are buff. The long uppertail-coverts are fuscous not black, and the tail is dark brown. Adults from Karkar (Dampier) Island had extremely clearly defined white wing-bars.

Juvenile Short uppertail-coverts hazel, otherwise it is similar to juvenile *L. t. tristissima*.

SOUTHERN STREAK-HEADED MANNIKIN
L. tristissima bigilalei
Restall, 1995, *Bull. Brit. Orn. Club.* 115 (3), 140 - 157.

Adult male Entire body brown, darker on the primaries and tail, ventral region and undertail-coverts. White streaks run from forecrown over the head to become faint and buffish on nape, mantle, scapulars and lesser wing-coverts. The white streaks are noticeably brighter on the hind ear-coverts, sides of the neck and sides of the upper breast. The buffish spots on the median wing-coverts become brighter on the greater wing-coverts forming a distinct bar. There are buffish edges to the ends of the tertials. The centres of the feathers of the sides of the breast and

upper flanks are amber. The rump is slightly darker than the mantle. There is no black band between the rump and short uppertail-coverts. The short uppertail-coverts are creamy yellow. The long uppertail-coverts are fuscous.

Female Very similar, very slightly smaller and with the spots not always so bright. The yellow of the rump was not quite so bright.

Juvenile Slightly duller version of the adult and lacks the yellow short uppertail-coverts.

KIUNGA STREAK-HEADED MANNIKIN
L. tristissima ' kiungae'
Undescribed.

This form has been reported (Hicks *in litt.*) from the Kiunga area in Central Western Province of Papua New Guinea, not far east of the Irian Jaya border and near the Lake Murray region. No details of geographic range, behaviour or plumage distinction, if any, are known.

HYBRIDS A specimen in the natural history museum in Leiden which appears to be a perfect intermediate between Streak-headed Mannikin and White-spotted Mannikin was described as a probable hybrid by Mees (1958). It was taken in the Bivakeiland area in the region of the Noord River in territory normally populated by White-headed Mannikins.

Coates (1990) assumes that the population in the south-east is an intermediate, apparently hybrid population without giving any references or description. What it would be intermediate between is uncertain. White-spotted Mannikin has been recorded only once in the south-east (Restall 1995b) – museum specimen rather than a field observation. The excellent specimens in the Port Moresby museum left me in no doubt that the population referred to by Coates is a distinct race of pure Streak-headed Mannikins.

CONSERVATION The species covers a considerable range across the island of New Guinea. There seems to be no cause for concern over habitat. The species is virtually unknown in aviculture and never appears on traders' lists.

REFERENCES Baptista (1990), Clement *et al.* (1993), Coates (1990), Diamond & LeCroy (1979), Gilliard & LeCroy (1966), Immenmann *et al.* (1977), Lindgren (1975), Mees (1958), Rand (1942), Rand & Gilliard (1967), Restall (1995b).

17 WHITE-SPOTTED MANNIKIN
Lonchura leucosticta Plate 7

Described as *Lonchura leucosticta* d'Albertis and Salvadori.

TAXONOMY The difficulty in dealing with the literature on this species is that some authors have regarded it as conspecific with Streak-headed Mannikin *L. tristissima* and because of this have melded any field observations into one. White-spotted Mannikin and Streak-headed Mannikin are distinct species with different behaviour patterns, thus, unless data includes details of location to enable sure identification of species or gives a trinomial, it might have to be ignored.

White-spotted Mannikin.

FIELD CHARACTERS This is a small warm brown munia with a pale throat, white spots on the head and wings, and a straw-coloured rump. It is cinnamon below with white spots on breast and flanks. The adult is fairly easy to recognise and can be told from the similar Streak-headed Mannikin by being noticeably more cinnamon in general, and having a pale throat. The areas where the two species occur are the Noord River, possibly north of Lake Murray, and in the greater Port Moresby area. The juveniles are very similar, but again the pale chin distinguishes White-spotted Mannikin.

STATUS Locally common.

HABITAT It is a lowland species that seems most likely to occur in open land between forest and marsh. It can be found in tall marshland grasses, areas of savanna and grassy areas along river banks. It seems to be particularly fond of bamboo, but almost certainly because the bamboo is seeding. There are no records of which species or types of bamboo occur in this area, let alone which bamboos are favoured by the birds. Field observations of White-spotted Mannikins in bamboo would be significantly enhanced in value if relevant details of the bamboo were recorded as well.

HABITS AND BEHAVIOUR It is a sociable species usually found in groups or flocks. Birds in captivity often react to a threat by dropping to the ground and remaining motionless, steadily watching the source of possible danger and only flushing and flying off if the threat approaches. They do not hide in the nest, and are much more prone to flee. They obviously feed on seeds from growing marshland grasses and similar plants, but they lack the large feet and long toes and claws of more typical marshland munias (e.g. Chestnut Munia *L. atricapilla*).

Also, the bill is small and comparatively fine. The inference I draw from this and their feeding behaviour in captivity is that the species is more specialised in its feeding habits than is known.

FOOD AND FEEDING It has been observed feeding on seeding grasses on the floating mats of vegetation on the edges of lagoons of the Fly River (Rand & Gilliard 1967), and may be seen in small flocks in tall marsh grasses and savanna near the forest edge. Rand (1938) found it feeding on the seeds of clumps of bamboo and found one flock in a clump of bamboo on a forested ridge some eighty metres from open country. Gregory (1995a) found a small party of about 10 birds at Lake Daviumbu, Papua New Guinea, feeding on the seeds of *Echinocloa* grass. In captivity I have found it to show a marked preference for the fresh unripe seeds of small grasses. Those grasses found in Hong Kong I have found to favour include *Lepturus* (*Rottboellia*) *repens, Axonopus compressus, Digitaria* spp., *Ottochloa malabarica* and *Isachne globosa*. The larger *Panicum maximum* was also taken readily, but only in small amounts. Large grasses like *Zea mays, Miscanthus floridulus* and *Saccharum arundinaceum* aroused very little interest. They readily sampled fresh lettuce every day.

MOVEMENTS Not recorded.

CALL The call note is a thin metallic *toot*, very reminiscent of the call of Zebra Finch *Poephila guttata*. When alarmed, the birds dive for cover with sharp cries of *peet* followed immediately by silence. I have noticed a short *tzurk!* warning note from birds I have studied in captivity.

Song of White-spotted Mannikin. The song itself lasts around 8 seconds but is usually repeated several times without a pause.

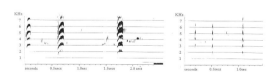

Male White-spotted Mannikin, loud contact call (left) and soft contact call (right).

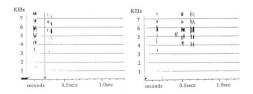

Calls of female White-spotted Mannikin.

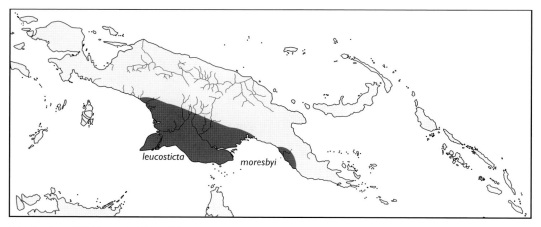

Distribution of White-spotted Mannikin.

There is a sequence of notes given by one bird that is sounding the alarm for the others. It begins with a sharp alarm note and ends with complaining sound, thus: *tchuk tchuk, tchuk tchuk, TCHZURK, TCHZURK, chzzz chzzzz chzzzzz*. The male and female loud contact *toot* notes are of a different tone from each other, the female's being lower in tone. I have noted a loud call by an estranged male *zweyr?* with a double note response from the female *tzer tzer*. Beehler (1986) notes a "short nasal buzz continually repeated in flight, quite unlike calls of other lowland *Lonchura*." Gregory (1995a) records a plaintive *seee*.

SONG The song of the male is described by Siegfried Kirschke (*in litt.*) who bred White-spotted Mannikin in Germany, as being "similar to that of other munias, croaking, squeaking and cackling sounds, some louder some softer and apparently somewhat ventriloquial". Oreste Piotto (*in litt.*) who successfully bred the birds in cages in England, commented on their distinctive voice. He described the song as being very noisy, a high-pitched wheezy, chirrupy trumpeting very reminiscent of a Double-barred Finch *Poephila bichenovii*, delivered with the bill open and body feathers fluffed out. In my own experience I found it to be anything but similar to other munias. It begins with three or four rusty *zwee* notes which are soon followed by a rising *zeee* and a higher, longer *tseee*. Then comes a low note and it continues as a 'roller coaster' of wheezes and buzzes with a few *tik* and *zee* notes along the way. It is different from the song of Streak-headed Mannikin and any of the *Poephila* grassfinches.

White-spotted Mannikin in directed song display.

COURTSHIP AND DISPLAY The advertisement song is delivered sitting fairly upright, neck stretched slightly, bill open with a slight mandibulation, but no bill closing, sometimes with the bird moving slightly from side to side. In the few observations I was able to make of the courtship, the male followed the female about, bursting into song if she stayed still long enough when he alighted alongside her. The directed display and song is usually given with feathers more erected, particularly on the nape, rump and flanks, with the head and tail turned towards the female. She invites copulation by leaning forward and tail-quivering. Copulation is followed by bill fencing and preening.

BREEDING Nothing at all is recorded of the breeding behaviour in the wild. Eggs from birds that I have kept were rather longer in proportion than is usual with *Lonchura*, being 15.5mm x 10.0mm. Oreste Piotto's pairs, liked to visit each other in their nests, being very active and curious. He found them to be very sociable, even while breeding. The pairs intermingled and engaged in mutual preening. For nesting material his birds showed a preference for hay, coconut fibre, white tissue and strips of newspaper. The clutch was 3–5 oval white eggs. Incubation lasted 14 days. The nestlings were orange-brown upon hatching, becoming darker within 2 or 3 days and feathering started at 7 days old. At 14 days dark rusty-brown plumage was apparent. The white spots of the adult became apparent around 10 weeks old. The young males also began singing about this time. The fledglings begged for food very noisily with quivering open wings.

DISTRIBUTION It is a bird of southern New Guinea. *L. l. leucosticta* ranges from the Fly River to the Noord River, and this boundary extends northwards above Lake Murray. *L. l. moresbyi* is recorded from a single specimen taken in in the Port Moresby area (Restall 1995a).

DESCRIPTION   **Plate 45**
There are two subspecies, similar in appearance and no doubt impossible to tell apart in the field, but the Port Moresby form is separated from the main area of distribution by an area of some 200km or more. It differs primarily by the male having dark grey undertail-coverts.

WHITE-SPOTTED MANNIKIN

L. leucosticta leucosticta   Plate 45

Former scientific name: *Munia leucosticta* d'Albertis
and Salvadori 1879, *Ann. Mus. Civ. Genova*, 14, p.88
Other common name: White-spotted Munia.

Adult male *c*.105mm. Wing length 52mm, culmen
11mm, height of the bill at the base is 8mm, tarsus is
11mm. From forehead to nape, ear-coverts, wings and
tail it is fuscous while the back is burnt umber. There
are white shaft lines from forehead to nape, thicken-
ing almost to terminal spots on the back and lesser
wing-coverts. There are white terminal spots on the
median and greater wing-coverts and also on the
tertials. The chin and upper throat is pale cinnamon
to white, quickly becoming tawny on the breast, belly
and flanks. There are white spots formed by the edges
of the feathers being white, and often arrowhead in
shape, that cover the chin, throat, upper breast, sides
of breast and upper flanks. The underwing-coverts are
salmon to pale buff. The thighs, ventral area and
undertail-coverts are black. The lower rump and short
uppertail-coverts are bright straw-yellow. The long
uppertail-coverts are black. The bill is pale blue-grey
or violaceous blue-grey. The irides are brown. The legs
and feet are grey.

Adult female 100–102mm. Wing length 49mm, culmen 11mm, height of bill at base is 7mm, tarsus
10mm. In general resembles the male but has a lightly
cinnamon-tinted chin, brown thighs and dark brown
vent and undertail-coverts. The short uppertail-coverts
may be slightly less bright yellow. The breast is less
rich tawny. In some females there are no terminal
spots on the tertials.

First-year Plumage of both sexes is slightly less richly
coloured, and some males might be dark brown on
the thighs, vent and undertail-coverts, though this is
darker than that of females. The undertail-coverts may
be tipped with buff or paler brown. It is possible for a
first-year male to be taken for a female if seen alongside an older male. The bill is usually a little narrower
at 7mm high at the base.

Juvenile Dull fuscous, slightly warmer on the rump,
darker wings and tail, with the long uppertail-coverts
very dark. The vent and undertail-coverts are darker
also and there may be pale edges to the undertail-
coverts. It has white shaft lines radiating from the forehead, lores, mesial and chin that fade on the nape,
breast and flanks. There are white terminal spots on
the median and greater wing-coverts. It may easily be
distinguished from juvenile Streak-headed Mannikin
L. tristissima by the pale chin and basal mesial.

LESSER WHITE-SPOTTED MANNIKIN

L. leucosticta moresbyi

Restall, 1995, *Bull. Brit. Orn. Club.*, 115 (3), 140 - 157.

Adult Wing length 47mm, culmen 9mm, tarsus 14mm.
From the forehead to the lower back, wings and tail it
is fuscous, with white shaft lines radiating back from
the face over the head to the back and wings, with
terminal spots on the wing-coverts and tertials. The
mesial and chin are creamy white, radiating in whitish
spots onto the throat, sides of breast and upper flanks.
These spots have dark brown subterminal marks, and
there are also dark brown edges to the feathers on

Comparison between *L. l. leucosticta*, **on left, and** *L. l.
moresbyi* **on right.**

either side of the whitish spots, throwing them into
sharp relief. The underwing-coverts are salmon. The
breast, belly and flanks are tawny to cinnamon, more
like the female *L. l. leucosticta*. The thighs, vent and
undertail-coverts are dark greyish-brown.

Palate markings of nestling hybrids *L. leuocosticta* x
Poephila guttata castanotis.

HYBRIDS Nothing is recorded from the wild. Piotto (*in
litt.*) subsequently bred hybrids between White-spotted
Mannikin and domestic Zebra Finch *Poephila guttata
castanotis*. He recorded the gape markings of the nestlings
but they died before moulting into adult plumage and
there is no record of plumage or voice. It is interesting
that the three spots on the roof of the palate are identical
to those on the roof of the palate of Zebra Finch; those
on the sides of the gape, tongue and lower part are missing. The palate markings of the nestling White-spotted
Mannikin are not known.

CONSERVATION White-spotted Mannikin is trapped in
small numbers for the bird trade. It is caught in the
grasslands outside Merauke along with Black Mannikin
L. stygia, Grey-crowned Mannikin *L. nevermanni*, and
Crimson Finch *Neochmia phaeton*. From 1985 to 1990 there
was a marked interest in it in Europe, but it proved to be
extremely difficult to breed and birds would become
listless and lethargic. It also appears to be short-lived in
captivity. Interest and demand lessened. By late 1994 I
found birds in holding establishments in Jakarta and
Singapore that had been waiting to be shipped for over a
year and the flow of freshly-caught birds had become small
and slow. This suggests that the bird trade does not
represent a threat to the species.

REFERENCES Beehler *et al.* (1986), Gregory (1995a),
Rand (1938), Rand & Gilliard (1967), Restall (1995b).

INTRODUCTION TO THE CHESTNUT MUNIA GROUP

In his seminal revision of the subfamily Estrildinae in 1943, Jean Delacour united three separate munia species into one. The three were *Lonchura malacca*, *L. atricapilla* and *L. ferruginosa*. He gave the name *ferruginosa* for the combined species, overlooking the fact that *Loxia malacca* Linnaeus (1766) antedates *Loxia ferruginosa* Sparrmann (1789). Since then several authors have questioned the wisdom of this. Wolters (1979) regarded *L. ferruginosa* as a good species and Sibley and Monroe (1990) follow him. Goodwin separated *L. malacca*, *L. atricapilla* and *L. ferruginosa* into three groups but retained them as a single species. Other writers generally follow this treatment, but there is a trend to regard *L. ferruginosa* as a good species, e.g. MacKinnon and Phillipps (1993). The specific integrity of *L. ferruginosa* now appears to be beyond doubt and I certainly feel it should be treated as a good species. Regardless of the status of *L. ferruginosa*, I have come to the conclusion that *L. malacca* and *L. atricapilla* must be regarded as distinct species (Restall 1994a and 1995b).

Tricoloured Munia *L. malacca* occupies a clearly demarcated range within India, quite separated from *L. atricapilla* by a strip of land some 250km wide at the closest point (Ali and Ripley 1987). In contrast, *L. atricapilla* has an extensive sprawling range within which various subspecies intergrade and even overlap.

Within *L. malacca* there are five distinct morphs, by far the commonest being the familiar black-headed chestnut-backed bird with a white breast band and white flanks and a clearly defined black belly patch merging with black undertail-coverts. This form accounts for 95% or more of any population. The other four variants are as follows. The first has a noticeably irregular zig-zagging of the division between the black and the white on the flanks. The second has a fine wavy black barring over the white feathers similar in pattern to that on African Silverbill *L. cantans*. The third has a very light cinnamon wash over the white with the edges of the feathers darker cinnamon, giving a scalloped appearance; and the fourth has the white replaced by uniform cinnamon. Obviously the species has a propensity for colour variation on the white. Only one of these resembles *L. atricapilla* and that is the cinnamon-flanked variant. But when compared side-by-side, the cinnamon-flanked form of *L. malacca* does not match any of the variations of *L. atricapilla*.

Chestnut Munia with Tricoloured Munia

Although I have not been able to hold live nestlings side by side for direct comparison, it appears that the palate markings of *L. malacca* are different from those of *L. atricapilla*. The similarity between the palate markings of *L. a. atricapilla* and *L. a. jagori* shows a homogeneity right across the range of Chestnut Munia that reinforces the case to regard the two as distinct species.

In behavioural terms, both in the wild and in captivity, *L. malacca* and *L. atricapilla* self-select for partners and pair bonding, in preference to

In contrast there is considerable variation within the different geographic forms of Chestnut Munia *L. atricapilla*. The different races have varying shades of brown on the upper surfaces, including a pale scalloping on the mantle. There are also different shades of brown on the breast and flanks and a considerable variety of colouring of the rump, uppertail-coverts and tail. In addition there are variations of head colouring, both from race to race and sometimes within a race, from black to brown and even pale grey on the nape. The belly varies from an extensive irregular black to a total absence of black, the belly and vent to undertail-coverts being the same brown as the flanks. In all this variation, within which there are many confusing intergrades and some abrupt contrasts, there is no clear trend nor cline. All the variation is of the black and brown coloration. More significantly there are no cases of morphs showing white anywhere on the body, let alone on the breast and flanks.

 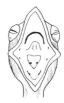

Palate markings of nestlings of *L. malacca*, left, *L. a. atricapilla*, centre, and *L. atricapilla jagori*, right.

crossing or mixing. Both species occur in Hong Kong where *L. atricapilla* is a migratory summer visitor and the introduced *L. malacca* is resident. Mixed pairs have not been recorded. It has been reported that intermediates between the two species occur (Viney *et al.* 1994) but I understand from Clive Viney (*in litt*) that this conclusion was based on observations of seeing both species entering the same reedbeds carrying nesting material. These would almost certainly have been male birds in each case, with which crossbreeding is unlikely. It would be impossible to divine the parentage of juveniles or moulting first year birds without seeing fledglings being fed by the parents. It seems certain that the two species do not interbreed there.

REFERENCES Ali & Ripley (1987), Delacour (1943), Goodwin (1982), MacKinnon & Phillipps (1993), Restall (1994a & 1995b), Sibley & Monroe (1990), Viney *et. al.* (1994), Wolters (1979).

18 TRICOLOURED MUNIA
Lonchura malacca   Plate 8

Other scientific names: *Loxia malacca* Linnaeus, 1766 *Syst, Nat.*, ed. 12, 1, p. 302 *Munia malacca orientalis*, Stuart Baker, 1925. *Lonchura ferruginosa bakeri* Delacour, 1943.
Other common names: Black-headed Munia, Southern Black-headed Munia, Tricoloured Mannikin or Nun, Three-coloured Munia, Mannikin or Nun.

FIELD CHARACTERS This is a medium-sized munia with a black head and chestnut body, contrasting white lower breast and flanks, with a black belly and undertail-coverts. The adult is unlikely to be confused with any other munia or finch. White-rumped Munia *L. striata* is clearly distinguished by its white rump.

The juvenile is indistinguishable from the juvenile Scaly-breasted Munia *L. punctulata* except for having a pale bill; that of Scaly-breasted Munia is black. Juvenile Red Avadavat *Amandava amandava* is similar but also has a dark bill.

STATUS Resident, locally common.

HABITAT It is a bird of grassy places, tending to favour wet or marshy areas where the grass is rich and long, and where seeding heads at various stages of development are plentiful.

HABITS AND BEHAVIOUR It is very gregarious, gathering in flocks of up to 40 or 50 birds. More often one sees small family groups. It frequents areas where the grasses grow tall, such as sugar cane fields and other tall crops standing in swampy ground (Baker 1926). It is a frequent visitor to rice paddies and can become a pest if large flocks descend on the crops.

In the south of India, it appears to associate with Streaked Weaver *Ploceus manyar* (Betts, in Ali & Ripley 1987). This latter species is also a bird of marshland and reedbeds, in which it breeds in small colonies of three or four pairs together. One or two pairs of Tricoloured Munias may attach themselves to the weaver colony, flying about and perching on the nests, which are beautifully and strongly woven among the reeds. They often breed among the weavers, but it is not recorded if they will use a deserted or unfinished weaver nest. The closely-related White-headed Munia *L. maja* is known to use weavers nests (Restall 1994b) and Tricoloured Munia will take to a basket in captivity, so it is possible it does. They do not feed with Streaked Weavers.

Ali & Ripley (1987) describe it as feeding on the ground, flying in undulating rabbles up into the tree-tops

when disturbed, soon to descend again in twos and threes to resume feeding.

Oberg (1975) describes Tricoloured Munia as a 'distance' species, with individuals normally spacing themselves about 2cm apart when perching. I have observed a trio in my study collection where two of the birds habitually clump and roost in contact, and occasionally all three birds perch in contact with each other.

FOOD AND FEEDING Whilst it will feed on the ground, taking fallen seeds, or will feed from the head of a grass that has been borne to the ground by the weight of the bird, it prefers to feed from seeds on growing grasses and weeds. It has large feet with long claws. Normally the claws are the same length as the toes, which enable the birds to climb stems with great agility. They can grasp several stems at once, quickly climbing up to the seeding head, and after feeding a little they will reach out to an adjacent stalk, grasp it with the bill, pull it within reach and, grasping it under the foot, feed on some of the seeds or step across onto the new stem. When disturbed the birds fly to cover uttering contact calls as they fly. They will quickly return to feed once the cause of disturbance has passed.

MOVEMENTS It is normally resident and sedentary, with some monsoon-related movements (Ali & Ripley 1987). Small flocks of immatures wander and are no doubt responsible for pushing the boundaries of the range into irregular and inconsistent patterns depending on the weather and availability of seeding grasses and rice paddies. There seems to be a little altitudinal migration but no author has commented specifically on this in the literature. In Sri Lanka it occurs up to over 2,100m (Warakagoda pers. comm.) and up to 2,100m in Southern India (Ali & Ripley 1987).

CALL The note is described by Baker (1926) as being a very pleasant chatter; no doubt his impression was gained from hearing several birds together in the field, for a single bird only utters monsyllabic-sounding notes. There is a quiet and unusual *tcht tcht* contact note, uttered by both sexes, that is difficult to hear more than a couple of metres away. At a louder level it takes on a metallic timbre. There are several variations of note from *pit* to *peet* among birds in a social activity, and one has been described as a plaintive little *ink* (Nichols in Ali & Ripley 1987). The loud contact call is a distinct and quite strong *peet!* that is more metallic or vibrato than pure. There is a different tone between that of male and female. The flight call is a triple chirp (Ali & Ripley 1987).

SONG The song, starting with a short series of squeaks virtually inaudible to the human ear, zips upwards several times, ending with a clear descending *peeeeee*. It is extremely quiet and impossible to hear in the field, although one might just catch a little of the final extended note, and the whole would normally only be heard by young ears.

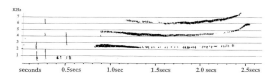

Tricoloured Munia in high intensity song.

Drawings from sound spectrographs of vocalisations of Tricoloured Munia, after Guttinger (1970).
Above, the bill-clapping at the start of the song, followed by the main legato, or *weeee*. Below, soft quiet song (?subsong).

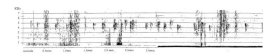

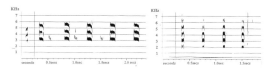

Above, calls of a bonded pair of Tricoloured Munias, male left, female right.

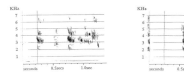

Mewing sounds from two males when roosting. Left is an unpaired male, on the right a bonded male roosting with a female.

COURTSHIP AND DISPLAY I think that Tricoloured Munias must be the original 'song and dance' bird, being a popular cage bird across most of India because of its display and song. The male, having flown about with a length of grass in his beak will perch alongside a female and, dropping the stem, will begin his display with a bob-bing up and down that becomes sufficiently energetic for the bird to be actually jumping up clear of the perch. In posture he is upright, with head pointing down, bill open, and nape and belly feathers erected. The song appears to be the result of having been pumped up but is very quiet to the human ear. A receptive female will lower herself to a near horizontal position with head and tail both turned slightly towards the male soliciting coition. The male will lean forward, turning head and tail towards the female, stop singing and mount her. There may be a little bill-fencing afterwards.

BREEDING Both sexes share in building the nest. The nest is a rather loosely-built spheroid, somewhat oval in shape with the entrance at one end, and rather large for the size of the bird compared to that of other munias. It is an untidy structure made of green grass and strips of leaves and bamboo leaves, etc. The main body is constructed of fine grasses and panicles or florescences, the lining being of the softer and finer ones. Some of these project out of the entrance forming a porch. Ali & Ripley (1987) describe this as the flowering grass-heads of the lining forming a trumpet-like tube all round the entrance. The structure is usually supported by the stems of some of the reeds in which is is built. Usually any leaves growing on the stems will be caught in the construction and thus are worked into the sides of the nest to provide some anchoring.

The nest may be built in a bush near human habitation (Harrington, in Baker 1926) but is more usually found in reeds and grass swamps well away from man (Baker 1926), two or three feet from the ground or over water (Phillips 1948), It is not a colonial species but often several nests will be built near each other. It will build in the company of Streaked Weavers *Ploceus manyar*.

The clutch is usually about 4 or 5 in Sri Lanka, but apparently 7 is normal in India (Phillips 1948). The eggs are white, oval, slightly rounder at one end. An average size taken from some 50 eggs in Baker's collection is 16.3 x 11.5mm. Incubation lasts about 12 or 13 days. Both birds take turns during the day to incubate, and both birds are in the nest at night. The young are brooded for between 8 to 10 days and fledge in about three weeks.

The nestlings are reared entirely on vegetable matter and there is no evidence that insects are taken at all. The food given to the nestlings is almost certainly soft, partially ripe seeds, with perhaps buds and the flowering heads of grasses before the seed properly forms.

Palate markings of nestling *L. malacca*.

DISTRIBUTION It is a bird of southern India south of a rough line from Bombay to Raipur, down to Sri Lanka where it occurs mostly in the north and east of the island, but it is uncommon in the south-west.

It has been released, accidentally or deliberately, in several locations, including the vicinity of Tokyo from where there is a fine colour photograph in Daisaku (1981). It occurs in the New Territories of Hong Kong, where it is a breeding resident in the Mai Po marshes, but the population seems to be declining there. It is also established on Oahu in the Hawaiian islands, but Pratt *et al.* (1987) do not mention this form, presumably not recognising it as a full species, and only *L. atricapilla* is illustrated; the latter also occurs there.

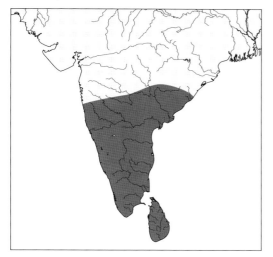

Distribution of Tricoloured Munia.

DESCRIPTION
Plates 46–47
Monotypic.

Adult male *c.*115mm. Wing length 55–57mm, culmen 12–13mm, tarsus 12–13mm. The entire head, throat and breast are jet black. The centre of the belly to the undertail-coverts and the thighs are also black. A broad band of pure white divides the breast from the belly and continues on the flanks. This is creamy-white in first adult or freshly moulted plumage. The upperparts are warm chestnut, darker brown on the flight feathers. The rump and uppertail-coverts are deep reddish-maroon. There is usually a little gold edging to the long uppertail-coverts and edges of the two central tail feathers, which are slightly pointed. The underwing-coverts are whitish to cream with some warm buff or rufous edging to the feathers. The irides are brown. The bill is pale bluish-grey. The legs and feet are grey and the large scales may be darker.

The sexes are alike but males may be detected in the hand by the more pronounced ridge to the culmen. This may be felt by gently rubbing the edge of the fingernail along the crown towards and over the edge of the culmen. It is virtually impossible to see under field conditions but it may give the male a slightly larger-looking bill. The males tend to be about 5mm longer when several birds are measured. The female also has a tendency to have paler fringes to the uppertail-coverts, the male conversely being more richly reddish-maroon. These features are usually apparent when a known pair is studied, but it is not possible to judge the sex of a single bird with any degree of certainty.

Colour variants The adult described above is the normal form and the only one described in most of the literature. However, there are four other morphs or varieties I have

Normal Tricoloured Munia with scaly-breasted variety.

discovered, which occur apparently at random and most certainly in small quantities. They occur in both males and females and from observations of birds I have kept in captivity it appears that they are constant forms which moult true.

In the first morph each of the white breast and flank feathers is edged with rufous, and the central quill shaft is also rufous. The effect is a light warm rufous scaled effect. It is not absolutely consistent and some specimens are more boldly marked than others. The strength of the marking does not alter with the age of the bird. I have seen this form in birds in western India and it has been recorded several times in Sri Lanka.

The second morph has the edge of the black belly and the white flanks scalloped in a zig zag line instead of a smooth continual line. This form is more rare, perhaps only 1% of the population.

The third morph has the breast and flanks a shade of cinnamon, the intensity and depth of which may be variable from pale to rich. I have found this morph among birds for sale in Crawford Market in Bombay on three occasions. It has been recorded in the wild in Sri Lanka (Deepal Warakagoda pers. comm. and Legge 1880). This morph does not look like a Chestnut Munia, and the cinnamon, regardless of tone, is quite distinct from that found in any of the many races of the congener.

The fourth variant has fine irregular grey and white barring all over the white breast and flanks.

Variety of Tricoloured Munia with grey barring on the breast and flanks.

Juvenile Warm brown above, buffish below. The irides are dark brown. The bill, feet and legs are horn-grey upon fledging but soon change to the colouring of the adult once the bird is feeding independently. There is some variation of tone and colouring within the juveniles of a given population.

Baker (1925) described birds from the southern third

of the range as having the black of the belly smaller and viewed this as a subspecific discriminator. He termed the form the Madras Black-headed Munia *L. m. orientalis*. This was regarded as synonymous with *L. m. malacca* by Paynter (1968).

HYBRIDS No natural hybrids have been recorded. Usually considered, incorrectly I believe (Restall 1995b), to be conspecific with the Chestnut Munia, but no intermediates between the two have been recorded by Ali & Ripley (1987) in India. This is not surprising considering the two ranges do not overlap nor even meet. Viney *et al.* (1994) reported interbreeding between *L. malacca* and *L. atricapilla* in the Mai Po marshes in Hong Kong, but the two different species have not been seen at the same nest, nor have they been seen feeding the same fledglings (Viney pers. comm.) and it appears that the assumption of cross-breeding had been made on observing birds of both species carrying nesting material into the same reedbed. It is the male that carries nesting material to the nest site, where the female works on the construction of the nest, often with the male's help. It thus seems that the Mai Po observation was only of males, and the only reasonable conclusion is that both species were nest-building, and possibly breeding, in the same reedbed.

Tricoloured Munia has hybridised with several other munias in captivity (Gray 1958), including Chestnut-breasted Mannikin *L. castaneothorax*, the Bengalese *L. striata*, White-headed Munia *L. maja*, Chestnut Munia, and Scaly-breasted Munia *L. punctulata*. There is a report of a cross-breeding between Tricoloured Munia and Zebra Finch *Poephila guttata*, (Pyman, in Gray 1958), but the report uses the word 'presumed', and an even more doubtful hybrid with the domestic Canary is mentioned.

CONSERVATION There appears to be no cause for concern. This is a species vulnerable to loss of habitat caused by marsh drainage, so the potential problem is there. The depredations of the bird trade are insignificant over most of the species' range, and are unlikely to have an effect on levels of wild populations.

REFERENCES Ali & Ripley (1987), Baker (1925 & 1926), Clement *et al.* (1993), Daisaku (1981), Gray (1958), Oberg (1975), Paynter (1968), Phillips (1948), Pratt *et al.* (1987), Restall (1994b & 1995b), Viney *et al.* (1994).

---

19   CHESTNUT MUNIA
Lonchura atricapilla   Plate 8

Described as *Lonchura atricapilla* Vieillot
Other common names: Chestnut Munia or Mannikin, Black-headed Munia, Nun or Mannikin.

Chestnut Munia

TAXONOMY There has been much debate and indecision in the literature over recognition of races in this species. It was formally regarded as conspecific with Tricoloured Munia, but I have argued that the two are separate species (Restall 1995b). Most of the confusion with this bird centres around the Philippine forms where the inconsistent variation in head colouring encourages most authors to lump everything into one single race *L. a. jagori*. In deciding upon the following races I have of course referred to the literature. I have also studied the collection of skins in the Natural History Museum at Tring, the AMNH in New York and the National University of Singapore Zoology Department. I have corresponded with field ornithologists, studied Chestnut Munias in the field in the Philippines, Hong Kong, Thailand, Malaysia, Vietnam and Indonesia and made observations of birds in captivity when I have kept most of the races for detailed study. The following notes do not pretend to be definitive and the conclusions are my own.

The descriptions and plumages depicted in the identification plates are my own selection of birds typical of each race. I have no doubt at all about the validity of the three Philippine races *L. a. formosana*, *L. a. jagori* and *L. a. brunneiceps*, having kept all three in aviaries and watched *L. a. jagori* in the field. It is possible that *L. a. jagori* could be divided into Borneo and Philippine races, but considerable field work would be required. There is evidence that *L. a. brunneiceps* and *L. a. jagori* overlap in south Sulawesi without interbreeding. From my own observations both the voice and the display of *L. a. brunneiceps* are sufficiently different from that of *L. a. jagori* and *L. a. sinensis* as to raise interesting questions about the integrity of *L. a. brunneiceps* as a subspecies. It is significant that the palate markings of the nestlings of Indian Chestnut Munia and nestling Chestnut Munias from northern Sulawesi are the same. If the palate markings of the nestling Brown-headed Munia proved to be different then the evidence that the latter should be considered a separate species would be significant.

I have been able to study live birds from south and west Kalimantan and concluded by virtue of the uppertail-coverts and fringes of the tail feathers that they are racially distinct from the Philippine *L. a. jagori*, and I have described two races, *L. a. obscura* and *L. a. selimbauensis* (Restall 1995b).

There are intergrades between the races wherever they are not clearly divided by non-contiguous geographic boundaries. My colour plate and the identification chart together show the discriminators for each race. The reader seeking help in identifying a form is invited first to look at the rump and uppertail-coverts, then the black of the heads and finally the belly. The males of the three Philippine races consistently have darker heads and more extensive black bellies than females.

FIELD CHARACTERS It is a chestnut-brown munia with an all-black head and black or dark brown on the belly, and under the vent and tail. The adult is unlikely to be confused with any other munia. The juvenile is indistinguishable from juvenile White-headed Munia *L. maja*. These two both occur in similar habitat in south Vietnam, peninsular Thailand, Malaysia, Sumatra, Java and Bali. The juvenile is also extremely difficult to tell apart from juvenile Scaly-breasted Munia *L. punctulata* in the field. The latter begins to show an all-black bill or black on the upper mandible before beginning the moult into adult plumage, and starts to show small scale-markings on the breast and flanks within a few months of fledging. Scaly-breasted Munia occurs over the whole of the range of Chestnut Munia. Both it and White-headed Munia are likely to mix with Chestnut Munia in rice paddies.

STATUS Scarce, locally common to abundant.

HABITAT It is essentially a bird of swampy grassland, but readily frequents tall grasses and will gather in substantial numbers to feed on the rice in paddy fields. MacKinnon and Phillipps (1993) describe it as an abundant munia of the lowlands in Borneo. It is not only a bird of lowland swamps. Watling (1983) found it common in rice-growing areas in both lowlands and upland valleys in Sulawesi. Here it is said to be present wherever rice is grown, but where there is little or no grass it inhabits the alang-alang scrub (Stresemann 1940). It often occupies relatively new clearings in the Sulu Archipelago (duPont and Rabor 1973). In the Himalayas it ranges up to over 1,230m (Baker 1926). It is found there in cultivations, tall grass and swampy ground (Ali and Ripley 1987) but keeps more to bushes than the lowland race *L. a. atricapilla* (Baker 1926). In some areas it is a forest edge species (Clement *et al.* 1993). In Cebu and north Sulawesi I found it to be a bird of gardens, breeding literally within arm's reach of human residences.

HABITS AND BEHAVIOUR It is said to form large flocks that do not mix with other birds, and which move through the paddy fields with a whirring of the wings as they rise and settle (MacKinnon and Phillipps 1993). In my own field observations I too have usually seen it in small flocks with no other species present, but in south Vietnam White-headed Munias may often be found in small numbers within Chestnut Munia flocks, and in north Sulawesi I found it feeding in the company of Scaly-breasted Munias and Moluccan Munias.

It is highly sociable, groups and flocks staying together throughout the year. They become predominantly comprised of juveniles during the breeding season when the older birds spend more time at the nest. They gather in cane beds, rushes and tall grass to roost in flocks. Breeding birds and recently fledged birds roost in the nest.

On two occasions I have observed an individual *L. a. brunneiceps* raise the far wing when threatened. In Sulawesi, I have also seen fledglings of the race *L. a. jagori* in northern Sulawesi raise the far wing when competing against other fledglings to be fed (Restall 1990). Hitherto, this behaviour by *Lonchura* species has only been recorded in the literature for African mannikins.

I have observed peering in the wild, when a male engaged in high intensity song to an adjacent female was seen by two other males that were drawn to the action. The closer of the two others stood within about four centimetres of the performer, leaning closer, and with head at a higher level, peering. As soon as the singer stopped, the peerer attacked it with fierce bill-fencing, soon driving it off, and leaving me wondering whether the peerer might have been the real mate of the female.

FOOD AND FEEDING Many years ago on the island of Badian, off the coast of Cebu in the Philippines I was able to observe Chestnut Munias in the garden. What appeared to be different groups wandered by every half hour or so. The smallest flock was of eight birds, the largest 14. They appeared every morning and afternoon feeding on the ground in the garden around my bungalow and around the swimming pool. On several occasions the birds came too close for my binoculars to focus. I had studied and often kept munias on and off for 40 years but this was the first time I had seen them in their natural wild habitat and it was fascinating. When disturbed, the birds would fly into the nearby bougainvillea or another shrub and sit still. Not for the first time was I amazed at how brightly coloured birds (and do not be fooled, a chestnut-and-black munia on green grass in tropical sunlight is brightly-coloured) can virtually disappear when sitting still in a tree. Very soon they would drop back to the ground with *zitt zitt* contact calls.

The birds were feeding on grasses dotted with weeds of the Compositae family; some looked like dandelions, others groundsel. A bird would fly at a bunch of stalks with feet spread and grasp several stems of grass. Its forward momentum would bend the bunch over slightly and the bird would be able to reach at the seeding heads where it would take up to half-a-dozen beakfuls before flying on. Sometimes a bird would land on a single stem of grass when its weight would bear the stem to the ground, whereupon it would quickly hop along to the head of the grass and take several bites. The groundsel-type weeds would invariably be borne to the ground where part of the seeding head would be bitten off and eaten. I also noted that a bird which had grasped a particularly thick stem, would reach out and pull another stem within grasp, adding it to the stem it was already gripping, and feed from the florescence of the new plant. The flock moved on, covering an area roughly 5–10 square metres at a time, never exhausting the seed supply. After they had gone, there was no sign that they had been there feeding, no grass stems were broken and all had sprung back up again.

I was able to make extensive observations of a small population of Chestnut Munias in North Sulawesi during January when the birds were breeding. There were four pairs with nests in palms and trimmed ornamental bamboos within a few metres of the dining room where I was staying. Two of the bamboos were within a metre of the edge of the balcony. There were fifteen fledglings that must have left the nest within a few days of each other. These juveniles gathered together, forming a crèche, usually on a small bougainvillea and were so unafraid of humans that I was able to catch one in my hand to draw the palate markings. They mobbed any adult that came to feed them, with up to seven fledglings at a time climbing over each other to get to the obliging adult. On a few occasions an adult would rebuff a soliciting fledgling which would respond by going into a high intensity begging posture, calling more loudly and more intensely, whereupon the adult would then feed it. When the adult or adults, for sometimes two or three would be feeding the youngsters at the same time, flew off, the fledglings would immediately begin a sort of ritual foraging. They would chew the dead bougainvillea flowers if they were on the bush, or chew grass stems, leaves and seeding inflorescences if they were on the lawn. They were not actually ingesting much, if anything, as far as I could tell. It seemed very much as if the various adults were flying to the youngster that begged most noticeably, and ended up sometimes feeding the three or four birds that were the most hungry. After very careful observations of this I concluded that there were only three adults that were feeding the fledglings regularly and they were feeding to demand, from any bird rather than their own brood. As a result every adult that approached the crèche was treated like an equal provider; I have called this behaviour 'crèche-feeding' (Restall 1995a).

MOVEMENTS It is generally sedentary, but there is some wandering particularly by flocks of mostly first-year birds. In Hong Kong it is a summer visitor, but where it migrates to is not recorded.

CALL There is a clear *pee, pewt* or *peet* call note in all the races I have noted and a loud contact call, *Pink! pink!* The call note is a tone higher in the female compared to the male. Ali and Ripley (1987) describe a "triple chirp" flight call, but I have not heard this myself. Birds I have released have flown off calling to each other a loud *fleep! fleep!* Birds I studied in North Sulawesi flew calling a clear single note *seep! seep!*

In the case of *L. a. brunneiceps* I have heard a soft croaking *queck* in addition to the *peet*, but I have not heard this in other races. This is worth remembering when studying this particular subspecies.

On several different occasions, with different pairs of *L. a. sinensis* kept in cages, both apart and together, I have recorded antiphonal calling, the two notes being slightly different. Fledglings call loudly and persistently when begging or competing with each other to be fed, but do not call to attract the attention of the adults. The call is like *psi psi psi psi*.

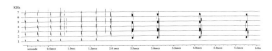

Call notes of Chestnut Munia *L. a. brunneiceps*, female on left, male on right.

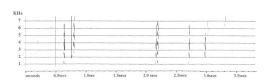

Call notes of Chestnut Munia *L. a. sinensis*, female on left and centre, male response on right.

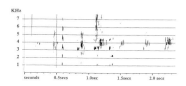

Female *L. a. sinensis* calling to the male.

SONG The song begins with a series of virtually inaudible clicks, followed by an extended legato *weee* (the whine of Hall 1962) ending with a series of slurred notes. The male in advertisement song will stretch upwards and with head

pointing down a little will utter a short series of clicks, as if winding himself up. This is followed by the bird bobbing slightly, bill open and still pointing downwards but without any audible (to human ears) sound. Then having apparently wound himself up completely he releases one or more long drawn-out whistles that descend in tone slightly.

Male Chestnut Munia in high intensity song directed at a female.

COURTSHIP AND DISPLAY In full courtship display, the male will usually fly about with a straw or length of grass held in his bill. He utters a sharp call as he does this. Then he alights beside the female and in a fairly upright position, body feathers fluffed erect, neck stretched and head pointed downwards, but turned a little towards the female. He drops the straw and begins to sing as described above. The bobbings up and down become full hops with his feet lifting clear of the perch in the inverted curtsey (Morris 1958), and he may edge closer to her in this way. If receptive, the female will crouch and quiver her tail, whereupon the male will mount her. This is usually followed by some bill-fencing and mutual allopreening. It seems as if all the elements of the straw display (Baptista and Horblit 1990) are present with the exception of the tail twist. In Sulawesi I made a drawing of a male that appeared to be displaying to its mate on a stem just outside the nest. It can be seen clearly exactly which feathers are erected and which remain smooth. All the black feathers of the head are raised, with a noticeable contrast at the breast where the feathers of the upper belly are smooth. The mantle is raised, contrasting with the smooth rump. The flanks and lower belly feathers are also raised.

Nest of Chestnut Munia in Thailand (from a photograph by Colin Ogle).

BREEDING The nest is an oval with the entrance at one end. Smythies (1981) describes it as being shaped like a rugby football with an entrance hole in the side. I made a sketch from a fine photograph by Colin Ogle (*in litt.*) of a nest found in long dense grass in an area some 120km north of Bangkok in Thailand which appears to be typical of the species. My second sketch is of a nest I found about 1.5m from the ground in a small ornamental palm alongside the swimming pool at the Manado Beach Hotel, in north Sulawesi. It was clearly the odd shape due to grasses falling down into the crotch of the palm leaves that formed the site. It contained recently-hatched young, and was being brooded by the female who returned some fifteen minutes after I had disturbed her, accompanied by the male. This nest was made entirely of fine twigs and stems, lined with fine grass stems. There appeared to be no strips of palm or broad-leaved grasses used at all. Other nests in the vicinity were usually built in densely trimmed, inverted pear-shaped bushes of bamboo, near the crown and some 3m from the ground. These were impossible to define from the outside, but were essentially oval balls of grasses and palm leaf strips.

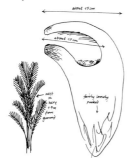

Cross section and location of Chestnut Munia nest in *Cyrtostachis* palm in N. Sulawesi.

The nest is usually made of fresh green leaves on the outside, although these quickly dry, becoming paler and browner. The bulk of the nest is of fine grasses and feathery panicles which both line the chamber and project out of the entrance forming a porch, and perhaps providing some concealment. It is usually constructed among rushes and reeds, or in shrubbery within a metre or two of the ground. In some localities it may nest higher, especially in palm trees. In the Himalayas *L. a. rubroniger* keeps more to bushes and prefers high sites for nesting, often building quite high up in comparatively lofty trees (Baker 1926). Both sexes share in the building of the nest.

Hahn (1988) records living in Brunei, where "... a pair of Chestnut Munias had built their domed nest in one of the pot plants of 7GR Officers' Mess which were moved each morning by the mess cleaners in order to clear the verandah. This did not stop the pair raising youngsters which actually flew while I was staying in the mess."

The eggs are small, oval and white. Clutches range from 3-8, with 5 or 6 being usual in the wild, 3-5 in captivity. Male and female take it in turns to incubate the eggs during the day, while both birds are in the nest at night. The incubation period is 12 or 13 days. The young are brooded for 8–10 days and apparently fledge in three weeks, but have taken up to four weeks to fledge when bred in captivity. They appear to be raised entirely on grass seeds and other vegetable matter, and there is no evidence that they take insects to feed their young or at any other times. Both parents feed the nestlings and continue to do so for up to three weeks after fledging.

Palate markings of nestling *L. a. atricapilla* (left) and newly-fledged *L. a. jagori* (right).

DISTRIBUTION The species ranges from the foothills of the Himalayas of central Nepal and the adjacent part of India (*L. a. rubroniger*), from lowland eastern Nepal and Sambalpur in east-central India across Bangladesh and southern north-east India to Burma (*L. a. atricapilla*) as far east as northern Yunnan in China and southwards through Burma, tailing off very irregularly in the western part of Thailand (*L. a. deignani*). From southern Yunnan it ranges into northern Thailand (*L. a. yunnanensis*) but Stevens (in Kinnear 1924) did not find it in Tonkin and today it is rare in most of Thailand. I corresponded with Ogle who, during over two years of field work in an area 120km north of Bangkok found only 3 individual birds. Philip Round (*in litt.*) says it is found only in really swampy areas in Thailand and sent me the map that indicated the fragmentary nature of the species' distribution; incidentally, this may give a clue to the wide variation of plumage in this part of the bird's range.

Its status in Indochina is not clear although I found *L. a. deignani* west of Ho Chi Minh City in the Mekong Delta in 1993. It seems reasonable to assume it ranges from northern Thailand across eastern Indochina, but I did not find it in the area of Hanoi and the bird sellers in the market usually only had White-rumped and Scaly-breasted Munias although on one occasion one stall had a pair.

It continues down peninsular Thailand into Malaysia and the entire north-eastern lowland half of Sumatra (*L. a. sinensis*), and the northern highlands of Sumatra, especially Batakana (*L. a. batakana*). However, it is a summer and autumn migrant to the Mai Po marshes in Hong Kong (*L. a. deignani*) so is possibly irregular from southern

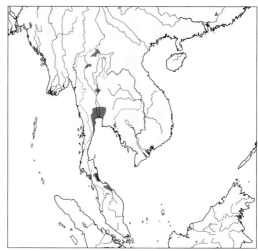

Swampy areas in Thailand where *L. atricapilla* is recorded (Philip Round *pers. comm.*)

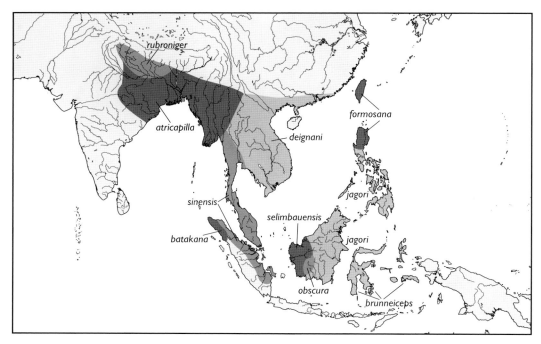

Distribution of Chestnut Munia.

Yunnan as far as Hong Kong and even beyond. It appears not to occur on the island of Hainan. The species occurs on the island of Taiwan and northern Luzon, (Isabela province) in the Philippines (*L. a. formosana*). The race *L. a. brunneiceps* is found in the southern part of Sulawesi, as well as on Muna and Butung and also Ambon. In between these last-mentioned two races is the wide-ranging *L. a. jagori*, which occurs from Luzon to Borneo, where it is found up to 1,800m, to Sulawesi and the Moluccas.

The black-headed (and often brown-naped) race *L. a. jagori* has been reported as far south as Parepare in Sulawesi (Andrew & Holmes 1990), well within the range of the brown-headed *L. a. brunneiceps*. This raises very interesting questions of racial or specific integrity and the possibility that the very distinct and smaller *L. a. brunneiceps* might be a sibling species. The biological species concept, when applied to sympatric populations is unambiguous (Mayr 1970, and Ratti 1980). It is clear that comparative field observations in the area of apparent sympatry are called for, and specimens of both forms collected and described. Its existence on the island of Ambon (Bishop 1992), also within the range of *L. atricapilla jagori*, further enriches the issue. The Ambon population has not been described and, considering how far it is from south Sulawesi, might well be distinct.

L. a. selimbauensis occurs in south-west Kalimantan, southern Borneo, and in one apparently small area of unknown size is the dark *L. a. obscura*, described by Mayr (1938) from Parit and which I was able to obtain live from a trader from Sampit (Restall 1995b). Riley (1938) suggested that the population on Halmahera might be an introduction to the island and White and Bruce (1986) concur, but it does look like a natural extension of the range of the Philippine *L. a. jagori*.

By nature it is a sedentary species. No doubt flocks of wandering juveniles are primarily responsible for pushing the boundaries of the species' range. There may be some altitudial migration, up to 5,000 feet (1500m) when conditions are ideal (Smythies 1986) and some marginal migration at the edges of the species' range, particularly along the northern boundaries when seasonal factors will affect food supplies. The summer population in Hong Kong appears to be an example. But this has not been studied and it is not known where the birds come from or go to.

It has been introduced by man into several locations, some no doubt the result of accidental escapes from avicultural stocks. One example was a pair that I watched nesting in reedbeds in Haslemere, England, many years ago. I expect those birds died during the following winter and probably stood little chance of ever establishing themselves. They have become naturalised in more than half a dozen locations around the world. Lever (1987) cites Japan, with a breeding colony as recently as 1981 in an area north of Osaka and I have seen it established in swamps and marshes around Tokyo. Nests with immatures have been recorded in Tamagawa. Suzanne Steiner (pers. comm.) reports it as breeding in Okinawa. These birds are possibly natural migrants from Taiwan, but the subspecies is not recorded.

Lever (1987) cites Puerto Rico, where it may be found in grassy areas and is a pest in rice fields, but it is not mentioned by Bond (1971) who does, however, mention *L. cucullata*. Catherine Levy, of Gosse in Jamaica (*in litt.*) reports it being established as a breeding bird in Jamaica, following the escape of a significant quantity of birds escaped from a bird trader's establishment during a bad storm. In Australia it has established itself in small numbers in swamps around Sydney where it is considered rare, sedentary and has not significantly increased in numbers.

	head all black	head black, dark brown nape	head dark brown	head dark brown with paler nape	head dark brown with greyish nape	belly black	belly dusky	belly dark brown	belly brown	undertail-coverts black	undertail-coverts dusky	undertail-coverts dark brown	undertail-coverts brown	uppertail-coverts as rump	uppertail-coverts orange	uppertail-coverts yellow-orange	uppertail-coverts yellowish	tail brown or maroon as rump	tail edges orange	tail edges yellow-orange	tail edges yellowish
L. a. atricapilla	●								●			●				●	●				●
L. a. rubroniger	●					●				●					●			●			
L. a. deignani	●						●	●				●			●			●			
L. a. sinensis	●							●	●			●	●			●	●		●	●	
L. a. brunneiceps			●	●			●				●	●		●	●				●		
L. a. jagori		●				●				●							●		●	●	
L. a. formosana				●	●	●				●							●			●	
L. a. batakana	●					●				●					●			●			
L. a. obscura	●					●				●					●						
L. a. selimbauensis	●					●				●									●		

Guide to identification of Chestnut Munia by subspecific differences.

Whilst most Australian bird books mention it, Immelmann (1965) chose to ignore it. The Australian race is *L. a. atricapilla*. Pratt *et al.* (1987) consider it to be well established on Palau, Guam and the Hawaiian Islands; the colour illustration is presumably *L. a. atricapilla* for it is certainly all black-headed and Lever (1987) mentions that birds had been imported to the islands from Calcutta.

DESCRIPTION Plates 48–55

Ten subspecies are described below. The chart is to aid in the identification of the different races.

INDIAN BLACK-HEADED MUNIA
L. atricapilla atricapilla

Former scientific names: *Loxia atricapilla* Vieillot, 1807, Ois. Chant., p. 84, pl.53, *Munia atricapilla novana* Matthews, 1929.

Other common names: Eastern Black-headed Munia, Indian Chestnut Munia.

Adult 110mm. Wing length 46–52mm, culmen 9–10mm, tarsus 12–14mm. The entire head, throat and upper breast are jet black. The upperparts are more amber than chestnut, a little lighter on the mantle, darker on the wings. The rump is rich maroon-red. The uppertail-coverts and the tail feathers are fringed with golden-yellow or orange. The underwing-coverts are warm buff. The lower breast and flanks are a lighter chestnut than the back. The ventral region and undertail-coverts are black in Indian birds and dark brown in those from Burma, intergrading from one to the other. The irides are brown. The bill is bluish-grey. The legs and feet are grey. The sexes are alike in colouring but males have a tendency to have slightly heavier bills, noticeable in the ridge of the culmen being slightly more prominent.

Juvenile Uniform clay or cinnamon above, buffish to tawny-olive below. The bill is horn-grey upon fledging but soon turns to light grey as the bird becomes independent.

NEPAL BLACK-HEADED MUNIA
L. atricapilla rubroniger

Former scientific name: *Munia rubro-niger*, Hodgson, 1836, *Asiatic Researches*, p. 153.

Adult 115–120mm. Wing length 52–54mm, culmen 11–12mm. The entire head, throat and breast, centre of belly to undertail-coverts and thighs are jet black. The upperparts from the mantle to the lower back and wings are warm chestnut, darker on the wings. The rump, uppertail-coverts and edges of the tail feathers are deep reddish-maroon with very little difference between the rump and the uppertail-coverts, which are slightly redder. A broad band of brick red divides the black of breast and belly. The flanks are the same brick red.

MALAYSIAN CHESTNUT MUNIA
L. atricapilla sinensis Plates 48–49

Former scientific name: *Munia sinensis* Blyth, 1852, *Cat. Birds Mus. Asiatic Soc.*, p. 337

Other common name: Chinese Chestnut Munia.

Adult 100–110mm, exceptionally 115mm. Wing length 47–52mm, culmen 11–12mm, tarsus 11–12mm. The entire head, throat and breast are black. The mantle, lower back, wing-coverts, lower breast and flanks are amber to a chestnut that is paler than in other races, and sometimes has a pale scalloping on the upper mantle, and sometimes with a whitish, almost silken lustre. The rump and uppertail-coverts are reddish-maroon, darker than the brown of the back but paler than in other races, and the long uppertail-coverts are described by Riley (1938) as aniline yellow inclining to xanthine orange or even amber-brown. The tail is brown with yellow or pale orange edging to the feathers. The centre of the belly, thighs, ventral area and undertail-coverts are variable, ranging from a barely darker brown of the breast to dark brown or chocolate, with some birds tending to blackish or near-black on the vent and undertail-coverts. When I have been able to verify the sex, I have found these darker-vented birds to be males.

FORMOSAN CHESTNUT MUNIA
L. atricapilla formosana   Plate 50

Former scientific name: *Munia formosana* Swinhoe, 1865, *Ibis*, p. 356.

Other common names: Taiwan Chestnut Munia, Taiwan Black-headed Munia, Grey-faced Munia.

Adult male 114–117mm. Wing length 49–52mm, culmen 11mm, tarsus 12mm. The entire head, throat and breast are dark brownish-grey, darkest on the face, brownish-grey on the nape. The mantle, lower back and wings are rich chestnut. The rump is bright reddish-maroon. The uppertail-coverts and tail are yellow. The sides of the lower breast and flanks are reddish-chestnut. The centre of the belly is black, extending upwards to join or almost join the blackish breast at the centre. The remainder of the underparts are black.

Adult female Same length or slightly shorter. Wing length 48–50mm, culmen 10–11mm, tarsus 11–12mm. The entire head, throat and breast is a lighter version of the male, particularly greyer or lighter grey-brown on the neck where a barring or pale scalloping caused by the edges of the feathers being buffish might be noticeable. This is more the case in fresh plumage. The black below is less extensive and there is a clear bar of reddish-chestnut dividing the breast from the belly.

DEIGNAN'S CHESTNUT MUNIA
L. atricapilla deignani   Plate 51

Former scientific name: *Lonchura malacca deignani* Parkes, 1958, *Proc. U.S. Nat. Mus.* 108, p. 290.

Other common name: Indochina Chestnut Munia.

Adult 105–110mm. Wing length 52–54mm, culmen 10–11mm, tarsus 12mm. The head, throat and breast are black. From the mantle to the lower back and wing-coverts it is mahogany-red. The rump, uppertail-coverts and the edges of the tail feathers are somewhat reddish-chestnut with the long uppertail-coverts and central rectrices deep orange-red. The flights of wings and tail are dark brown. The lower breast, upper belly, thighs and flanks are chestnut, becoming paler on the upper edges of the flanks. The ventral region is dark brown or blackish and the undertail-coverts are dark brown. The sexes appear to be alike.

BROWN-HEADED MUNIA
L. atricapilla brunneiceps   Plate 52

Former scientific name: *Munia brunneiceps* Walden 1872, *Trans. Zool. Soc.* London, 8, p.73, pl.9.

Adult male 100–105mm. Wing length 48–49mm,

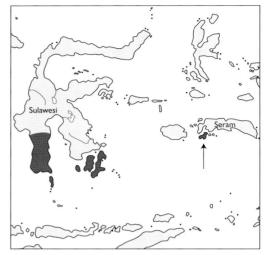

Range of Brown-headed Munia *L. a. brunneiceps*

culmen 10–11mm, tarsus 10mm. The entire head is dark grey, brownish on the ear-coverts, blackish on the throat and breast. The black graduates from the throat over the face until it becomes dark dull brown on the nape. The mantle is brown but this is not a pure colour, being washed with greyish-brown, purest and brightest on the shoulder. The rump is the same cinnamon-walnut of the flanks, changing to rich lustrous brick red on the uppertail-coverts. The tail is dark brown with a little lustrous orange-brick red suffusing the surface. The black of the underparts joins or almost joins the breast and extends to the undertail-coverts. The thighs are black.

Adult female 95–100mm. Wing length 47mm, culmen 10mm, tarsus 10mm. It is similar to the male but paler on the rear crown and nape. The black on the face may be sufficiently restricted as to cover only the breast, but more commonly suffuses the front of the face and bib as well There is a bar of cinnamon-brown between the breast and the dull black or dark brown belly. The brown is more extensive on the flanks and includes the thighs which may be entirely brown or barred black and brown.

First year Generally duller and males lack the richer black on the belly and breast which usually comes with the second-year moult.

PHILIPPINE CHESTNUT MUNIA
L. atricapilla jagori

Former scientific names: *Munia (Dermophrys) jagori* Martens, 1866, *Journ. Ornith.* 14, p.14. *Lonchura malacca gregalis* Salomonsen, 1953.

Other common names: Philippine Munia, Philippine Black-headed Munia.

Adult male *c*.115mm. The entire head, throat and breast are deep brown to blackish, but this is highly variable from location to location, and even within local populations. According to duPont and Rabor (1971) birds from the northern part of the Philippines have proportionately browner heads. Parkes (1958) recognises a tendency for this race to have darker heads the further south one proceeds, but it is too inconsistent to be regarded as a cline. In my

Brown-headed Munia *L. a. brunneiceps* **(left), Philippine Chestnut Munia** *L. a. jagori* **(centre) and Malaysian Chestnut Munia** *L. a. sinensis* **(right).**

experience in the field in the Philippines and Sulawesi, the colour appears to change depending on the angle of view, appearing deep chocolate in some lights and black in others. Add to this the fact that museum specimens have a tendency to fox with time, and it is apparent that comparative work should be done with fresh specimens of the same age, in the hand. In contrast, birds from Borneo are much more consistent in colouring on the heads than birds from the Philippines and in general have blacker heads. Salomonsen (1953) identified the Borneo black-headed birds as *L. a. gregalis*, but undermined his proposal by including a range that embraced variable, brown-headed birds in Mindanao. A case could probably be made for separating the north Borneo birds. From the mantle to the lower back and wing-coverts it is deep chestnut, darker on the flight feathers. The rump is deep reddish-maroon as are the short uppertail-coverts, but the long uppertail-coverts and edges of the tail feathers are rich gold. The sides of the lower breast and flanks are reddish-chestnut. The centre of the belly, from an upper point where it often touches or fully joins the black of the breast to the undertail-coverts including the thighs is black, the black edges along the flanks being usually, but not always, an irregular line, occasionally appearing to be almost barred.

Clearly marked examples of Philippine Chestnut Munia *L. a. jagori*, **male on the left.**

Adult female Slightly smaller, about 105–110mm. The entire head, throat and breast are black to dark brown. Again, the museum skins are more varied than the birds appear in life, but in my experience the heads of the females are consistently more brown, or lighter than in those of males in the same population. The female usually has a far less extensive black belly patch

and the brown of the flanks invariably joins across the lower breast. The long uppertail-coverts and tail edgings are a less rich and less extensive gold, tending more to straw.

I carried out a careful analysis of 45 museum specimens from the Philippines and northern Borneo where the sex had been positively recorded at the time of preparation. All the birds with jet black heads were males, all those with black heads but brown napes and brown rear crowns were females. When males had brown napes there was a distinct tendency for their heads to be darker than those of females from the same locality.

SELIMBAU CHESTNUT MUNIA
L. atricapilla selimbauensis
Restall, 1995, *Bull. Brit. Orn. Club*, 115 (3), 140 - 157.
Adult male 105–110mm. It has the entire head and upper breast black. The back and wings are chestnut, the lower rump and uppertail-coverts are brick red and there is a little orange edging to the tail feathers but not the uppertail-coverts. A narrow bar across the breast and the flanks is brick red (i.e. slightly darker than the chestnut back). The underwing-coverts are buffy-yellow with chestnut centres to the longer feathers. The belly to undertail-coverts and thighs are black, and the line where the black meets the flanks is irregular.

Adult female 98–105mm. The entire head is black but may be dark greyish-brown on the nape. The bar across the breast, the flanks and back are all uniform chestnut. The uppertail-coverts are maroon and there is a little orange edging to the tail feathers.

DARK-BACKED CHESTNUT MUNIA
L. atricapilla obscura   Plate 54
Restall, 1995, *Bull. Brit. Orn. Club*, 115 (3), 140 - 157.
Former scientific name: *Fringilla minuta* was the first naming of the bird now known as *Lonchura atricapilla jagori* by Meyen in 1834, but this name was already preoccupied by *Fringilla minuta* Temminck, 1807. In discovering these dark-backed birds, Mayr (1938) obviously referred back to *minuta* to distinguish them, but I have renamed them to solve the problem of misnaming.

Adult 100–105mm. The head is entirely black, tending to a very rich deep chocolate on the nape. The back, sides of breast, which barely join across the breast, and flanks are deep dark chestnut. The rump and uppertail-coverts are deep maroon, wrapping round on the sides to merge into the chestnut of the lower flanks. The wings are deep chestnut, the sepia flight feathers being edged with chestnut, the tertials and inner secondaries edged with a paler chestnut. The tail is sepia edged slightly with maroon. The underwing-coverts are flesh-ochre. The centre of the lower breast, belly, thighs and undertail-coverts are black. The bill is pale grey, the irides chestnut, the legs and feet grey.

Juvenile 95–100mm. The forehead and crown to lower back is cinnamon-brown, the wings darkening to brown, the median, greater wing-coverts and flight feathers edged with amber. The rump and uppertail-coverts are a warm clay colour; the tail is sepia. The chin and throat are pale drab, the remainder of the underparts including the underwing-coverts are buffy-cinnamon. To appreciate the richness of the colouring of the juvenile the measured drawing of juvenile *L. a. obscura* should be compared with that of juvenile *L. atricapilla sinensis* from Thailand.

BATAKANA CHESTNUT MUNIA
L. atricapilla batakana
Former scientific name: *Munia atricapilla batakana* Chasen and Kloss, 1929, *Bull. Raffles Mus.*, 2, p.23.
Other common name: Batakana Munia.
Adult *c.*110mm. The entire head, throat and breast, centre of belly to undertail-coverts and thighs are black. From the mantle to the lower back and wing-coverts it is chestnut, darker on the flights. The rump and uppertail-coverts are deep reddish-maroon. A bar across the lower breast and the flanks are rich chestnut.

HYBRIDS The only report of a natural hybrid, between Chestnut Munia and Tricoloured Munia *L. malacca*, is from Hong Kong (Viney *et al.* 1994), but it seems this report was based on observations of birds of both species carrying nesting material, flying into the same reedbed (Viney *in litt.*). Mixed pairs were not recorded, nor were both parents seen feeding fledglings. Since it is the male that carries nesting material to the nest site, where the female is busy making the nest, it is most likely that only males were observed. The proper assumption then would have been simply that both species were breeding in the same reedbed.

Grey (1958) records several cross-breedings in captivity. Those with munias include Chestnut-breasted Mannikin, *L. castaneothorax*, Bengalese, White-headed Munia, both Silverbills *L. cantans* and *L. malabarica*, Scaly-breasted Munia and Tricoloured Munia. There is a remarkable record of a cross with a Village Indigobird *Vidua chalybeata*.

CONSERVATION It appears that there can be no concern for a species that is so widespread and apparently numerous. Yet it is not only local but scarce in Thailand, and population figures are not available from other countries where it is trapped regularly for the bird trade. In Thailand it has been trapped in considerable numbers for the bird trade in the past. That demand is now being met largely by supplies from Vietnam, peninsular Malaysia (illegally), and south Sulawesi. Whilst the species as a whole is apparently secure, awareness of local population levels should be encouraged and comparative audits carried out. The numbers quoted in TRAFFIC data given to me informally suggested that exports of *L. malacca* (which includes *L. atricapilla*) from all the countries in Asia amounts to little more than 10,000 birds in the entire period from 1980 to 1992. In my personal observations I have witnessed single shipments of 7,000 at a time being exported from Vietnam, and it is certain that exports of the Chestnut Munia from that country alone significantly exceed 10,000 birds in a single year.

REFERENCES Ali & Ripley (1987), Andrew & Holmes (1990), Baker (1926), Baptista, & Horblit (1990), Bishop (1992), Bond (1971), Clement *et al.*(1993), duPont & Rabor (1973), Hahn (1988), Hall (1962), Immelmann (1965), Kinnear (1929), Lever (1987), MacKinnon & Phillipps (1993), Mayr (1938 and 1970), Morris (1958), Pratt *et al.* (1987), Ratti (1980), Restall (1995a & b), Riley (1938), Salomonsen (1953), Smythies (1986), Stresemann (1940), Viney *et al.* (1994), Watling (1983), White & Bruce (1986).

20 BLACK-THROATED MUNIA
Lonchura ferruginosa
Plate 9

Former scientific names: *Loxia ferruginosa*, Sparrman, 1789, *Mus. Carlsonianum* pls. 90, 91 *Munia ferruginosa*, *Lonchura malacca ferruginosa*, Paynter, 1968. *Lonchura atricapilla ferruginosa*.
Other common names: Javan Maja Mannikin or Munia, Javan White-headed Munia or Mannikin.

TAXONOMY This species was placed in *L. malacca* by Delacour (1942) and Paynter (1968) and continues to be regarded as conspecific by some authors, including Mason and Jarvis (1989) and Clement *et al.* (1993). Goodwin (1982) recognised it as a '*ferruginosa* group' within *L. malacca* which also contained an '*atricapilla* group'. MacKinnon (1988) first treated it as a race of *L. malacca*, but later gave it tentative specific recognition (MacKinnon and Phillipps 1993). Immelmann *et al.* (1968-72) say the voice of Black-throated Munia is different from that of Tricoloured Munia. It was considered to be a full species by Wolters (1979) and is accepted as such by Sibley and Monroe (1990) and I have followed them (Restall 1995b).

One unfortunate result of a form being regarded as a race of a widespread species is that it tends to become overlooked as a separate entity, and any observations of it that are recorded become lumped with those of the presumed conspecific. Inevitably, details of any distinguishing behaviour and other subtleties are lost. This I believe to have been the case with Black-throated Munia. There is little data based on field observations.

FIELD CHARACTERS It is a medium-sized munia, white on the head with a black throat and underparts, chestnut-brown above. It is readily distinguishable from White-headed Munia *L. maja* by the black throat. The juvenile is indistinguishable from juvenile White-headed Munia and extremely difficult to tell from the juvenile Scaly-breasted Munia. The race of the latter that occurs in the same range as Black-throated Munia is *L. punctulata nisoria* which has only the upper mandible black in the adult, the lower mandible being grey. The bill of the juvenile is all grey in recently fledged birds, and these are indistinguishable from juvenile Black-throated Munias but the upper mandible darkens as the bird matures towards the first-year moult and becomes a diagnostic feature.

STATUS Local, and probably scarce.

HABITAT The Black-throated Munia is a bird of grassy areas, tending to favour wetlands where grasses, reeds and sedges grow in abundance and provide food all the year round.

HABITS AND BEHAVIOUR It favours the rice paddies when the rice is fattening and is regarded as a pest when it flocks, usually in the company of White-headed Munias, but also with other munias. Once independent the juveniles wander off and join the juveniles of other species of munia in flocks that increasingly wander further afield, and may be seen feeding in rice paddies.

FOOD AND FEEDING It feeds on the seeding heads of various grasses, climbing and hopping nimbly up and down the stems and crossing over from stem to stem with great agility. Its large feet and long claws are well adapted to this feeding behaviour. It is able to reach forward to grasp a nearby stem of grass or rice and pull it close so that it may be held with one of the feet while the seeds are taken, without the bird having to fly to another stem.

MOVEMENTS Fairly sedentary, but young birds wander in the company of other immatures.

CALL Described as *veet veet* by Goodwin (after Immelmann *et al.* 1968-72). In my own notes I have the call transcribed as *psitt psitt* or *pseet pseet*.

SONG The song begins with an almost inaudible series of clicks and wheezes. This is followed by a long drawn out *wheeee*.

COURTSHIP AND DISPLAY The full display contains most of the elements of the straw display (Baptista and Horblit 1990). The male begins by first flying about with a stem or blade of grass in its bill and when perceiving some encouragement will drop the item and perch nearby the female and begin its song and dance display. In this the male stands more or less erect, leaning forward slightly, with feathers erect, most noticeably on the head, nape, the belly and flanks. With the head pointing slightly down it will bob up and down, the feet sometimes leaving the perch in a full inverted curtsey (Morris 1958).

The male begins to sing with an audible opening and closing of the bill. He then bobs up and down slightly, appearing to be pumping himself up, with an almost inaudible series of clicks and wheezes. During the long, drawn out *wheeee* the bill is kept open. An unreceptive female will either fly away or stand fairly upright seeming to stare down on and thereby disconcerting the performer. A receptive female will lean forward to a near-horizontal position, and turn both her head and tail slightly towards the male. He will stop singing and will attempt to mount. Some bill-fencing takes place following this, especially if copulation has occurred.

BREEDING The nest is usually built in grasses or reeds within a metre or so of the ground. Some leaves of the growing grasses are bent back and entwined, and fresh green leaves and strips are formed with them into a melon-shaped structure with a side entrance. The green leaves soon dry out forming a harder and more rigid nest. The inside is lined with grass heads and inflorescences which project a short way out of the entrance forming a short porch which may serve to conceal or shelter the entrance hole.

The clutch may be anything from 3 to 7 eggs, but I have no details of an average number. Four or five seem normal in captivity. Incubation is probably 13 or 14 days but is recorded up to 17 days in captivity, and is shared alternately by both sexes during the day. Both birds stay in the nest together at night. The young are brooded for up to 10 days and fledge in about 3 weeks. They are fed by both parents for at least two weeks after fledging and they all spend the first few nights in the nest together.

DISTRIBUTION The Black-throated Munia is found only on the islands of Java and Bali. It has been introduced on the island of Babelthuap, largest of the Palau Islands in the Pacific (Lever 1987).

DESCRIPTION Plate 56
Monotypic.
Adult male 105–116mm (average 110). Wing length 53–55mm, culmen 12–13mm, tarsus 12–13mm. The forehead,

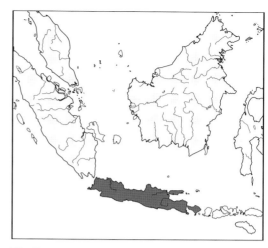

Distribution of Black-throated Munia.

lores and ear-coverts are buffish-white shading to pale drab grey on hind crown, nape and sides of neck. The mantle and all upperparts are brown, particularly rich deep maroon on the rump and uppertail-coverts. The flanks are very clearly chestnut-maroon and join to form a bar across the lower breast. There is a variant that has the underparts entirely jet black from chin to undertail-coverts, with perhaps a little chestnut-maroon on the flanks covered by the wings. I have seen both forms in mixed flocks in Java and in Bali. It seems most likely that the birds with all-black underparts are males. There is no reference to this form in the literature, but Frank Mason (*in litt.*) in Bali has kindly carried out field observations and agrees with this. The black form is nowhere near as common as the birds with maroon flanks and breast bars. The irides are brown. The bill is pale blue-grey with pale to white cutting edges, and the culmen may be noticeably more ridged at the forehead and curved than on the female. The legs and feet are grey or dark grey.

Adult male Black-throated Munia, right, with variant showing all-black underparts on the left.

Adult female *c.*105mm. Wing length 50–52mm, culmen 11–11.5mm, tarsus 11–12mm. The brown band across the lower breast is usually wider in the female, sometimes two or three times the width of the same bar in the male.
Juvenile *c.*105mm. Wing length 50–52mm, culmen 11–12mm, tarsus <13mm. The head is cinnamon, paler on the cheeks, becoming pale horn on the chin and throat. It is darker on the back, washed with raw umber. The rump is brown. The wings and tail are fuscous, edged with raw

umber or brown. The bill is pale blue-grey, paler on the cutting edges. The legs and feet are grey.

HYBRIDS No hybrids are recorded.

CONSERVATION It is included by MacKinnon and Phillipps (1993) in their list of threatened or endangered species that are found within the Meru Betiri Game Reserve, the Baluran National Park and the West Bali (Bali Barat) National Park. The authors describe it as locally common but there is no indication of either actual population levels, or the kind of population density needed for the species to survive. It is trapped for the bird trade in both Bali and Java, but appears only spasmodically in the markets, always in very small numbers and always with White-headed Munias. With the erosion of natural habitat due to greater government pressure to increase rice production, combined with intensified efforts to eradicate bird pests in the rice fields, this is a species that could well become seriously endangered.

REFERENCES Baptista &Horblit (1990), Clement *et al.* (1993), Delacour (1943), Goodwin (1982), Immelmann *et al.* (1968-72), Lever (1987), MacKinnon (1988), MacKinnon & Phillipps (1993), Mason & Jarvis (1989), Morris (1958), Paynter (1968), Restall (1995b), Sibley & Monroe (1990), Wolters (1979).

21 FIVE-COLOURED MUNIA
Lonchura quinticolor Plate 10

Former scientific name: *Loxia quinticolor*, Vieillot, 1807, *Ois. Chant.*, pl. 54, p.85 *Munia wallacii*.
Other common names: Chestnut-and-White Mannikin or Munia, Hopping Finch (USA).

Five-coloured Munias.

TAXONOMY Goodwin (1982) recognises only one race but admits (*in litt.*) to having overlooked the second race *L. q. wallacii*. White and Bruce (1986) also include *wallacii* in *L. quinticolor*. However, I am quite certain there are at least three races (Restall 1995b) which I describe below. This conviction arose first as a suspicion when studying reports from aviculturists of two distinct forms, a golden-rumped form and a maroon-rumped form. Certainty came that there were three races, and the suspicion of a fourth, when I studied the skins in the Natural History Museum collection at Tring and those in the American Museum of Natural History in New York. Later, I came across shipments of two distinctive forms from West Timor and Sumba and I subsequently saw all three forms in the wild.

The colour plate shows these three races. Defining the locations and full range of each of the three forms is not so easy and there may be a cline between yellow-rumped and orange-rumped birds in Timor and Flores, but the paucity of skins in the museums and difficulty of engaging in comprehensive field work means that my distribution map is approximate. It could be that the orange-rumped populations can be grouped into distinct subspecific or intermediate groups. A detailed study of the species would include records of the palate markings of the nestlings of the different forms, and sonograms of the vocalisations.

FIELD CHARACTERS It is a medium to fairly large munia, depending on the race. The head is dark brown with distinctive striations on the ear-coverts. The rest of the upperparts are various shades of rich brown, with the rump and uppertail yellow, orange, or maroon. The breast, belly and flanks are white. The undertail-coverts are black. The bird is quite easy to spot when it is feeding in rice or grassy places because of its bright white breast. At a distance it is possible to confuse it with Moluccan Munia *L. molucca*, which has a whitish breast and belly with black vermiculations which are not noticeable at a distance in the field. But the black of the face and breast of Moluccan Munia extends lower than it does on Five-coloured Munia, and the pale rump of Moluccan Munia when it flies is a good distinction. Juvenile Five-coloured Munia is indistinguishable from juvenile Scaly-breasted Munia *L. punctulata* or Pale-headed Munia *L. pallida* and all three may well be feeding in the same rice paddy together.

STATUS Uncommon or local.

HABITAT It is primarily a bird of grasslands and rice paddies, but may be found in hillside scrub, gardens and cultivated land especially where cereals are being grown. It said to be a bird of lowlands and foothills, occurring up to 1,100m (Immelmann *et al.* 1968-72). I have seen it almost at the edge of the tree line on the slopes of the Keli Mutu volcano in the Flores highlands, at about 1,600m. This was well above the level where there was any rice growing, although it would have been only a short migration downhill to many hectares of rice paddies. These birds were feeding in gardens where I noted maize in flower.

HABITS AND BEHAVIOUR I first saw this species on the island of Sawu, when a small group of estrildid finches was flushed by a goat herder and his goats. It was in a mixed flock with Zebra Finches *Poephila guttata*. Then on the island of Roti I spent an hour or so watching a flock of about 35 Scaly-breasted and Five-coloured Munias on the edge of a rice paddy, working their way along a ditch where rice was growing casually, and which seemed to be riper than that growing in the paddy proper. About half the Scaly-breasted Munias were immatures but I was unable to identify any immature Five-coloureds. As with Pale-headed Munias in rice, they were easy to see at a distance with the naked eye, the bright white standing out clearly against the solid green. They are very agile, grasping several stalks at a time, crossing over from one stalk to another with ease, and working down a bending stem as easily as they worked up one. They were well spaced as they fed, usually a metre or so apart, and showed none of the behaviour of Scaly-breasted Munia where several birds will gather on a single stem. I also noticed that Five-coloured Munias would eat only a little seed from a head and then move on, never cleaning out a head entirely, or almost so, as Scaly-breasted Munias seem to do.

It is a sociable species, but does not gather in the numbers that typify Scaly-breasted Munia. Whenever I have seen them feeding together the latter outnumbered Five-coloured Munias by at least three to one. The largest number I saw in any mixed flock was about ten birds.

In captivity the birds will perch close to each other but do not exhibit heavy clumping behaviour. I have recorded allopreening and peering. In a group of birds where several males are present, any one that begins undirected song will attract one or two peerers immediately.

Five-coloured Munia peering. As the male on left begins singing, the second male hops closer and peers until it is almost touching.

FOOD AND FEEDING It can usually be found feeding on the seeding heads of various grasses which it climbs with the agility of other grassland munias, having the same big feet and long toes. It has a definite liking for rice and is the target of the rice farmers. Birds I saw in gardens in the highlands of central Flores were apparently feeding on the male inflorescences of Indian corn *Zea mays*.

At Aileu, at about 1,400m in northern East Timor, there were extensive grasslands and rice paddies around the town and I was able to get an excellent view of both Five-coloured Munia and Moluccan Munia *L. molucca* feeding together in the same area. I could see the birds leaving the grass, which at times stood well over 2m tall, and flying into the paddy in small groups of 4 or 5 birds. Both species were easy to spot due to the white on their plumage and equally easy to separate from each other. I noticed the clear tendency of Five-coloured Munia to post a lookout, and there was always a bird or two sitting on guard, high on a tall stem. This was both in the tall grass and in the rice. The only bird of prey I saw in the vicinity was a Eurasian Kestrel *Falco tinnunculus* but it was clear the main predator is man.

MOVEMENTS Not known.

CALL The loud call note of the female is a single sharp *peet*, while that of the male is a double *triprip*. With one pair I studied, the female called the male with a single loud querulous *weet!* and he always replied instantly with a trisyllabic rapid *trtrtrtr*. It was not until I caged them apart that I was able to ascertain with certainty that what had sounded like a call from a single bird was effectively duetting.

Burkhard (1980b) describes a close contact call *veeveevee*, which I have not heard. My birds in close contact used a softer tone of the loud contact call in which the sexual differences were less apparent. At dusk, when settling down, they will make the mewing sounds that many, if not all munias make. This is an intimate sound made by birds settling into a roost together or in close proximity but when one is prevented from joining the other. A single

bird in a nest in daytime will also make the sound, apparently inviting its mate to join it. It might be this note that Burkhard mentions.

SONG The song is long, about 10 seconds, beginning with some almost inaudible *te te te* which becomes not one but two legatos followed by a series of soft but complex *pti-pti-pti-pti*.

COURTSHIP AND DISPLAY When displaying, the bird stretches upwards, looking straight ahead, raising the feathers around the head and neck, with the belly, lower flanks and ventral feathers only slightly raised. In high intensity display the male turns towards the female. The whole is rather similar to that of Chestnut-breasted Munia *L. castaneothorax*, although in the latter there is a greater variety in the actual display (Green 1986).

BREEDING Virtually nothing has been written about this bird in the wild, with no description of nest, eggs, or any behaviour. The eggs of birds I have bred in confinement were white, ovoid but tapered at one end, 12mm wide at the base, 17mm long.

At Aileu I found a dozen or so munia nests collected by boys who had been sent into the tall grass to collect them as part of the on-going war against rice-eating birds. There were spilled and broken eggs, some still inside the nests. It was impossible to know which species had made which nest but there were only two species resident, Five-coloured and Moluccan Munias and two very distinct kinds of nest. One type was perfectly round, about 16cm across. The walls were about 4cm thick and dense, and incorporated a lot of fine soft fluffy grass heads in them. The round entrance hole was in one side. There was no entrance porch, although there was effectively an entrance tunnel. The other kind of nest was slightly more loosely made with fewer of the fluffy grass heads, slightly ovoid with the entrance at one end and a hint of an entrance porch and overhang.

The first breeding recorded in captivity is usefully detailed (Green 1986). The pair built their own nest, a spheroid made entirely of grasses in a clump of grass about 1.25m from the ground. It was small and compact, measuring 17cm long x 10cm across. The actual nest chamber measured only 7cm across. Six eggs were laid. Both sexes incubated during the day but only the female sat at night. The young hatched in about 14 days and were light pink with white down. They were brooded until about 10 days and were reared on a diet of soaked white millet and soaked canary seed, small maggots (blow fly larvae), a proprietary brand of egg-rearing food lettuce and occasionally some other green food. Upon fledging the young had dark horn bills, legs and feet and appeared to be dull buffish-grey, whitish on the abdomen. They were extremely nervous, a feature mentioned in reports of breeding from Germany. The parents were very protective of the young, incessantly calling them to roost together in a disused nest box. The young were feeding themselves within a week of fledging, but the parents continued to feed them for two weeks, after which they built a new nest in a ball of wire and went on to rear a second brood of four.

Green (1986) comments that they are sociable birds, but did not clump nor alloapreen, and when sitting together always stayed a few inches apart. Colin Rowe (*in litt.*) noted that at about 5 months the male birds began moulting first, and were definitely whiter on the breast than the females. All his second generation pairs were

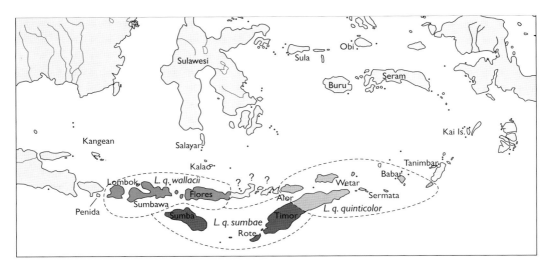

Distribution of Five-coloured Munia.

selected on this basis without one mistake. Green also was able to separate the sex of his birds the same way. When breeding in the outdoor aviary Rowe's birds fed their nestlings with both egg-rearing food and live food, but always refused both when rearing in cages.

Rowe ended 1988 with a colony of 19 birds, twelve of his own breeding and seven acquired adults. He noticed that in this colony situation only the dominant pair bred, the others showing no apparent interest. He noticed a lot of bickering, sometimes serious and some birds died. In this colonial environment he noted that the immatures took longer to moult, the last brood taking almost a year before assuming adult plumage.

 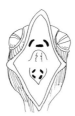

Palate markings of nestling Five coloured Munia bred in captivity. Left, according to Rowe (*in litt.*), and right according to Sproule (1994).

DISTRIBUTION Five-coloured Munia is restricted to the islands of the Lesser Sundas and the south-eastern Moluccas. *L. q. quinticolor* ranges from the eastern end of East Timor, although it has been taken as far south as Camplong, eastwards to Moa, Sermata and Babar. At the western end of its range, *L. q. wallacii* occurs on Lombok, Sumbawa and possibly western Flores. The third race, *L. q. sumbae*, ranges from eastern Flores to Sumba, Roti and West Timor, where it has also been collected at Camplong. I do not know which form occurs on the islands from Lomblen to Alor. Goodwin (1982) shows the species on Bali in his map but properly does not mention this island in his text as it does not occur there (*vide* Mason and Jarvis 1984).

DESCRIPTION   Plates 57–59

Three subspecies are described (Restall 1995b). The eastern Timor race has a yellow rump, the central islands race from Sumba has an orange rump and the western race from Lombok has the rump maroon.

TIMOR FIVE-COLOURED MUNIA
L. quinticolor quinticolor   Plate 57
Former scientific name: *Loxia quinticolor* Vieillot, 1807, *Ois, Chant.*, pl. 54, p. 85
Adult *c.*125mm. Wing length 54–55mm, culmen 12.5–13mm, tarsus 14mm. It has the lores, forehead and forecrown chestnut, the rear crown to nape chestnut with blue-grey subterminal lines on either side of the quills forming rows of V-markings without the point. This extends irregularly onto the mantle which is cinnamon-brown. The supercilium and ear-coverts are cinnamon with pinkish striations caused by pale feather quills. The chin and throat are reddish-maroon. The wing-coverts and lower back are cinnamon like the back, the wings and tail being darker brown. The rump, uppertail-coverts and edges to the tail feathers are orange-yellow. The breast, belly, ventral area and flanks are white with a silky texture to the edges of the feathers that give a scaly appearance in some lights. The underwing-coverts are creamy-white. The thighs and undertail-coverts are black. The irides are reddish-brown. The bill is blue-grey, tending to lilac at the base, with white cutting edges. The legs and feet are grey.
The culmen is more pronounced on the male and males average larger bodies up to 5mm longer, with wings similarly a few millimetres longer.
Juvenile Drab above, from forehead onwards, darker on wings and tail, warmer on the rump and uppertail-coverts. The ear-coverts have whitish quill striations, a sure way to distinguish this species from other juvenile munias, although this character cannot normally be seen under field conditions. From throat to undertail-coverts it is buffy, warmest on breast and flanks. The bib is very pale. The bill is pale blue-grey. The legs and feet are grey.

SUMBA FIVE-COLOURED MUNIA

L. quinticolor sumbae   **Plate 58**

Restall, 1995, *Bull. Brit. Orn. Club.* 115 (3), 140 - 157.
Adult 105–120mm with most birds being around
120mm. Wing length 52–57mm, culmen 10–12mm,
tarsus 12–14mm . These measurements suggest a considerable variation in size. In my observations the birds
from a given location or island are all roughly the
same size, but it seems there is some variation in size
from population to population. The face, forehead,
supercilium, line through the eye, mesial, chin and
throat are maroon, the ear-coverts are maroon with
pink quill striations. From the crown to mantle and
lower back, wings and tail chestnut, with similar but
less noticeable blue-grey 'broken V' markings on the
nape; they may extend from crown to upper mantle.
The rump, uppertail-coverts and edging to the tail
feathers are all chrome-orange. The breast, belly,
ventral area, flanks and underwing-coverts are white.
The thighs and undertail-coverts are black. Bill, legs
and feet are as for the nominate race.

From the descriptions of the rump colouring it is probable that the birds kept by both Green and Rowe were
of this race. They both found it easy to tell the sexes
apart by the whiteness of the breast, males being
distinctly whiter. I have not been able to observe this
distinction either in live birds or in museum specimens.

Juvenile Same as the juvenile *L. q. quinticolor*.

LOMBOK FIVE-COLOURED MUNIA

L. quinticolor wallacii   **Plate 59**

Former scientific name: *Munia wallacii* Sharpe, 1890,
Cat. Birds Brit. Mus., 13, p.339

Other common names: Wallace's Five-coloured
Munia, Golden-rumped Five-coloured Munia.

Adult *c*.115mm. Wing length 58mm, culmen 12.5mm,
tarsus 14.5mm. The entire head is burnt umber, paler
to almost cinnamon on the ear-coverts, and blackish
on the chin and throat. There are white quill striations
on the ear-coverts, and one short row of white quills
on the supercilium. The mantle and wing-coverts are
maroon-chestnut, the wings chestnut, and the tail dark
brown. There may be faint broken V-markings on the
nape of freshly-moulted birds, but these tend to
abraid, leaving solid colour. The rump and uppertail-
coverts are maroon, reddish-maroon on the edges of
the tail and from the breast to ventral area. The flanks
and underwing-coverts are white. The thighs and
undertail-coverts are black. The bill, legs and feet are
blue-grey.

Male birds of this race that I kept for painting and
observation had a noticeably bolder culmen than the
females, and this could be felt by rubbing one's fingernail from the crown onto the culmen.

It is important to note that the above descriptions are
of fully adult birds in fine plumage condition. Young
birds in their first year are not as boldly coloured.
The underparts tend to be cream rather than white,
and the rump and uppertail-coverts are not so brightly
coloured.

Juvenile As described for the nominate race.

HYBRIDS No hybrids are recorded.

CONSERVATION Five-Coloured Munia is listed by the
International Council for Bird Preservation (Collar and

Andrew 1988) in the Near-threatened category. At best it
means that this species should be watched carefully. At
worst it means that habitat destruction or trapping for the
bird trade will tip population levels below that of self-
sustaining and the species will become genuinely
threatened. In my visits to dealers and bird markets in
Singapore and Indonesia between 1990 and 1992 I became
seriously alarmed at the regularity with which Five-
coloured Munias were being trapped from most of the
islands on which it occurs, particularly Lombok and Timor.
By late 1994 it was appearing in smaller quantities in the
Jakarta holding stations and stock was sitting there for up
to a year. The reason, I was told, was that there is no longer
any demand for it. Demand is a function of fashion and if
bird keepers decide to take an interest once more then I
fear it could become a race between the slow-down of the
bird trapping activities and developing restrictions on the
bird trade in Indonesia on the one hand, and the ability
of the species to maintain a viable population on the other.
It is quite possible that while the species may survive, some
island populations with distinct subspecific characteristics
might not.

REFERENCES Burkhard (1980b), Collar & Andrew
(1988), Goodwin (1982), Green (1986), Immelmann
(1972), Mason & Jarvis (1989), Restall (1995b), Sproule
(1994), White & Bruce (1986).

---

22   WHITE-HEADED MUNIA
Lonchura maja   Plate 9

Described as *Lonchura maja* Linnaeus
Other common names: White-headed Nun, White-headed
Mannikin, Maja Munia.

White-headed Munia

FIELD CHARACTERS This is a white-headed munia with
a reddish-brown body, black belly and undertail-coverts.
The only possible confusion is with Black-throated Munia
L. ferruginosa on Java and Bali, but the latter has a distinct
black throat. Possible escapes of Pale-headed Munia *L.
pallida* on Bali would cause confusion; look for the dark
to black belly on White-headed Munia. Juveniles of all
three of these species are indistinguishable in the field.
Juvenile White-headed Munia is also very similar to juvenile Scaly-breasted Munia *L. punctulata*. The two species
flock together in the paddy fields. In south Vietnam White-
headed Munia consorts with Chestnut Munia *L. atricapilla*
and again the juveniles are virtually identical.

STATUS Locally common, or locally scarce (Vietnam).

HABITAT In Sumatra it is found in open country with grassland, rice fields, cultivation and village gardens, in lowlands and fields up to 1,500m (van Marle & Voous 1988). Madoc (1956) emphasises that in Malaysia it is a bird of lowlands. Van Marle and Voous (1988) go on to say it is very common, often in large flocks with Scaly-breasted Munias and other species in ripening rice fields. Mason and Jarvis (1989) say it invades the lowland fields in swarms, apparently in the company of other munias. In Vietnam I have only been able to find it in the vicinity of rice paddies. However in Da Lat, a local bird trapper told me it was fairly common in the grassy areas outside the town, the altitude in this area ranging from 1,300m to 1,500m.

Hails (1987) says of it in Singapore that it is uncommon in parks and gardens, favouring rural areas and showing a clear preference for invading land which has been cleared for development and has become overgrown with wild grasses. Some of the largest flocks he has encountered (100) have been on or near to areas of reclaimed land, a very useful adaptation for a bird in Singapore.

HABITS AND BEHAVIOUR This is a sociable species, gathering in large numbers to feed and roost. It is frequently seen with Scaly-breasted Munias in Java, and many thousands of first-year birds of both species are trapped for the bird trade in Jakarta. It also flocks with the Scaly-breasted Munia in Malaysia. In contrast, those birds that are caught in the inner Mekong Delta in Vietnam are in the company of Chestnut Munias. The flocks roost in reedbeds and cane fields.

Of the various munias I have observed in Bali, White-headed Munia is the only one that appeared to show any sign of feeling the heat. Birds will hop around with their bills open, panting, a behaviour not seen in other species.

Oberg (1975) observed that White-headed Munia is a 'distance' species, with individuals spacing themselves up to 6cm apart when perching. Whilst this may be so, I have observed them clumping in captivity.

FOOD AND FEEDING Tweedie (1960) described its feeding habits as typical of the genus, moving in small flocks over the ground, feeding on the grass seeds. The flock constantly moves forward by the hindmost birds flying over the birds feeding in front of them, going a few yards and settling in front of the foremost. These flocks usually contain more than one species. Bernstein (in Goodwin 1982) found it was unable to cope with fully ripe rice and thought that it flocked to the rice stubbles to feed on seeds of wild grasses or weeds there. I am sure Bernstein is right in his second assumption for it is undoubtedly a lover of weedy, recently worked ground. However, I have seen cages of the birds in the bird market in Surabaya fed on nothing but bunches of hard dry rice and stocks in transit in the bird trade certainly live for months on nothing else but this.

Goodwin (1982) suggests the species might take some invertebrates, referring to Gocht's birds in Germany that eagerly took greenfly, although the species normally rears its young in captivity without taking live food. I have referred to this eagerness with which captive munias will take greenfly elsewhere in this book (in particular see the account on Java Sparrow *L. oryzivora*) and I am convinced the greenfly is seen by the birds as their typical ideal food – soft green grass in flower, or when the seed is just swell-ing, being rich in protein and the easiest to eat, and (certainly to human taste) the sweetest and most delicious. Look at the young green seeds of *Poa annua* or several of the *Pannicum* millets to see the similarity with greenfly. I think that munias would, or do, take greenfly in the wild – for the same reasons.

MOVEMENTS Birds of the year form focks with the young of other munias, particularly Scaly-breasted Munias, and wander in search of food, especially cultivated areas with ripening rice. Otherwise it is fairly sedentary.

CALL The call is a soft *preet*, or *prit*, and the local name for all munias in Bali is *prit* and in Malaysia it is known as *pipit*. The note of the male is at a different pitch, higher and usually longer than that of the female. A solitary bird has a loud and penetrating *peep*! as it seeks to make contact with its mate, or others of its kind. I have heard a lone bird, thought to be a male, coaxing another bird into its nest at roosting time with a purring kind of wheeze, *waaaargh waaaargh*. I have also heard a similar, louder, mewing call made by one bird as it flew into a tree, followed by its mate.

SONG The song begins with beak clicking which then becomes a *weeeeee heeeheeheeeheeeeheee*. One young male from Vietnam in my posession began singing while still in juvenile plumage. His song began with beak clicking then a wheezing note before beginning the long whine or *weeeee*. One song I heard in Bali, I transcribed in my notes as *peee wik wik wik*, followed by a drawn out *weeeee*.

COURTSHIP AND DISPLAY On one occasion a pair came to our garden in Bali and perched in a shrub that loomed over a fountain and small pool. The female flew down to the pool, drank and bathed. The male stayed on a branch and immediately sang, stretched and looked down watching his mate. The female flew up to join him and both preened and tidied their feathers as if both had bathed. When they flew the female flew first and the male followed, as is usual with bonded pairs of munias. In fact whenever I have been sure of the sexes of pairs of munias under observation, it has invariably been the female that flew first, with the male following close behind.

On another occasion the male sang while alone on a branch. The female flew up to join him and moved a few hops up the branch. The male, in a more upright position, edged down to be closer then began to sing again. He displayed by bobbing every 2 seconds or so. On completion of the song there was a little bill-fencing and the female flew off, the male following closely.

The male in full directed display draws himself upright, whether perched or on the ground, the feathers of the head and body being fluffed out, the bill held forward horizontally and open while singing, and all the time bobbing up and down.

The song begins with the neck stretched, head slightly tilted downwards and turning from side to side. The flanks and belly feathers are somewhat erected, and the tail is spread.

BREEDING Breeding normally takes place after the rainy season but may happen at any time of the year if weather and food supply is appropriate. Although White-headed Munias will nest in the vicinity of others of their own species, or other munias and weavers, it is not a colonial nester.

The nest is a spheroid, more round than the tall ellipse

of Chestnut Munia or the flatter ball of White-rumped
Munia. It is built with stems and blades of grasses, bamboo
and other long leaves, lined with finer stems and fibres.
The entrance is at the side with a downward sloping porch
made of the longer inner roof linings. Both sexes take
part in building the nest but in my observations it seems
that only the male carries material to the nest. Both birds
incubate the white, oval eggs. The clutch numbers from
3–7. Incubation is usually 12–13 days after hatching, and
the young fledge in about 21 days. Breeding normally takes
place after the rainy season but may happen at any time
of the year if the weather and food supply is appropriate.

I once stayed at the Hotel Oberoi on the southern-
most part of Bali and found White-headed Munia to be
common in the grounds of the hotel and in the adjacent
country. It was the middle of the breeding season and birds
were engaged in nesting activity all around. Single birds
assumed to be males were gathering nesting material, and
if one hopped around the ground for long it was sure to
be joined by another, or a passing pair. One male regularly flew to the edge of the lawn where it abutted a dry
stone wall and small tufts of grass, which, having escaped
the mower, had grown to 20 or 30cm in length. The bird
would bite at the base of the stem, and lean back, tugging
until a blade or complete stem would break off. Then it
would fly to its nest in the head of a swamp palm about
3m from the ground at the edge of the lawn. The nest, an
ovoid of grass blades, dried and straw-coloured was wedged
snugly in the base of the palm leaves. Whilst I did see the
occasional White-headed Munia flying by with a length of
dry straw, suggesting nest-building at an early stage, all
the nests I observed were clearly being lined and finished
off with soft fine green grass. One pair was nesting in a
deserted or abandoned nest of a Streaked Weaver *Ploceus
manyar*. The male of the pair would fly down to the lawn,
search for a stem of grass some 10 to 15cm long then fly
up to the nest which was suspended from a proud branch
about 5m from the ground. Within 20 seconds he would
fly out, having left the blade inside with the female who
was working away at the new fresh lining.

**White-headed Munia adapting a nest of the Streaked
Weaver.**

They have bred in captivity many times. Siegfried
Kirschke (*in litt.*) was particularly successful with them in
Germany. He confirmed my own observation that pairing
naturally occurs while the birds are still in juvenile plumage. If several young birds are kept together and pairs
allowed to bond, they will settle very well and breed easily.
They normally rear on an all-seed and green food diet,
green food being particularly important. They do not
normally show any interest in insect food.

**Palate markings of nestling
White-headed Munia.**

DISTRIBUTION *L. m. maja* ranges from southern peninsular Thailand, down the Malaysian peninsula and Singapore to Sumatra, Java and Bali. It is also found on the
islands of Simeulue (Simalur), Nias and Batu. I have found
the Vietnamese race *L. m. vietnamensis* among the rice-
growing area in the grasslands of the Mekong Delta, near
the Cambodian border up from Tay Ninh, and further to
the north-west at Da Lat. The area of distribution for Vietnam shown on the map is an approximation.

It appears to have been released and is established as
a breeding bird on Okinawa, and may also be established
north of Osaka in Japan (Lever 1987).

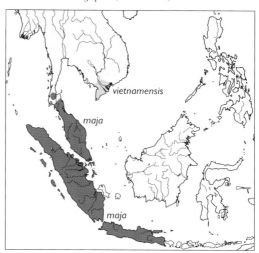

**Distribution of White-headed Munia. The area shown for
Vietnam is an approximation. The small pocket shown for
the species in peninsular Thailand is after Lekagul and
Round (1991) and indicates the fragmented nature of the
bird's distribution.**

DESCRIPTION   **Plates 60–63**
Two subspecies are described. The Vietnamese race is
slightly darker, with a more distinct brown bib and throat,
and generally darker on the head. In both sexes of the
Vietnamese race it appears that the black of the belly
touches the breast. In the nominate race *L. m. maja* the
brown of the flanks joins in a bar between the breast and
the black of the belly, invariably in the female and often
in the male.

WHITE-HEADED MUNIA
Lonchura maja maja   **Plates 60–62**
Other scientific names: *Loxia maja*, Linnaeus, 1766,
Syst. Nat. ed. 12, 1, p.301. *Loxia leucocephala*, Raffles,
1822. *Munia maja zapercna*, Oberholser, 1926. *Munia
maja simalurensis*, Oberholser, 1926.

Adult male 115–120mm. Wing length 55–59mm, culmen 12–13mm, tarsus 13mm. The entire head is slightly off-white in first-year birds, becoming whiter with each moult. There is a buffish tinge on the nape. This is variable according to the age of the bird, and is usually drab in a first-year bird. In older birds it pales with each moult and can become pure white. From the mantle, the wings to the lower back and upper rump it is brown. The lower rump, down from level with the middle tertial, to the uppertail-coverts and tail, it is very deep reddish-maroon with a crimson edging to the tail feathers. The breast is drab. The flanks are almost the same as the back but tend to be slightly more vinous and become the deep reddish-maroon of the lower rump on the lower flanks. In many if not most old males the black of the belly extends upwards to reach the drab breast, dividing the brown of the flanks. The underwing-coverts are dark pinkish-buff. The thighs are black. From the centre of the lower breast to the undertail-coverts is black. The irides are brown. The bill is pale bluish-grey with white cutting edges. The legs and feet are dark grey, black on the large scales.

Adult female 110–115mm. Wing length 54–57mm, culmen 11–12mm, tarsus 12–13mm. Similar to male but usually sufficiently different to be distinguished. The thighs are black. The buff of the nape is more extensive, reaching the crown, and similarly tinging the bib. In paired birds of similar age, the head of the female can be seen to be duller than the male's, particularly on the crown. The throat is fawn graduating to cinnamon-brown on the breast and upper flanks. The flanks are the same vinous burnt umber of the male but are broader, joining in a soft bar across the lower breast. The thighs are fuscous. In some females the central tail feathers are tinged deep crimson. The bill is pale grey. The legs and feet are vinous-grey with blackish large scales.

Juvenile Cinnamon above, buffy to cream below, with a grey bill and dark grey feet. However I have examined birds from Malaysia that were distinctly paler lilac-grey on the bill, more pale greyish on the head and more straw-coloured on the entire body. I examined a large number of juveniles from Java and noted considerable variation among them but they were all darker than the straw-coloured Malaysian juveniles.

VIETNAM WHITE-HEADED MUNIA

Lonchura maja vietnamensis   **Plate 63**
Restall, 1995, *Bull. Brit. Orn. Club.*, 115 (3), 140–157.
Adult male 104mm. Wing length 52mm, culmen 12mm, tarsus 12mm. From forehead to nape is pale brown, chin and ear-coverts beige, supercilium, lores and the forepart of beneath the eye off-white. The back and wings are warm brown. The lower rump is very dark reddish-maroon. The tail is dark brown with mahogany edging to the feathers. The breast is cinnamon-brown. The flanks are chestnut, almost burnt sienna, which joins the uppertail-coverts at the lower flanks. The underwing-coverts are light cinnamon. The thighs are black. From the centre of the lower breast to the undertail-coverts is jet black. The bill is blue-grey with white cutting edges. The irides are very dark brown. The legs and feet are mid violaceous-grey.
Adult female 105–106mm. Wing length 52–56mm,

culmen 12mm, tarsus 14mm. It is whitish on the front forehead and around the eyes and sides of the face, tinted with pale cinnamon-brown. The rear forehead is light drab to dark drab on the nape. The back and wings are burnt umber. The rump to tail is rich maroon-red with some crimson glistening on the longer uppertail-coverts and central tail feathers. From throat to breast it is dark fawn, almost olive-brown. The flanks are chestnut. The underwing-coverts are warm buff with dark brown edges or tips. From the centre of the breast to the undertail-coverts it is dull black. The bill is light blue-grey with the cutting edges pale to white. The irides are dark brown. The legs and feet are violaceous-grey with blackish large scales.

Juvenile 104mm. From forehead to back it is light cinnamon-brown to rufous, lightest on the top of the head, darkest on the back and wings. The flight feathers and greater wing-coverts are dark brown edged with rufous. The lower rump and uppertail-coverts are raw sienna. It is buffish on the throat, around the eyes and ear-coverts, becoming pale clay on the rest of the underparts. The flanks become pale brown under the wings. The underwing-coverts are chamois. The irides are very dark brown. The bill is pale blue-grey with paler cutting edges. The legs and feet are dark violaceous-grey with black larger scales.

HYBRIDS No hybrids are reported in the wild, but several have been produced in captivity (Gray 1958). These include cross-breedings with Cut-throat *Amadina fasciata* and Black-throated Finch *Poephila cincta*, and at least seven species of munia.

CONSERVATION Despite a regular and heavy toll by the bird trade in Indonesia, particularly in Java, there does not seem to be cause for concern for this prolific species there, yet. However the status of the species in Vietnam is virtually unknown. It seems to be uncommon and local, probably scarce. The birds that I have seen formed only a small percentage of the flocks of Chestnut Munia feeding in the paddies. Bird trapping in the south of Vietnam is rampant and widespread. The birds are caught for human consumption, for release at buddhist shrines and also for export to Singapore and Taiwan. In one shipment of 7,000 Chestnut Munias that I intercepted in Singapore there was only one White-headed Munia. In a shipment that I understood had consisted of a few thousand munias that I found in Taiwan there were perhaps two hundred White-headed Munias. The dealer said he could get a thousand to order. In the absence of better data on the populations of munias in Vietnam, especially White-headed Munia, it should be regarded as potentially threatened.

REFERENCES Delacour (1943), Goodwin (1982), Gray (1958), Lekagul & Round (1991), Lever (1987), Madoc (1956), Mason & Jarvis (1989), Oberg (1975), Restall (1995b), Tweedie (1960), van Marle & Voous (1988).

23   PALE-HEADED MUNIA
Lonchura pallida   **Plate 9**

Described as *Lonchura pallida* Wallace
Other common names: Pallid Munia or Mannikin, Pale-headed Nun, Pale Sunda Munia and Pallid Finch.

Pale-headed Munia

FIELD CHARACTERS Pale-headed bird, brown above with buffish nape and mushroom breast that becomes cinnamon on belly and flanks. At a distance the head is very pale-looking and this prevents confusion with any other species in its range. I have seen Pale-headed Munia on sale in the bird market in Denpasar and know they have escaped from time to time. It is thus worth double-checking identification of White-headed Munias on Bali. White-headed Munia *L. maja* has a slightly whiter head, but the real distinction is its dark breast and belly. The juveniles are indistinguishable in the field.

STATUS Locally common.

HABITAT It is a bird of grassy scrub, grasslands and cultivated areas. I have seen it emerging from woodland to venture into rice paddies, and have seen it retreat into wooded areas when disturbed. It is found in grassland and cultivation to 1,000m (White & Bruce 1986) and up to 1,400m (Clement *et al.* 1993); in the lower Palu valley it occurs below 400m, breeding the year round.

HABITS AND BEHAVIOUR Virtually nothing is recorded about this bird in the wild. It has been seen in rice paddies in mixed flocks with Chestnut Munia *L. atricapilla* in Sulawesi. From my own limited observations of the bird in the field and more extensive studies of birds in captivity it seems to be the geographic representative of White-headed Munia. I found a feeding flock on the island of Sawu, consisting 90% immatures which were particularly noticeable by their dark bills. They would feed close together, often 2 or 3 to a stem. The very few adults were alert, perching high in the grass where it was obvious they were keeping a look out. I saw a few adults either feeding alone or with Scaly-breasted Munias *L. punctulata* in green rice or ripening rice in East Timor, Flores and Sumba. The pale head looked very white at a distance and they are very easy to notice when one is scanning the paddies for munias.

On the island of Liran I watched them on a number of occassions; the largest group consisted of 7 birds. They frequented trees on the edge of open grassy areas and would descend nervously. When feeding, one or two birds would keep watch, and quickly alarm the others into retreating into the tree tops where one or two birds would be visually prominent, looking out for the threat that had caused the alarm. They were usually seen feeding with Zebra Finches *Poephila guttata* and Scaly-breasted Munias neither of which were as jumpy. It was a clear contrast in comparative behaviour to observe the three species when disturbed. The Zebra Finches would fly into the trees and be lost from sight. The Scaly-breasted Munias would fly away over the grass, undulating and corkscrewing, descending into the grass again, usually about 25 metres away. The Pale-headed Munias would fly up into the trees where, quite obvious and easy to see due to the pale colouring of their heads, they kept watch until they judged it to be safe enough to descend once again to the grass. Liran is virtually uninhabited with no rice cultivation to explain their wariness of man. The Scaly-breasted Munias fed peacefully, coming to within 2 metres of me before flying up. If there were any Pale-headed Munias amongst them they would be much more alert than Scaly-breasted Munias, some keeping high-stalk sentry, and they would fly off in alarm long before the Scaly-breasted Munias saw me, or took any notice. Pale-headed Munias fly swiftly and direct with little undulation, contact calling loudly as they fly.

FOOD AND FEEDING In my observations it feeds on the seeds of various growing grasses and rice. It probably takes the seeds of weeds that grow in among the grasses. From observations of birds in captivity it also takes dry seeds that have fallen to the ground. When breeding, I found that it feeds the young on green food as well as succulent half-ripe seeds. It will take a little rearing food of the kind given to breeding canaries. My birds showed no interest in mealworms.

MOVEMENTS Nothing known.

CALL They are quiet birds, similar to White-headed Munias, and not given to the loud contact calling of Chestnut Munias. The call of the male is *pseet!* while that of the female is *psit!* There is a louder *peep!* when the birds are in flight, or one is apart from the group.

SONG A lone male I kept briefly indoors with two males of another species, each in its own cage, sang very sweetly during the night. It was a sweet warbling song with the typical munia *weee* but included an often repeated phrase which I transcribed as *chopipichow chippichow*. The main song I have noted as a series of rattling notes that end with a high-pitched extended *weeeeeeeeee*.

Male bowing at start of direct courtship display.

COURTSHIP AND DISPLAY The courtship display contains most of the elements of the straw display (Baptista and Horblit 1990). The male begins courtship by bowing low, turning towards the female, with his tail also turned slightly towards her. In this position he bobs up and down. If the female stays nearby, the male then stands more upright, somewhat stretched and leaning forward slightly, head pointed slightly downwards, and facing the female. The flanks and belly feathers are fluffed out. In this position he performs the inverted curtsey (Morris 1958) and also moves his head from side to side. During this performance, his bill is open, the mandibles opening and closing as he sings. The more upright the stance, so the more open the bill and more pronounced the mandibulations. After completing the display, the males wipes his bill two or three times, then launches right back into a repeat, picking up at the inverted curtsey.

Siegfried Kirschke (*in litt.*) described the display of the male with its head and neck feathers erected. If the female is interested she hops near to the male and pecks gently towards him. He displays more intensely until the female crouches and quivers her tail, at which point copulation takes place. He says that after copulation both birds peck in a friendly manner towards each other but without touching.

Inverted curtsey display with the male head-twisting.

BREEDING The pair that furnished the observations described above built a nest of dry grasses and straw, finishing it with fine, soft grass stems and completing the lining until the entrance was only 3 or 4cm across and had a rough wide porch over it. Four perfectly oval eggs were laid 12mm wide x 15mm long. Subsequent clutches by other birds had the same measurements. Both sexes shared incubation. The clutch was 5 eggs and these were incubated for 14 days. After fledging the young were led back to the nest to roost for the first few nights. The nestlings were very dark-skinned with distinctive palate markings and white papillae. They were reared on a mixture of canary-rearing food, hulled millet and Barleygreen which was made fresh every day. The parents also took dry hard seed and fresh lettuce. The nestlings called loudly when the parents were at the nest or were entering it. The fledglings begged very noisily. They were sampling lettuce at one week and were very agile at 10 days, easily perching on vertical grass stems. They had blackish bills upon fledging, and these did not begin to pale until the birds were about 10 weeks old. The young males were singing around this time.

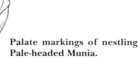

Palate markings of nestling Pale-headed Munia.

DISTRIBUTION Pale-headed Munia ranges over southwest and south-east Sulawesi, throughout the Lesser Sundas from Lombok to Babar with most of the islands in between mentioned by both Goodwin (1982) and White & Bruce (1986), but neither sources mention Wetar or Timor. Goodwin does embrace both in his distribution map, which is correct, for I have observed birds on Timor myself and I have observed the bird on Liran, one of Wetar's offshore islands and on Babar.

According to Watling (1983) the chestnut-bellied race *L. p. subcastanea* is found only in the lower Palu Valley (below 400m) of the Lore Lindu Reserve in northern-central Sulawesi. However, he says, it is quite common there and breeds all year round.

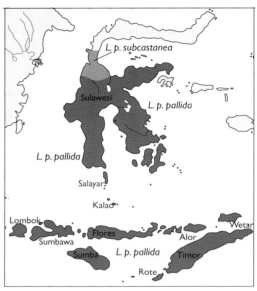

Distribution of Pale-headed Munia.

DESCRIPTION   **Plates 55 & 64**

There are two subspecies described. The Palu Valley race has significantly darker underparts and comparison with the nominate race is not necessary for identification. There is undoubtedly considerable variation of colouring within the birds presently defined as *L. p. pallida* despite the implication that there may be fading with wear (Goodwin 1982). The opportunity exists to study them across their distribution, particularly comparing types from the dark Lombok group, those from Saon and Sermatta which have the belly a pale, washed-out cinnamon, a particularly distinctive group with the belly cinnamon from Kisser, and those from Tanimbar and Sulawesi which have the belly more tawny-cinnamon.

PALE-HEADED MUNIA
L. pallida pallida
Former scientific name: *Munia pallida*, Wallace, 1863, *Proc. Zool. Soc. London*, p.495

Adult male 109–112mm. Wing length 54–56mm, culmen 11–12mm, tarsus 11 to 12mm. The head is pale creamy-white becoming buffish on the crown and nape. From mantle to lower back and wings it is rich earth-brown. The rump, uppertail-coverts and tail are deep reddish-maroon, with the tail slightly paler, finely washed with a tinge of orange. The face and throat are creamy-white graduating soon into a mushroom-coloured breast. This in turn becomes cinnamon on the belly, thighs and flanks. The ventral area and undertail-coverts are reddish dark brown. The irides are dark brown, the bill pale grey and the legs and feet grey.

Adult female 105–110mm. Wing length 52–54mm, culmen 11mm, tarsus 11mm. Similar to male but the crown and nape is usually a little darker, while the entire underparts are a little paler. There may be a light greyish scalloping on the cinnamon upper belly and the undertail-coverts are not so dark nor so clearly demarcated as in the male. In some birds I studied in Timor (and subsequently bred in confinement) the difference between the sexes was immediately apparent. The breast of the male was a richer colouring than that of the female which was noticeably paler.

Juvenile The juvenile has the top of the head olive-brown with the cheeks pale tawny-olive. The mantle is pale brown, the rump and uppertail-coverts are warm brown. The tertials and secondary wing feathers have the leading edges warm cinnamon. The primaries and tail feathers are dark brown with paler edgings. Below, the chin and throat are very pale tawny-olive, the breast and flanks are warm tawny-olive, and the undertail-coverts are tawny-olive. The bill is black upon fledging but gradually lightens after fledging. The legs and feet are dark horn.

PALU VALLEY PALE-HEADED MUNIA
L. pallida subcastanea
Hartert, 1897, *Novit. Zool.* 4, p.161.
Other common name: Chestnut-bellied Pale-headed Munia
This race is similar to *L. p. pallida* but is distinguished by having the lower breast, thighs and flanks chestnut, instead of cinnamon. The female is similarly darker on the underparts while being overall paler below than the male. In size it appears to be similar to the nominate race and the two juveniles appear to be similar.

HYBRIDS No hybrids have been reported.

CONSERVATION No information, but no apparent cause for concern. The species occasionally occurs in the bird trade, but the demand is insufficient at present.

REFERENCES Baptista & Horblit (1990) Clement *et al.*(1993), Goodwin (1982), Morris (1958), Watling (1983), White & Bruce (1986).

---

24   GRAND MANNIKIN
Lonchura grandis   Plate 11

Described as *Lonchura grandis* Sharpe
Other common names: Great Munia or Mannikin, Great-billed Munia or Mannikin.

Grand Mannikin

TAXONOMY On the basis of morphology and distribution, Grand Mannikin probably forms a superspecies with Thick-billed Mannikin *L. melaena* and New Ireland Mannikin *L. forbesi*.

FIELD CHARACTERS This is a large mannikin. It has a massive bill, a black head and is nearly all black below. It is chestnut or reddish-brown on the back and wings, with orange, golden or yellow uppertail-coverts. It is unlikely to be confused with any other species.

STATUS Uncommon or locally common.

HABITAT It is found both at low levels and in the foothills up to mid-montane levels, all the while found in open grassland, swampy grassland, cane breaks and cane-grass swamp.

HABITS AND BEHAVIOUR It tends to occur in small parties of a few birds up to medium-sized flocks of up to 20 birds (Diamond 1979, and Hicks pers. comm.) but it is often recorded in mixed company. Clement *et al.* (1993) state that it occurs in flocks of up to 300.

According to Rand and Gilliard (1967), when the whole country around the Idenburg River was flooded in the period March to May there were extensive beds of floating marsh grass and in these the birds were common. Although they were breeding, it was usual to find them feeding on the seeds of the marsh grasses and moving around in small compact flocks.

Baptista (1995) observes that adults behave as 'distance' species, always keeping a minimum distance between individuals when sitting together, but juveniles have been seen clumping. In a large flight cage containing eight Grand Mannikins (seven of which were males) I noticed clumping occur between two males on several occasions, although they would normally sit one to a few centimetres apart. I have also (rarely) observed allopreening.

I have also seen what I have called 'peering-enforced singing' (Restall 1995a). In this behaviour a male pushes itself firmly alongside another male that has recently sung, leaning over it with the tip of its bill almost touching the culmen of the singer, peering at it almost menacingly. The put-upon bird edges away but the aggressor overbearingly edges after it. The second male then, seemingly reluctantly, begins to sing and completes a full song cycle. On completion, the peering enforcer visibly relaxes and the performer flies away.

FOOD AND FEEDING Baptista (1990) reports visiting a grassy field about half a hectare in area, in front of the Baitabag Community School in Madang. Having heard the call of mannikins he sought them and located a flock consisting mostly of Grand Mannikins, smaller numbers of Chestnut-breasted Mannikins *L. castaneothorax* and a few Streak-headed Mannikins *L. tristissima*. He found this flock on three separate occasions during the month of January. On two occasions he also identified a single individual of a fourth species, Hooded Mannikin *L. spectabilis*. He tried to estimate the number of mannikins in the field by counting them as they broke up into small flocks and flew to their night roosts, and estimated a total of 328.

All four species were observed plucking seeds from the *Roettboellia exaltata* grass, a species that grows up to 2m tall and produces seeds as large as rice grains. Although the leaves and stems were brown in most of the plants, the seeds were green and milky. The bills of some of the birds were stained green from eating the half-ripe seed heads. Grand Mannikins were also seen plucking seeds from wild sugar cane *Saccharum robustrum* at several locations in the region and also the seeds of *Cyperus* and *Brachiaria* grasses (Baptista *in litt.*). Hicks (pers. comm.) has observed the species many times in the foothills outside Port Moresby and says it appears to have identical feeding habits to Chestnut-breasted and Grey-headed Mannikins.

The large bill of the species does not appear to have evolved in response to specialised feeding behaviour or any particular food source, and its feeding behaviour appears to be hardly any different from that of Hooded Mannikin, a bird almost half its size. From my own observations of birds in captivity, I relate the bill size to sexual attraction.

Baptista (*in litt.* and 1991) observed Grand Mannikins grasping a spikelet of a seeding grass head and running its bill sideways along the stem from base to tip, thereby collecting several soft seeds along the way. Assuming the seeds were then mashed and eaten whole, this would be a more efficient way to collect food than picking seeds one at a time and one presumably made possible only by the size and strength of the bill. Smith (1991) reports on studies of Black-bellied Seedcrackers (*Pyrenestes* spp.) in Zaïre which showed that birds of that genus with larger bills have different feeding habits from those with smaller bills. If this were the case with Grand Mannikins the males would have an advantage over females, if the spikelet scraping observed by Baptista was a normal feeding method. I have been unable to repeat this observation with captive birds despite supplying many different kinds of fresh grasses; those in my care invariably took seeds from inflorescences one at a time in the usual way, even from the smallest and finest seed stems.

MOVEMENTS Mostly sedentary, with some altitudinal movements likely.

CALL They are very vocal with a considerable variety of notes as they converse together. The general sound is of a tinkling of similar high-pitched contact notes. The loud contact call is a *quip*, different in tone between male and female, almost like *peep* and *pipi*. However, when a pair is separated, or one bird is separated from the group, the contact call becomes a loud *quire*, very loud when a mate replies, when both birds' calls take on a distinctly anxious tone (to anthropomorphic human ears). At this point the difference between the call of the male and the female is easy to hear.

Another voice I noticed was when a pair of *L. g. destructa* in my aviaries took possession of a nest cavity in one of the straw-filled nesting banks in an indoor flight. From within the nest the male emitted a long, drawn out *weeee* the source of which, to human ears, is very difficult to locate. The female was drawn slowly, but almost hypnotically, to the site. She would go right up to the entrance hole, but I never saw her go in. I have obtained a similar but more complex sound from caged male birds in the night by innocently provoking them with the tiny *beep*! of an electronic pocket diary.

SONG The song is very quiet and impossible to hear in the wild with normal human hearing. It begins with a series of fairly rapid *tk tk tk tk*, lasting from 5 to 15 seconds followed immediately by a descending legato *wwhheee-eeeeeeeeeeeeee* that lasts from 3 to 5 seconds. There may be a *peep* or *tchip* at the end.

COURTSHIP AND DISPLAY In a large aviary I have seen the male chase the female about in a kind of ritual pursuit, the pair doubling back and forth, round and round,

Song enforcement by one male peering menacingly across another bird until it begins to sing, whereupon the enforcer visibly relaxes to a mild level of peering.

and clearly she is not in fear of being caught or hurt. The male pursued her with a kind of butterfly flight, each bird pausing momentarily from time to time before setting off again. Sometimes the other pair in the enclosure would also join in. On one occasion it seemed to me the two males were fighting in some way, turning and tumbling, until they soon fell to the ground in a close grasp in exactly the way a female sparrow *Passer* will grasp a male sparrow before the two fall to the ground. In this case the remaining two birds, which I took to be the females, hopped excitedly from perch to perch, barely a metre above the two on the ground. All the while there was an incessant, excited chirruping.

Suddenly one of the birds on the ground, I think it was the vanquished (?) male, would fly off to be followed immediately by its mate, in turn followed by the other pair. Normal group behaviour would then resume. A pair in a cage will chase each other around, as described earlier. A mixed pair comprising a male Grand Mannikin that was caged with a female Black Mannikin behaved in exactly the same way. I can only hypothesise that this behaviour is connected with pair bonding and ovulation. Perhaps there is a parallel with Bamboo Parrotfinch *Erythrura hyperythra* which indulges in a similar chasing, the function of which seems to be to stimulate ovulation.

My feeling is that the larger bill of the male is a clear sexual stimulus to females and from observations of birds in captivity both in the UK and in Hong Kong it seems that larger-billed males pair up before smaller-billed ones. I have kept the species in aviaries where they have been able to interact with other munias. It is interesting to note that females of two different species, *L. pallida* and *L. atricapilla brunniceps*, both apparently bonded to males of their own kind, were so attracted to the male Grand Mannikin as to stray from their natural mates.

Male singing solitary song, left, compared to the advertisement song, right.

In solitary song the male stands in a very upright position, legs at about 45° to the perch, head held high and level, bill wide open without any movement and virtually no movement of the head or body.

In advertisement song the male faces forward. The posture is upright with the head held level, the legs clearly visible but almost horizontal. The feathers of the nape are raised, and the feathers of the flanks and belly slightly raised. He sits quite still with a very small movement of both mandibles and the throat pulsing in a noticeably undulating movement. When another Grand Mannikin is nearby he will follow it with his eyes and keep this head pointed in the bird's direction. Another more intense form of solicitation has the male alight alongside the prospective mate; he will quickly bow forward and lean across in front of the other bird almost touching it, all the while singing strongly. I have only seen this happen when the attention was unwelcome. Then the bird that had been approached always stood stiffly, head slightly angled upwards. On completion of the song cycle it would jab at the singer, who was still bending around across the front of it but who would now sit upright; short burst of bill-fencing would ensue.

'Kissing statues'. The position following courtship display between a bonded pair.

When singing to the female he is paired to, the male will turn slightly towards her, leaning over her in a rather crouched position. Thus placed he will sway backwards and forwards, bow, then return to an upright position. This is repeated several times. At the end of the song the two birds touch bills and sit still for several seconds. They then resume normal activity, usually by the female flying off and the male following.

Grand Mannikin singing to female.

BREEDING Gilliard and LeCroy (1966) found 8 nests in a small patch of low, thick-leaved grass growing in swampy grassland 100m or so from the Sepik River. The nests were built of grass strips tightly intertwined among the small stems and green leaves of the outer limbs. They were dishevelled, ball-like structures with side entrances. Some were close together, others were 3.3m apart, from 3.7–9.2m above ground.

Rand (1942) found it nesting on the floating mats of march grass, in flooded areas of the Idenburg River region in March–May. The nests were placed sometimes singly, sometimes several close together, in shrubs and on floating logs or stumps with projecting branches. One stump, that projected only a metre or so above the water held ten active nests. The nests, shaped like 'lop-sided flasks lying on their sides' were built of broad dead grass blades and some nests also had lots of grass rootlets used in them. They were lined with the fluffy flowering heads of grasses, and seed panicles from which the seeds had been removed or had fallen. In captivity, breeding birds have lined the nest with feathers. One nest measured 10cm long, 13cm wide x 16cm deep with an inside chamber 9cm x 8cm with a 6cm-long entrance tunnel. From my own observations of birds in captivity, whilst the male will bring most of the building material to the site, both sexes work on building the nest. In a nest built in my bird room the male constructed an elaborate entrance tunnel that eventually completely obscured the entrance and the nest could only be entered from an oblique lower angle.

The clutch is 5 or 6 eggs. In my experience these are long and narrow, averaging 17 x 11mm. Incubation lasts about 14 days and both sexes share the incubation. When born the young are quite naked, with typical *Lonchura* horseshoe-shaped palate markings (Rudiger 1981). The nestlings are reared on half-ripe seeds. Oppenborn (1987) found his birds to be particularly fond of sprouted seed. They fledge in three weeks and are feeding independently within two weeks of fledging. The fledglings continue to roost in the nest for some nights after fledging.

When my birds in England were nesting seriously, the male would sit sentinel outside the nest and stave off any other munias coming close, and Oppenborn (1987) also found them to be aggressive in defence of the nest. I found them to be nervous nesters, especially the females, approaching the nest with caution then entering immediately. Despite the apparently aggressive behaviour of the males to each other – and the females did their own amount of chasing as well – I never felt any of the chasing and aggression to be negative nor harmful.

DISTRIBUTION The four races come from four separate and discrete locations on the island of New Guinea; there appear to be no overlaps or intergrades. According to Clement *et al.* (1993) the races are separated by only very short distances, isolated from each other by ridges or lines of hills dividing the valleys where they occur, but this only applies to the races *L. g. destructa* and *L. g. heurni* in northern Irian Jaya. The locations of the four races are as follows. *L. g. grandis* ranges from south-eastern New Guinea westward on the southern coast to Hall Sound and westward on the northern coast to the upper Watut River where it is a bird of the foothills. From Astrolabe Bay to the Ramu and Sepik Rivers, the race *L. g. ernesti* appears to be a bird both of the lowlands and the hillsides. Diamond (1979) found it at 1,350m in the grasslands surrounding the Okasa forest and appears unwilling to accept *L. g. ernesti*, raising the possibility of another race. My own interpretation of his description of the single specimen collected is that the bird in question was most likely *L. g. ernesti*. In Hollandia, bridging Irian Jaya and Papua New Guinea, is the race *L. g. destructa*, while further to the west *L. g. heurni* ranges up the Idenburg and Memberamo valleys of northwestern Irian Jaya.

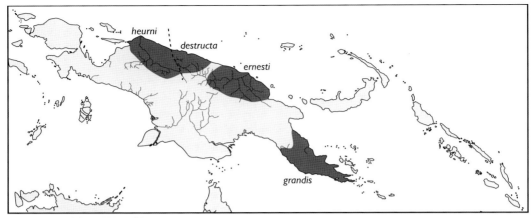

Distribution of Grand Mannikin.

DESCRIPTION   **Plates 65–66**

There are four distinct races of this species. The larger two have shades of chestnut on the back, the smaller two have shades of cinnamon. There is some variation in size, both within and between the races and of the males in particular, and some more subtle variation in colouring. While it might not be easy to define the race of a bird in isolation it would be easy to decide whether it is from the cinnamon-backed *grandis/ernesti* group or the larger and darker *destructa/heurni* group. I have given each race a different common name in an effort to help distinguish them.

GRAND MANNIKIN

L. grandis grandis

Former scientific name: *Munia grandis* Sharpe, 1882, *Journ. Linn. Soc. London, zool.*, 16, p.316

Adult male 120–130mm. Wing length 52–55mm, culmen 13–15mm. The heavy bill, 12–13mm deep causes the head to be larger so, although the body size may only be that of a Chestnut Munia *L. atricapilla*, it appears to be bigger and bolder. Tarsus is 13 to 14mm. The head is entirely black, the underparts from bib to undertail-coverts are black with some irregular cinnamon-rufous on the flanks. This may be largely hidden by the folded wings. The underwing-coverts are cinnamon-buff. There might be a slight green gloss on the black of the throat and breast. The mantle, back and scapulars are cinnamon. The lower back and wings are cinnamon-rufous. The rump graduates from cinnamon-rufous to chrome-orange on the uppertail-coverts. The edges of the tail feathers are yellow. The irides are chestnut, the bill, legs and feet are pale-grey.

Adult female 115–120mm. Wing length 51–53mm, culmen 13–14mm and 11–12mm deep, tarsus 13mm. Plumage is similiar to that of the male.

Juvenile Dark drab on the head, becoming more russet on the back and wings. The rump and uppertail-coverts are drab or buffy-drab. the tail is the same dark drab of the head.The bib is pale pinkish-buff. The throat and breast are tawny-olive flushed with drab with darkish streaks to the centre of the feathers. The rest of the underparts are pinkish-buff. The bill is large and distinctive, dark grey but usually paler along the cutting edges.

ERNEST'S GRAND MANNIKIN

L. grandis ernesti

Former scientific name: *Munia grandis ernesti* Stresemann, 1921, *Anz Ornith. Ges Bayern*, 1, p.33.

This is the smallest of the four races.

Adult male *c.*115mm. Wing length 50–53mm, culmen 14–15mm and *c.*12–13mm deep with the head correspondingly enlarged, tarsus 13–14mm. The entire head and underparts are black and there may be a little green gloss to it. The mantle, back and wings are cinnamon-rufous. The leading edges of the primaries are pale straw. There are irregular cinnamon patches along the flanks, the underwing-coverts are cinnamon-buff to salmon. The rump is reddish-amber graduating to deep orange on the uppertail-coverts. The edges of the uppertail-coverts are straw. The irides are chestnut or red to dark red (Gilliard and Le Croy 1966) The bill, legs and feet are pale blue-grey.

Adult female 110–115mm. Wing length 50–52mm. The bill is usually slightly less massive, culmen 13mm. Plumage similar to male.

Juvenile Like that of *L. g. heurni.*

GREAT-BILLED MANNIKIN

L. grandis destructa   **Plate 65**

Hartert, 1930, *Novit. Zool.*, 36, p. 42

This is the largest of the four races.

Adult male 130–145mm. Wing length 56–62mm. The culmen of the massive bill is 16–19mm, with a depth of 16–17mm, tarsus 14mm. The large head and entire underparts, except for the edges of the flanks, are jet black with a green sheen that shows well in some lights. The mantle, wings, and edges of the flanks (which may be largely covered by the folded wings, giving the appearance of the entire underparts being black) are rich deep chestnut. The rump, which starts level with the innermost tertial, is reddish-orange, the uppertail-coverts are orange, the edges of the tail broadly edged with yellow. The underwing-coverts are salmon. The irides are chestnut. The bill is pale blue-grey with paler to white cutting edges. The legs and feet are pale blue-grey.

Adult female 125–135mm. Wing length 53–56mm. The bill is massive but noticeably smaller than that of a large male, culmen 14–15mm and usually *c.*14mm

144

deep, tarsus 13–14mm.The apparent variation in the amount of chestnut on the flanks is not a sexual difference but in general the reddish-orange of the rump starts level with the second tertial.

Juvenile Similar in colouring to that of *L. g. heurni*. I have not seen them side by side but would expect juvenile *L. g. destructa* to be slightly larger.

HEURN'S GRAND MANNIKIN
L. grandis heurni   Plate 66
Hartert, 1932, Nova Guinea, *Zool.*, 15, p. 476.
Adult male *c*.130mm. Wing length 54–57mm. The massive bill has the culmen 16mm, and is about 16mm deep, tarsus 15mm. The entire head and underparts, except for some irregular chestnut on the flanks, are jet black with a slight green gloss. The mantle, back, lower back, wings and flanks maroon-chestnut. The rump is a clearly defined bar of reddish-orange, the uppertail-coverts clearly defined orange-yellow, the edges of the tail straw. The bill is pale blue-grey with white cutting edges. The irides are chestnut. The legs and feet are blue-grey.
Adult female 115–120mm. Wing length 53mm. Culmen 13mm with a depth of 13–14mm, tarsus is 12–14mm. In other respects it resembles the male.
Juvenile Similar to juveniles of *L. g. destructa* and *L. g. ernesti*. It is blackish on the face and forecrown, becoming brown on the crown and this colour extends to the lower back and wings. The wing coverts and flight feathers are edged slightly paler. The rump and uppertail-coverts are light brown. The tail is brown. The chin is whitish with dark edgings. From throat to breast it is light drab with dark streaks. The belly, flanks, underwing-coverts, thighs and undertail-coverts are all dull buff. The bill is grey, possibly paler on the cutting edges.

From the above descriptions it is obvious that males of the species range from 115mm to over 140mm, and females from 110–135mm. The difference within a race may be as much as 20mm but in my experience of them in captivity, females average 10% shorter than males. When compared to Chestnut Munia, with which it has a certain superficial resemblance, it is a more upright-standing bird, a factor that when combined with the larger head and bill, tends to increase the impression of size of Grand Mannikin. The brown on the flanks of the races is variable in appearance, depending on how much is covered by the folded wings. However this is not an indication of sex.

HYBRIDS A 'probable hybrid' between a Grand Mannikin and a Chestnut-breasted Mannikin is reported by Coates (1990) and repeated by Clement *et al.* (1993). The source of this rather improbable hybrid is a report by Tolhurst (1987) of the Pacific Adventist College near Port Moresby. The original description is given thus: "...The head, throat and chest were all dark: black or grey. The dark colour of the chest was uniform and extended well down, about half way down the front of the body. The cut-off line for dark colour was quite distinct. The belly was white. There was no chestnut on the front of the bird at all. At first I thought it might be a Black-breasted Mannikin *L. teerinki*. However it seems to be unlikely as this species is listed as being a mountain resident, found from 1,000 feet upwards. The College Campus is at only about 150m. The bird did not look like an immature Grey-headed Mannikin which is often seen on Campus. The

only other possibility would be an immature Chestnut-breasted Mannikin."

It is significant that Tolhurst, an experienced bird watcher who was very familiar with the birds of his area, including Grand Mannikin, thought that this might be a Black-breasted Mannikin which does not even occur in Papua New Guinea, rather than a Grand Mannikin which can be found only a short drive from the College. If there is any probability about this specimen it is that it was a Chestnut-breasted Mannikin that had the breast black instead of brown.

CONSERVATION There is not enough information about population densities, trends in populations, or any factors affecting habitat to be able to draw any conclusions about any conservation needs of the species. Trapping for the bird trade is small, with shipments of birds numbering in the dozens, judging from those I have been able to trace in Jakarta. These birds are almost invariably taken from populations in the region of Jayapura only.

REFERENCES Baptista (1990 & 1995), Clement *et al.* (1993), Diamond & LeCroy (1979), Gilliard & LeCroy, (1966), Oppenborn (1987), Rand (1942), Rand & Gilliard (1967), Restall (1989 & 1995a), Rudiger (1981), Smith (1991), Tolhurst (1987).

---

25   GREY-BANDED MANNIKIN
Lonchura vana   Plate 9

Former Scientific name: *Munia vana* Hartert, 1930, *Novit. Zool*, 36, p.42.
Other common name: Arfak Mannikin.

Grey-banded Mannikin

FIELD CHARACTERS This is a medium-sized grey-headed, mid-brown munia with the upper breast divided by a whitish band, and yellow uppertail-coverts and tail. It is the only mannikin occuring in the Vogelkop region of Irian Jaya and is unlikely to be confused with any other bird.

STATUS Scarce (Bostock, in Collar *et al.* 1994) or very rare (Gibbs, in Collar *et al.* 1994).

HABITAT It is described by Beehler *et al.* (1986) as being a shy inhabitant of mid-montane grasslands.

HABITS AND BEHAVIOUR No information.

FOOD AND FEEDING Nothing recorded.

MOVEMENTS Nothing known.

CALL The call is a high, thin *ts ts ts* (Beehler *et al.* 1986).

SONG Nothing has been described.

COURTSHIP AND DISPLAY Nothing known.

BREEDING Nothing known.

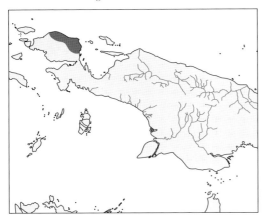

Distribution of Grey-banded Mannikin.

DISTRIBUTION It is found at high elevations, from 1,800 to 2,100m or more in the Anggi Lakes area, in the Arfak and Tamrau Mountains in the Vogelkop, north-western Irian Jaya.

DESCRIPTION
Monotypic.
Adult male 100–105mm. The entire head is a pale, drab grey, whitish around the forehead, eyes and lores. The mantle and wings are russet, The rump, uppertail-coverts, two central rectrices and broad edges to the tail are straw or creamy-yellow. The breast is drab, and scallopings of this continue more or less around the side of the neck and divide the nape from the mantle. The drab of the breast may extend to fully cover the nape. Immediately below the breast, dividing it from the cinnamon belly, flanks, vent and undertail-coverts, is a bar of the same grey as the head. The underparts are described as chestnut by Rand and Gilliard (1967), light chestnut or warm orange-brown by Clement *et al.* (1993) and brown by Beehler *et al.* (1986), but the museum specimens that I examined were definitely cinnamon. Goodwin (1982) states that the underparts may be intermixed with black but I did not see this on museum specimens I examined. The undertail-coverts may be tipped with black. The irides are dark brown. The bill, legs and feet are grey or dark grey.
   In the AMNH collection a male from Lake Anggi Gidji had the breast bar the same brown as the mantle. The belly was cinnamon with the narrow bar separating the breast from the belly the same white as the face. The crown was only slightly paler than the mantle. Another male had the crown and nape lighter, scalloped with the pale of the forehead. It seems that the adult plumage is variable, probably depending on age.
Adult female Resembles the male. It is possible there are differences between the sexes at the same age, but there is insufficient material available for study.
Juvenile Greyish-brown to drab from crown and nape to

lower back, darker on the wings and tail, with tawny on the rump and uppertail-coverts. It is light warm buff below, lightest on the throat. Clement *et al.* (1993) describe it as generally brown on upperparts with a grey-brown tinge to head and face, dull greyish-buff on the breast washed with pale yellowish on flanks and belly. A male in the AMNH collection, apparently in first-year plumage, had fawn showing on the long uppertail-coverts but no yellow. The breast bar of this bird is patchy on a fawn ground colour. The crown is scalloped with the pale of the forehead.

CONSERVATION Virtually nothing is known about this species, its habits or habitat. It has occurred at least once in captivity (Tay 1989) but I was unable to trace the source or route of supply. CITES Annual Report data (1994) showed that 700 birds appeared in the trade in 1986, but since the country of origin for 200 of these was listed as Senegal it is not even certain they were *L. vana*. There is no regular nor organised trade in wildlife from the Vogelkop and dealers in Jakarta say it is not possible to get birds from the Arfak region. It is rated Vulnerable in the Globally Threatened Species section of *Birds to Watch 2* (Collar *et al.* 1994).

REFERENCES Beehler *et al.* (1986), Clement *et al.* (1993), Collar *et al.* (1994), Goodwin (1982), Rand & Gillard (1967), Tay (1989).

26   GREY-HEADED MANNIKIN
Lonchura caniceps   Plate 12

Described as *Lonchura caniceps* Salvadori

Grey-headed Mannikins

TAXONOMY From the number of undescribed populations which are possibly new subspecies, it is obvious that this species merits serious and comprehensive field work.

FIELD CHARACTERS It is a dark, thickset munia with a grey head and noticeable bright orange uppertail-coverts. Within its range it is unlikely to be confused with any other species. It flocks and feeds with Chestnut-breasted Mannikins and it might not be easy to distinguish the juveniles from each other, particularly if they are moulting.

STATUS Common to locally common.

HABITAT It is a bird of grassland and savanna scrub, pockets of savanna in rainforest areas, pockets of swamp rice and any open man-made area where grasses will grow.

HABITS AND BEHAVIOUR I have seen it in small groups of half-a-dozen birds and in mixed flocks of up to 50 or so birds, perhaps a third of which were Chestnut-breasted Mannikins *L. castaneothorax ramsayi*. This was in July. Rand and Gilliard (1967) mention a flock of several hundred birds in June. When roosting, Grey-headed Mannikins clump, perching in actual contact with each other.

FOOD AND FEEDING It feeds on grass seeds, either on the stem or picking up seeds from the ground. I have seen it feeding on apparently dead *Rottboellia exaltata* extracting the large seeds from the dry heads. On one occasion I watched a single bird sitting in a bare sapling standing out of dense tall, dry grass by the roadside, it sang a simple advertisement song, then after 5 minutes or so flew down into the grass and disappeared. I carefully waded into the grass, which was about 1.5m high wondering if I might find a nest, when I flushed a small party of birds that had been feeding on the open ground beneath the grass which, although it was a matted mess at waist level and upwards, had plenty of space at ground level where the grass grew in thick-based clumps. In such circumstances it is easy to overlook the presence of the species.

In a swampy area overgrown with tall *Setaria* grass, I found Grey-headed Mannikins climbing with agility on the thick stems of the *Setaria* to the level of the seeding heads of the feral millet *Pannicum maximus*. They would reach out and feed on the seeds of the millet, grasping a stem in the bill and pulling it close so that by shifting a foot the millet stem could be grasped along with the *Setaria* stem. On other occasions I watched flocks descend to the ground and hop among and around such short grasses as goose grass *Eleusine indica* and *Eragrostis* sp., picking up seeds from the ground. Some birds were observed jumping up in the air to grasp the seeding heads then falling back to the ground with a head of grass held in the bill. These birds would then usually stand on the stem and peck out the seeding heads. We netted two mixed flocks totalling about 60 birds for banding and photography (and to select some specimens for me to paint) and found their crops were swollen with seeds that could easily be seen through the stetched translucent skin. The flocks comprised a mixture of adults and juveniles equally.

MOVEMENTS Somewhat nomadic (Filewood 1969, and Coates 1990). From personal observations in the Port Moresby area it seems to spread to the coastal area in the wetter part of the year, and retreat into the foothills and lusher interior in the dry season. Its movements are seemingly erratic, but obviously connected to food supplies.

CALL The contact call is a sharp *peet* and there is a slight tonal difference between the call of the male and that of the female. The contact call in flight is a *pziiitt*. When the birds are close by each other it is a shorter *psit*. I kept a few birds in a cage while I painted a study plate and noticed a singular lack of variety or vocabulary in the notes used by the birds. This was in marked contrast to a collection of Chestnut-breasted Mannikins *L. c. ramsayi* I kept at the same time for the same purpose, which had a varied and complex vocabulary.

SONG Undescribed.

COURTSHIP AND DISPLAY The male in plain undirected song sits with neck stretched and head held horizontally, bill open. The crown and rear crown or nape feathers may be slightly erected. The flanks and ventral

Undirected advertisement song of Grey-headed Mannikin.

region feathers are also held away from the body. The song is uttered simply without any bobbing or leg stretching. In advertisement song the head is turned from side to side through about 50°. I have not seen the male in direct courtship, but there is a good description in Baptista (1991). During courtship the male was seen to increase the erection of the feathers of the nape and belly, and also to fluff out the feathers of the rump. The bill is pointed downwards and the head moved from side to side – as in undirected singing. When a female is close by the tail and head are both inclined towards her and the male will hop closer. In contrast to the display of Chestnut-breasted Mannikin only the feathers of the lower belly are erected (Chestnut-breasted Mannikin erects feathers up to the lower breast). The bill is held wide open while the singing continues.

Full courtship display of Grey-headed Mannikin, with nape, flanks and belly all fully fluffed out.

BREEDING The breeding season is recorded as being in the wet season from October to April. I timed my visit to Port Moresby for July, reasoning that I would find birds in every plumage phase, which proved to be the case. However, the month of June that year, 1990, was extremely wet. The monthly net rainfall was 169mm, compared to about 16mm of rain the previous June. This must have stimulated breeding behaviour for not only did I see males in advertisement song, but there were also birds clearly engaged in serious nesting behaviour. Males could be seen leaving the feeding area and flying off in determined manner carrying lengths of grass leaves. I watched one male pulling and tugging until he successfully stripped off a long seed panicle from the head of a ripe *Pannicum maximum*, and then he flew off in a strong straight line towards a bougainvillea tree in the distance. In this particular location, the grounds of the Adventist College about 17km outside Port Moresby, the favourite nesting site of Grey-headed Mannikins was in the middle of bougainvillea bushes.

The nest is an ovoid made of grasses and lined with finer smaller strips and bits of panicles. It is usually placed in dense shrubs or trees. The male collects and carries

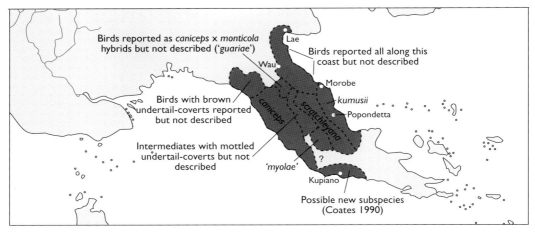

Birds reported as *caniceps* x *monticola* hybrids but not described ('*guariae*')

Birds reported all along this coast but not described

Birds with brown undertail-coverts reported but not described

Intermediates with mottled undertail-coverts but not described

Possible new subspecies (Coates 1990)

Distribution of Grey-headed Mannikin.

nesting material to the site where the female builds the nest. It is not woven, as *Lonchura* do not weave, but as each length of grass is pressed and pushed into place a certain amount of interlocking and entangling of the stems is inevitable. The normal clutch is four to six white oval eggs. It appears that both parents incubate and brood, and both are in the nest at night (Peckover and Filewood 1976). Several broods may be reared in one season.

The juveniles begin their moult into adult plumage around four months of age and complete it by six at which time they begin pairing up (Peckover and Filewood 1976).

There is a single record of the species in captivity, described to me personally by Eric Clewlow in Durban, South Africa. Clewlow kept his birds in a large planted aviary, some 14m x 3m x 2.5m high, which contained a mixed collection of small finches, waxbills, a waxwing, a robin and a sunbird. Growing in the aviary was a tall thick coarse grass, and it was in this that the mannikins built a nest. The birds were supplied with additional grasses, including a very fine one known locally as Teff grass which is very popular for nest building. The food supplied was a standard seed mixture, hard boiled egg, spinach and grated carrot, and nectar. Soaked seed was also given daily.

No record exists of the nesting details, but two youngsters fledged successfully, and Clewlow remembers the parents taking soft food and soaked seed. Like many aviculturists in South Africa and Australia, when he could find termite larvae, 'white ants', he fed them to the birds, and these were taken by Grey-headed Mannikins. The breeding occurred during May and June 1985.

DISTRIBUTION This is a bird from southeastern Papua New Guinea. *L. c. caniceps* ranges along the coastal savanna of the south from Hall Sound to east of Port Moresby. *L. c. scratchleyana* is found in the mid-montane grasslands from 1,000 to 2,000m (Hicks 1987). *L. c. kumusii* occurs in the grassy lowlands of the Northern Province north into Morobe.

As indicated above, other possible races of this species may occur, and Coates (1990) casts intriguing light on the obvious need for extensive and careful field study. On the distribution map I have identified locations for the three races mentioned above together with the Myola bird described by Hicks (*in litt.*). I have been unable to examine birds, nor find museum skins, from the other locations. In the south-east Central province to Kupiano Coates

(1990) suggests the birds may be subspecifically distinct without giving details. Similarly other locations include the area of Malalana in the Gulf province where the local birds are distinguished by having brown undertail-coverts. What shade of brown? In other respects are they just like *L. c. caniceps*? The species has been recorded near Lae (King 1979) and further south between Morobe and Wau. It is possible that this population is simply an extension of *L. c. kumusii*. Finally, Coates questions the highland populations around Myola, Chirima and Garaina. I discussed these at length with Roger Hicks but unfortunately all the birds recorded were assumed to be *L. c. scratchleyana* and were banded and released without any specimens being taken. But careful details of plumage variation were recorded by Hicks using Smithe (1975) colour charts throughout, and I have an excellent colour transparency of a Myola bird taken by Hicks. This population is the one described tentatively below as '*myolae*'.

DESCRIPTION Plate 67

Three subspecies have been formally described.

GREY-HEADED MANNIKIN
L. caniceps caniceps

Former scientific name: *Munia caniceps* Salvadori, 1876, *Ann. Mus. Civ. Genova*, 9, p.38.

Adult male 110mm. Wing length 52mm, culmen 10.5mm, tarsus 13mm. The entire head to nape and lower throat is smoke-grey to glaucous, olive-grey on the nape which quickly changes to dark russet on the back and wings. The rump is orange, blending to a fiery chrome-orange on the uppertail-coverts and edges of the tail. The glaucous of the throat graduates into a dark violaceous-grey on breast and flanks, to black on belly, vent and undertail-coverts. The underwing-coverts are buffy-yellow. The irides are dark brown while the eyelids are dark violaceous-grey. The bill is black with a pale blue-grey base to the lower mandible. The legs and feet are blackish.

Adult female 105mm. Wing length 48mm, culmen 9.5mm, tarsus 11mm. Said to be duller than the male but otherwise similar. In my experience with birds in the field and confirmed during a visit to the museum in Port Moresby (Restall 1991) the adult female is very similar to the male but the rump and uppertail-coverts are entirely chrome-orange, beginning at the level of the third tertial (compared to a brighter more yellowish-orange of the male's rump beginning level with the first tertial). There is also a tendency for the axilliaries of the female to be tinged with brown.

First-year Plumage is slightly duller and has the skin of the eye-ring blue-grey.

Juvenile 100mm. The head and back are fawn with some fine darker streaking on the top of the head, ear-coverts and mesial. The wings and tail are cinnamon-brown. The rump and uppertail-coverts are warmer, tending to amber. Below it is a light clay colour, paler on the chin, warmer on the undertail-coverts. The underwing-coverts are warm buffy-yellow. The irides are dark chestnut with the eye-ring blue-grey. The bill is black with a pale base to the lower mandible. The legs and feet are dark grey.

SHARPE'S GREY-HEADED MANNIKIN
L. caniceps scratchleyana
Former scientific name: *Munia scratchleyana* Sharpe, 1898, *Bull. Brit. Orn. Club*, 7, p.60.
Adult Head pale olive-grey, merging into dark tawny, often with some darker scalloping on the back and wings. The rump, uppertail-coverts and edges of the tail are buffy orange-yellow. The grey of the throat darkens to glaucous and becomes cinnamon-grey on the lower breast, belly and flanks. The lower belly, ventral area, thighs and undertail-coverts are dark greyish-brown or black (This might be indicative of sex difference) not light fulvous-brown as described by Coates (1990).

L. c. caniceps x *L. c. scratchleyana* intermediates
Coates refers to presumed intermediates between *L. c. caniceps* and *L. c. scratchleyana* as having the undertail-coverts patchily marked with black and brown. This is odd, because both races have very dark undertail-coverts and brown patches with black is the last characteristic one would expect in an intermediate between the two. Where would the brown come from? This population needs to be properly described.

HARTERT'S GREY-HEADED MANNIKIN
L. caniceps kumusii
Former scientific name: *Munia caniceps kumusii* Hartert, 1911, *Bull. Brit. Orn. Club*, 27, p.47
Adult Similar to *L. c. scratchleyana* but the back is a darker brown or russet. In the specimens I examined in the British Museum collection the birds were a darker grey on the nape, sides of neck and breast, with scalloping onto both mantle and lower breast. The belly and flanks were also greyer, described by Clement *et al.* (1993) as dark or slate-brown.

MYOLA GREY-HEADED MANNIKIN
L. caniceps 'myolae'
Adult Head, nape and lower throat smoky-grey, mottled on the forehead, crown and nape. The back and wings are warm brown, slightly paler towards the tail. The wings are dark brown. The rump and uppertail-coverts are buff. The breast and flanks are greyish-horn. The belly is jet black. The underwing-coverts are pale horn. The bill is blackish-grey with the base of the lower mandible a violaceous-grey. Hicks (*in litt.*) noted an interesting variation in plumage on the thigh, with some birds having a mottled thigh and others being plain. Those with plain thighs were larger

in all or most of the key measurements and might have been males.

GUARI GREY-HEADED MANNIKIN
L. caniceps 'guariae'
Coates (1990) refers to the local population at Guari as showing signs of hybridisation with *L. monticola* but gives no details. A comparison between the two species suggests that the characteristics on *L. caniceps* that would remind one of *L. monticola* would most likely be black on the face. Clearly this population has to be properly described.

HYBRIDS Grey-headed Mannikin has apparently hybridised with Chestnut-breasted Mannikin (Peckover and Filewood 1976).

CONSERVATION There is no cause for concern for the status of this species.

REFERENCES Baptista (1991), Clement *et al.* (1994), Coates (1990), Filewood (1979), Hicks (1987), King (1979), Peckover & Filewood (1976), Rand & Gilliard (1967), Restall (1991), Smithe (1975).

27 GREY-CROWNED MANNIKIN
Lonchura nevermanni   Plate 14

Former scientific name: *Munia nevermanni* Stresemann, 1934, *Ornith. Monatsb.*, 42, p.101.
Other common names: White-crowned Munia or Mannikin.

Grey-crowned Mannikin

FIELD CHARACTERS This is a medium-sized munia with a greyish-white head, black bib, and brown body. This is the only pale-headed munia in its area of distribution and it is unlikely to be confused with any other species. The juvenile would be impossible to tell apart from juvenile Black Mannikin *L. stygia* in the field. On close comparison, juvenile Grey-crowned Mannikin is a warm buffy colour while juvenile Black Mannikin is greyish-brown. There might be confusion with juvenile Crimson Finch *Neochima phaeton*, but the latter's more slender form and hint of red wash on the brown would separate it.

STATUS Common or locally common.

HABITAT It is primarily a bird of grassy marshland, found in reedbeds and grass banks along the sides of the rivers in the Trans-Fly in south-western Irian Jaya and Papua New Guinea. It usually occurs in groups in tall densely-grassed savanna, and can also be seen on the floating mats of rice grass in lagoons, flooded areas and rice fields.

HABITS AND BEHAVIOUR Within the more restricted range of Black Mannikin, the two species are usually found together, but Grey-crowned Mannikin is more numerous. It has a habit of stretching upwards with head at a normal angle, looking around alertly, when the head takes on an arrowhead appearance. The first moult is at 10–12 weeks. Males can be told at this stage by their vocalisations and young first-year males that look quite like females often stretch and display briefly in undirected advertisement song. I have noticed that unwell birds have a habit of standing or perching with the feathers of the nape raised, giving the impression the bird is hunched.

Unwell Grey-crowned Mannikin in 'hunched' position.

Non-breeding birds are very sociable and will all roost together in a tight clump or in a single nest box. This is one of the species of munia I have seen allopreening. Peering is a common phenomenon, and an undirected singing male will usually attract one or more peerers if they are all sitting up in a roosting tree or similar situation during the day.

FOOD AND FEEDING It habitually feeds on the seeds of growing grasses, climbing up and down the stems with great agility, often grasping several stems together as it flies onto them, thus securing a firm hold from which to select the seeding heads. Clement (*et al.* 1993) says it feeds largely on the ground. Neff (1979) found it necessary to provide ant pupae and other insect food, half-ripe wheat and millet, as well as soaked seed and chickweed when rearing young in captivity. However, birds I have bred in cages reared their young perfectly well on a diet of hard seeds, fresh seeding grasses, lettuce and canary rearing food.

MOVEMENTS Nothing recorded.

CALL The call made within the group is a single syllable *tseet*. The louder contact call is a double syllable *ps-eet*! Gregory (1995a) noted a musical *tink tink* from birds observed at Lake Owa in Papua New Guinea. As with most, if not all munias, the call note between male and female is distinct.

SONG The complete song consists of three parts, a whisper song that is virtually inaudible to human ears, a short series of *tiks* then a complex *whheeeeeee* sound. Oreste Piotto (pers. comm.) in England, has bred Grey-crowned Mannikins and kindly passed me his notes. He considers the song very close to that of Chestnut-breasted Mannikin *L. castaneothorax*, with the last trailing note a high clear bell-like sound. Colin Rowe (pers. comm.) in England, bred both species several times and is of the same opinion.

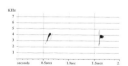
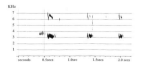

Sonograms of calls by Grey-crowned Mannikin males, soft call, left, and loud call, right.

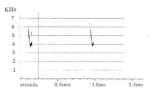

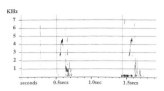

Soft call of female Grey-crowned Mannikin, above, and loud call, below.

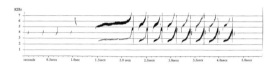

Sonogram of the song of Grey-crowned Mannikin. The opening *tik tik tik trik* is followed by the main song.

COURTSHIP AND DISPLAY Goodwin's (1982) description of the display as beginning with flying or hopping to and fro from perch to perch, I take to be observations of birds in cages or small enclosures. I suspect this is a function of confinement. In the wild or in a large aviary, where behaviour might be expected to be a little more natural, this is more likely to be manifest in chasing. In my own observations the male 'pushes' a female with a length of straw of similar material in his bill and perches alongside her. If he senses she is at all receptive he will drop the straw and begin displaying. Another behaviour I have observed several times is of a male grasping a length of grass at one end when he is in the company of his mate. He will fly off either to a chosen nest site, or a perch near it, and turn to see if she is following; if not he will return to her side and repeat the action, all the while carrying the material. What usually happens is that the female will fly to what she clearly has chosen as a nest site of greater potential or more to her liking and he will follow her. In my experience the female always dominates in this incident, the function of the male's abortive efforts being apparently to stimulate the female.

In undirected singing the male will sit upright, head pointing down, with flanks and belly feathers erect, singing without further ado. Peering may occur if this happens in a crowded social situation. The head may turn from side to side while singing (Meyer 1978) although I have not noticed this to be a noticeable feature of the display.

In full intensity display, a male includes all the elements of the straw display (Baptista and Horblit 1990). When perched alongside his bonded female he will sit slightly stretched upward but with head pointed down, giving an impressive 'arrowhead' shape to the head, the feathers of the nape, lower breast, belly and flanks erect. The bill opens and his tail is twisted a little towards her, as is his head. He bobs in a series of jerks in the inverted curtsey of Morris (1958), and then bows, turned towards her with tail twisted in her direction. If responsive enough she will lower herself and solicit copulation by tail quivering. Following copulation there will be some bill-fencing and allopreening. Oreste Piotto and Colin Rowe both consider the display of Grey-crowned Mannikin to be very much like that of Chestnut-breasted Mannikin.

Male singing at full intensity.

BREEDING The nest is built of grasses and reed leaves, etc., and is usually built among thickly-growing reeds or grasses. Some leaves of the growing stems may be built into the structure thus anchoring it well to avoid slipping as a result of movement of the stems by wind. The entrance is at one end with very little entrance porch. It is lined with fine stems and fibres. The male brings most of the material for the nest and the female does most of the building (Neff 1979). The male arrives with a length of material, passes it to the female who sits where the centre of the nest cavity is or will be and then pushes and pulls the material in position. She has usually accomplished this by the return of the male, which may be within a minute or two, but if not, the fresh material is simply included in the work. Once completed each bird continues to add fine pieces of fibre or lining material each time it returns to the nest and this continues throughout incubation (Plose pers. comm.).

Both sexes share in the incubation. The clutch numbers from 3–6 white oval eggs with 5 being usual. Incubation is recorded as 12–16 days in captivity with 13 apparently normal. Both sexes brood during the day, but only the female broods at night. The young are naked, flesh-coloured and have typical white *Lonchura* gape markings (Ehmke, in Nachrichten 1979). The gape marking of birds I bred in captivity had a simple inverted horseshoe marking on the upper palate.

They beg for food in the typical estrildid manner, wave their heads from side to side with gape open and tongues lifted. Their eyes open at 7–9 days from which time the parents no longer brood them continually. After this period the nestlings beg for food quite loudly. At least one parent continues to brood or roost with the young at night, probably the female, until they fledge at about 21 days. They continue to roost in the nest for a while after fledging. Neff reported that his parent birds led the young back to the nest to be fed for the first few days. In my experience they roosted naturally in the nest after fledging, but there was no way to tell if the parents led or called the young to the nest.

The young begin sampling and chewing seeds quite soon after fledging but are not feeding independently before two weeks. They soon wander off to join other immatures and form small compact groups of birds that wander about foraging for food.

Palate markings of nestling Grey-crowned Mannikin x Bengalese.

DISTRIBUTION New Guinea south of a line from Frederik Hendrik Island in the south-west, north to Lake Daviumbu and eastwards to the Fly River and Balimo.

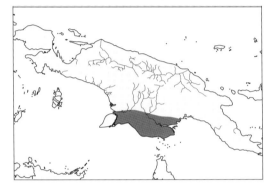

Distribution of Grey-crowned Mannikin.

DESCRIPTION   **Plate 68**
Monotypic.

Adult male 115–118mm. Wing length 55mm, culmen 11mm, tarsus 14–16mm. The forehead, crown, supercilium lores, ear-coverts and base of mesial white or whitish, with considerable variation from bird to bird. The crown to nape is washed heavily with fuscous, but the feathers, especially those on the nape, are edged with pale grey. The mantle, back and wings are umber (deep earth-brown). The rump is chrome orange, the uppertail-coverts and edges of the tail feathers are orange-yellow. The bib, mesial (except the base) and a small part of the collar below the ear-coverts are black. The breast, flanks and belly are cinnamon-rufous, and the underwing-coverts are a paler version of the same. The thighs, vent and undertail-coverts are black. The bill is blue-grey above, pale blue-grey below with white cutting edges. The irides are brown. The legs and feet dark blue-grey.

Adult female 110–115mm. Wing length 52mm, culmen 10mm, tarsus 12–14mm. The white of the head is restricted to the forehead, the fuscous of the crown beginning above the eye and the feathers having pale grey edges. As with the male, there is considerable variation from bird to bird. Older birds tend to be paler on the crown, lores and ear-coverts.

The species has a propensity to melanism, with individuals of either sex showing areas of black from bold spots on the upper breast or lower belly, to almost entire black underparts, and black on the rump with black spots on the uppertail-coverts.

First-year Forehead, supercilium and crown grey, the lores, ear-coverts, hind crown and nape are fuscous with darker centres and pale edges to the feathers, and the quill shafts of the ear-coverts are pale grey; the bib and mesial are black with brown edging to the feathers. The mantle is darker brown than the wings. The median and greater wing-coverts mat be edged with cinnamon. The under-parts are not so richly coloured as in the second-year adult and the feathers are edged slightly paler, usually only no-ticeable in the hand. The bill is an even blue-grey on both mandibles with paler cutting edges. Males in this plumage usually have the forehead and forecrown paler grey to whitish than females. This plumage is attained in the first year, not the second year as in Clement *et al.* (1993). It is very easy to mistake a first-year male for a female.

Juvenile Sandy-cinnamon or warm brown above, with the wings and tail fawn. Mees (1982) describes it as ochraceous-tawny below and overall darker than typical juvenile munias, but I would say the colours are warmer than on other juvenile munias. The rump is the same warm tawny of the breast and flanks. The bill is very pale on fledging but soon becomes grey.

HYBRIDS The record of an apparent hybrid between Grey-crowned Mannikin and Black Mannikin (Mees 1982) led Goodwin not only to question whether they might be conspecific, but to conjecture that Black Mannikin might be a dark morph of Grey-crowned Mannikin. This seems highly unlikely to me, not only on grounds of distribu-tion, but also because of behaviour. I have come across several individual Grey-crowned Mannikins that showed additional black and have included some of these in the identification plate in this book. From a bird dealer's ship-ment from Merauke I selected one that was very close to Mees' hybrid (see plate 14 and Restall 1993). My belief is that Mees' hybrid was a pure *L. nevermanni*, albeit melan-istic. The juveniles of the two species are quite different from each other, although they appear very similar in the field.

In a large aviary and bird room in England I had two unpaired male Grey-crowned Mannikins that persistently courted a female Black-breasted Mannikin *L. teerinki* while ignoring a single female Black Mannikin. I twice watched these two males hopping about a large tray of screenings with Black Mannikin and one of them hopped up to a ledge and began undirected singing actually facing away from her. In Hong Kong I have placed several juveniles of both species together and kept them through the moult but they have paired up preferring their own species, with two young male Grey-crowned Mannikins bonding to-gether. I failed to persuade the two species to hybridise. In conclusion, I agree with Mees (1982) that the two are good and distinct species and that Grey-crowned Manni-kin is possibly closer to Chestnut-breasted Mannikin than to Black Mannikin.

I cross-bred Grey-crowned Mannikin with Bengalese. The offspring were dark-faced, earth-brown above, and were evenly barred on the white underparts. Barring of the underparts is a common characteristic of munia hy-brids. They were quite distinct from Black Mannikin x Bengalese hybrid.

CONSERVATION The trade in estrildid finches from Merauke is steady, but not large. From my observations it does not pose a threat to the species. There is no sugges-tion that destruction of habitat is occurring, and I see no cause for concern about this species.

REFERENCES Baptista & Horblit (1990), Clement *et al.* (1993), Goodwin (1982), Gregory (1995a), Mees (1982), Meyer (1978), Morris (1958), Neff (1979), Restall (1989 & 1993).

28　HOODED MANNIKIN
Lonchura spectabilis　　　　　Plate 13

Described as *Lonchura spectabilis* Sclater
Other common names: Hooded Munia, New Britain Man-nikin or Munia, Sclater's Mannikin.

Hooded Mannikin

FIELD CHARACTERS A small munia that is whitish below, brown above and has a golden to orange rump. It is un-likely to be confused with any other bird within its range. The juvenile is similar in appearance to the much larger juvenile Grand Mannikin *L. grandis* but the significant difference in size between the two, and the proportionately larger bill of the latter should prevent any confusion.

It is a species deserving specialised study. I have recog-nised eight distinct forms, some of which do not have a type specimen, and only five have been properly described. The species has a remarkable propensity for plumage variation, and within distinct geographic types there is variation both among adults and juveniles. A pure white bird was described by Gregory-Smith and Gregory-Smith (1989) at Menyamya in Morobe Province.

STATUS Locally scarce (New Britain), locally common, or common (New Guinea).

HABITAT It is a bird of foothills and mid-montane grass-land, being particularly fond of land that has been cleared by man and which has produced a fine crop of feral millets and other grasses.

HABITS AND BEHAVIOUR It may be found in flocks of up to 30 or 40 individuals (Meyer 1930) and in central New Guinea, Diamond (1967) found the species so un-wary of man that it could be stalked and caught by hand.

In my experience a bonded pair stay close together, the male keeping sentinel, alert for danger, while his mate feeds. When bathing he will stay alert, waiting for her to bathe first. When she flies off, he follows immediately. I have often seen the male preening the female, both when sitting together, and when clumped with other Hooded Mannikins. However, I have not observed mutual preen-ing or allopreening. To the best of my observations preen-ing of members within a flock has only been of a male to his mate. The male of a pair will sing frequently as they move around, foraging or being part of a social group.

The song is undirected, and seems to function primarily as bond reinforcement communication. The male will also give an advertisement song from the entrance of the nest, directed at the female nearby, who, incidentally usually appears to be indifferent.

An interesting incident of gang rape occurred in my captive study group when four new birds were introduced to an enclosure that was occupied by three males. The first bird out flew up to join the three residents and was immediately raped by first one male and then another. The bird, a female, was then allowed to sit among the group, looking somewhat cowed. Exactly the same routine happened to the second bird (which also turned out to be female). The third bird resisted, standing up to its attacker, bill-fencing vigorously. It was sung to in high intensity by each one of the resident males in turn who attempted but failed to rape it. This third newcomer turned out to be a male and so was the fourth who suffered a similar but not so intense repeat of the third bird's experience.

Peering occurs and a peering bird may lean so close as to almost touch the singing bird. Peering-enforced singing (Restall 1995a) occurs. This is when one male leans almost menacingly over another male that has recently sung, in an exaggerated peering posture, thereby intimidating the second bird to sing again.

FOOD AND FEEDING Baptista (1990) observed it in numbers feeding on the seeds of the introduced grass *Rottboellia exaltata* a species that may grow as high as 2 metres or more and which produces seeds as large as rice grains. Although the leaves and stems were brown in most of the plants, the seeds were green and milky. The bills of some of the mannikins were stained green, apparently from eating the half-ripe seed heads. *Rottboellia* is a recent introduction in New Guinea, but Baptista found it growing abundantly at Baitabag and Nital where it is evidently an important food source for these mannikins and may be a factor in the apparently increasing distribution of the species in some areas of northern New Guinea. They habitually feed by clinging to the stems of the growing grasses and plucking seeds from the inflorescences. Immelmann *et al.* (1968-72) state that grass pollen is the most important food, although grass seeds are also taken. This reference had always puzzled me until I was able to discuss it with Immelmann in person. It turned out that he was referring to the habit if not preference of most *Lonchura* spp. to eat grass seeds while they are still latent and in flower with prominent beads of pollen showing. It does not refer to pollen-eating in the sense that the birds actively seek pollen to eat from flowers.

According to the Kalam people, Hooded Mannikins are very fond of the algae that forms a scum on stagnant pools and puddles, and the local boys will shoot them at these sites when the birds are on the ground preoccupied with their feeding. In their charmingly anecdotal book of the birds in the Kalam country, Majnep and Bulmer (1977) say the species is common in the grasslands and garden areas where there is *Thermedaor ischaemum* grass. They say that "...most people will eat (Hooded Mannikins) but some adult men will not, and neither on the whole will the young unmarried or newly-married men and women....because the mannikin has big families, and newly-married people don't want to have a whole lot of children very fast."

MOVEMENTS Apparently generally sedentary (Clement *et al.* 1993).

CALL The normal contact notes are *peep* or *seep*, and are similar when given by either sex. The loud call note is distinctively different between male and female, and it is comparatively easy to separate the sexes in this way. The loud call of the female is a double-noted *sileep!* or *tsilip!* The loud call of the male is a clear single note *seep!* or *tseep!*. *L. s. sepikensis* has a thin down-slurred *zeee zeee* (Jonkers and Roesma 1990).

SONG The song appears to consist almost entirely of a series of high-pitched *weee* notes. After pumping up several *weees* the male may produce up to 20 or 30 *peee* notes, one after another. There is a soft, more complex subsong, uttered by a male both in a social situation or when alone.

Hooded Mannikin in undirected advertisement song.

COURTSHIP AND DISPLAY Hooded Mannikin has much of the straw display (Baptista and Horblit 1990) in its repertoire, but some parts are modified and others missing. An unpaired male in fine healthy condition will sing advertisement songs directed at apparently nothing in particular. He will begin singing with his head level, and bill opening and closing and a slight hint of bobbing, but the body soon becomes motionless. This appears to be an atrophied version of the inverted curtsey (Morris 1958), which is often missing altogether from the high intensity display, only occurring when the male is actually hopping closer to the female.

High intensity display of Hooded Mannikin. When a female is alongside, the male lowers himself and edges along the perch and twists towards her.

In directed display the male may preface his display by flying about with a bit of nesting material (Goodwin 1982) but I have never seen this as a significant or contributory factor in my observations of the bird. An enthusiastic, promiscuous male, engaged in opportunistic courtship, will approach another bird regardless of sex or species. He will begin to sing with body mainly upright, head pointed towards the bird or, if he has landed between two birds, with the head staight forward. The head is held level or slightly downward, the throat is pumping and the *weee*

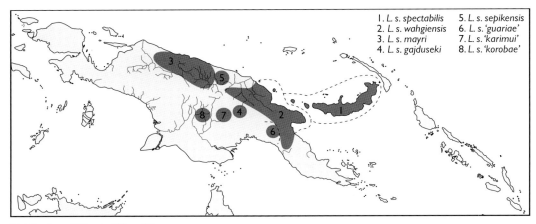

Distribution of Hooded Mannikin.

1. *L. s. spectabilis*   5. *L. s. sepikensis*
2. *L. s. wahgiensis*   6. *L. s. 'guariae'*
3. *L. s. mayri*   7. *L. s. 'karimui'*
4. *L. s. gajduseki*   8. *L. s. 'korobae'*

becomes pulsating. The flanks and belly feathers are fluffed out. In the final stage of this display the head is stretched up fully, the bill is held wide open without any movement of the mandibles and the head is turned from side to side. He then edges towards her as if with intention to mount.

When a female is alongside he will edge towards her, maybe with little hops, and, turning from left to right with a slight bobbing, will bend forward with the bill held open. There is no noticeable movement and the song is a continual high-pitched trill. The male will sing while sitting in the nest, head poking out, apparently to attract a female to the nest, or to call in his mate if she is within sight or sound.

In the last part of the high intensity display of Hooded Mannikin, the bill is held open and there is no body movement. This is when the high extended *peeeeeeeeee* part of the song is uttered.

BREEDING "They nest at the time the taro is setting its new shoots (in about October) and may lay five or six eggs, occasionally seven. If you find a nest with droppings in it, you'll know that a whole family are using it for a roost, and you can catch them there. We call this a young men's house. And, as with Chestnut Rail *Rallicula forbesi*, if you kill one and leave it in a roost others gather to mourn over it, and you catch a lot that way" (Majnep and Bulmer 1977).

The nest is a flattish ovoid of grasses, straw and finer stems, panicles and fibres. It is placed in grasses or in a bush, and the choice of site undoubtedly influences the size and shape of the nest, as with most munias. Neff (1971 and 1972) records that in some nests his birds built in captivity, there was an area immediately opposite the

entrance hole where the wall of the nest was extremely thin. When he blocked the entrance of the nest with his hand the sitting bird escaped through this weak part of the opposite wall. I have not observed this feature in any nest built by birds in my care.

The clutch is 3–5 tiny white eggs thicker at one end than the other. Those laid by my birds were more like those of a Guillemot *Uria aalge* egg in shape than a blunt-ended oval usual with estridids. Incubation is about 14 days and the young fledge in three weeks.

The nestlings of birds bred in captivity have been reared on a vegetable diet, no doubt soft green unripe seeds and flowering grasses, etc. There is no evidence whether wild birds take any insect food for themselves or when feeding their young.

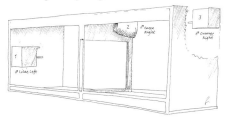

Two metre long cage in which three pairs of Hooded Mannikin nested.

DISTRIBUTION Nominate *L. s. spectabilis* comes from the island of New Britain, Long Island and Rooke Island. The remaining races all occur on mainland New Guinea. Only one race, *L. s. mayri*, is known to occur in Irian Jaya, ranging from the northern lowlands of the Lake Sentani area and the Cyclops Mountains across into western East Sepik in Papua New Guinea. The yellow-rumped race, *L. s. wahgiensis*, ranges across the foothills of the Herzog, Saruwaged and Bismarck Mountains of Morobe and Madang Provinces. What appear to be recently evolved races are *L. s. gajduseki* in the eastern part of Chimbu Province, *L. s. 'karimui'* in the western part of Chimbu, *L. s. sepikensis* in the Sepik plains and two undescribed, tentatively new races I have not been able to see live or in skins, *L. s. 'korobae'* from Koroba near Lanke Kopiago, and *L. s. 'guariae'* from the Guari area in Central Province. Information concerning distribution is very limited.

Diamond (1972) believes the rapid evolution of distinct racial characteristics could have happened in as short a period as 15 years, when forest is cleared by man and left to waste, and this seems to be accepted by Jonkers and Roersma (1990). The waste land quickly begins to regenerate with grasses and the subsequent islands of new and suitable habitat are found by wandering flocks of munias. In this way small isolated populations may rapidly evolve distinctive characteristics, presumably if there is any tendency for aberration present in the limited gene pool. Jonkers and Roersma (1990) found *L. s. sepikensis* another very distinct race, in precisely such a man-made grassland in the vicinity of the Urimo cattle station in the Sepik Plains. In this case, primary rainforest had been cleared, and the soil having been exhausted and left for waste developed into scrub grassland. Recent studies of morphological changes in Darwin's Finches *Geospiza/Camarhynchus* in the Galapagos (Grant 1991) and Rock Doves *Columba livia* (Johnston 1990) show that response to changes in environment can be much faster than was supposed. It is certainly possible to establish a stable, self-perpetuating population of a variant *Lonchura* in captivity in as few as 8 years.

DESCRIPTION
Plate 69

Eight distinct forms are recognised here, but three have not been formally described.

NEW BRITAIN MANNIKIN
L. spectabilis spectabilis
Former scientific name: *Donacicola spectabilis* P.L. Sclater, 1879, *Proc. Zool. Soc. London*, p.495.

Adult male *c*.100mm. Wing length *c*.45mm, culmen 10–11mm, tarsus 14mm. The entire head is black, graduating in a series of scallops onto the mantle. The mantle, lower back, scapulars and wings are dark russet. The breast, belly and flanks are creamy-white. The rump and uppertail-coverts are rich chrome-orange. The tail is brown with orange to yellowish edges. There may be some faint brownish barring on the lower flanks or greyish barring across the upper breast and on the sides of the breast down the flanks in some birds. The ventral region, thighs and undertail-coverts are black. The bill is grey, typical munia in its proportions, slightly longer than deep, and large when compared to the other races. The legs and feet are dark grey.

This race has a form that is barred from the upper sides of the breast down the flanks. I have no information of its geographic occurrence nor whether it is an irregular or predictably occurring morph.

Adult female 90–95mm. Wing length 43mm, culmen 9–10mm, tarsus 13–14mm. The entire head is black, as is the tail, ventral region, thighs and undertail-coverts. The breast, belly and flanks are creamy-white or pale straw, and in some birds there may be faint or indistinct fine brown barring on the sides of the breast and flanks.

First-year Plumage is more buffish below and is usually slightly barred on the upper breast and flanks.

Juvenile Dark buffish to drab above, darker on the face with some dark radiations on the ear-coverts and the pale cream chin. The entire head may be brown with blackish streaking on the face and throat. The lower rump and uppertail-coverts are tawny to cinnamon. The underparts are light cream, with some fawn flush on the breast in some individuals. The bill is black while the legs and feet are grey.

MAYR'S HOODED MANNIKIN
L. spectabilis mayri
Plate 69

Former scientific name: *Munia spectabilis mayri* Hartert, 1930, *Novit. Zool.*, 36, p. 42.

Adult male 100–112mm. Wing length 47–49mm, culmen 9–10mm, tarsus 12–14mm. The entire head is black as are the tail, ventral region, thighs and undertail-coverts. The breast, belly and flanks are creamy-white or pale straw appearing white flushed with yellowish. In some individuals there is a light brown barring on the flanks. The nape, mantle, lower back and wings are brown, more amber than chestnut and there may be soft white terminal spots on the median wing-coverts, particularly in first-year birds. The rump and uppertail-coverts are light orange-ochre, halfway between yellow ochre and orange-yellow. The bill is pale blue-grey, small and stout, darker on the culmen. The irides are chestnut. The legs and feet are variable and may be vinous-grey, dark grey or even black.

Adult female 92–98mm. In other respects the sexes are alike.

First-year Usually cream below with some buffish barring on the breast and flanks, and the rump is faintly barred with brownish. Wild-caught birds that I studied in captivity had black spots on the large underwing-coverts.

Juvenile Similar to juvenile *L. s. spectabilis* but do not have dark streaking on the chin or throat.

GAJDUSEKI'S HOODED MANNIKIN
L. spectabilis gajduseki
Diamond, 1967, *Amer. Mus. Novit.*, no.2284, p.14.

Adult *c*.105mm. Wing length 49–52mm, culmen 9–10mm, tarsus 12mm. The entire head is black, as are the ventral region, thighs and undertail-coverts. The upperparts from nape to lower back, wings and tail are chestnut. The rump and uppertail-coverts are orange (midway between those of *L. s. spectabilis* and *L. s. mayri*). The breast, belly and flanks are buff-yellow. The sexes are alike.

Juvenile Resembles the juvenile *L. s. mayri.*

WAHGI HOODED MANNIKIN
L. spectabilis wahgiensis
Mayr and Gilliard, 1957, *Amer. Mus. Novit.*, no.1577, p.7.

Adult *c*.100mm. The entire head is black, graduating on the nape in a series of black scallops. The back, lower back and wings are cinnamon-brown. The rump, uppertail-coverts and edges of the tail are orange–yellow. The breast, belly and flanks are creamy-white, sometimes pale buff, and medium buff in immatures. The ventral region, thighs and undertail-coverts are black. The bill is a neat stout cone, blue-grey; the irides are chestnut; the legs and feet are variable from vinous-grey to dark grey. The sexes are alike.

Juvenile Resembles juvenile of *L. s. gajduseki.*

URIMO HOODED MANNIKIN
L. spectabilis sepikensis
Jonkers and Roersma, 1990, *Dutch Birding* 12 (1) 22-25.

Adult Measurements are not recorded. The entire head is black. The breast, belly and flanks are cinnamon with the central region and undertail-coverts black. The mantle and wing-coverts are brown, the primaries dark brown with paler brown edges to the outer webs. The uppertail-coverts and tail are orange-brown.

Juvenile Not described.

KARIMUI HOODED MANNIKIN
L. spectabilis 'karimui'

Adult *c.*95mm. The entire head is dark chocolate brown, or charcoal-brown (Clement *et al.* 1993) The upperparts from nape to lower back, wings and tail are chestnut. The rump is chrome-orange graduating into straw-yellow on the long uppertail-coverts and edges of the tail feathers. The breast, belly and flanks are warm buff. The ventral region, thighs and undertail-coverts are black.

This is the bird referred to as the dark form of *L. s. gajduseki* by Coates (1990).

KOROBA HOODED MANNIKIN
L. spectabilis 'korobae'

This bird is recorded by G.C. Clapp in Coates (1990) as having fawn underparts. In view of this quite distinctive characteristic and the isolated location of the record it merits tentative subspecific recognition subject to being properly described.

GUARI HOODED MANNIKIN
L. spectabilis 'guariae'

Coates (1990) refers to 'hybridisation occurring' between *L. spectabilis*, presumably *L. s. wahgiensis* and Alpine Mannikin *L. monticola* in the Guari area between 1,700 and 1,860m. The bird is described as having the "head and upper throat blackish, becoming dark brown on nape and hindneck; back brown; uppertail-coverts buffy-ochraceous; breast and belly buffy-ochraceous, with or without indistinct dark markings across the mid-breast and down the flanks, suggestive of the pattern found in *L. monticola.*"

HYBRIDS I am highly suspicious of presumed 'stable hybrid populations' of *Lonchura* and on principle do not accept them without irrefutable evidence. In the case of Guari Hooded Mannikin the birds described show all the characteristics of being yet another local variation of a highly variable species and not those of a hybrid. The barring that may appear on the breast and flanks is already in evidence in the species in *L. s. spectabilis* and *L. s. mayri*. It may well occur in other, or indeed all the races. I therefore take Coates' (1990) description of the Guari population as being effectively a clear indication of another distinct form of *L. spectabilis* and, subject to proper description, ascribe it provisional racial status. This position is reinforced by the physical differences between *L. spectabilis* and *L. monticola* being such that a true hybrid between them would be remarkable for showing aspects of both. Obviously detailed field work needs to be carried out and descriptions recorded.

CONSERVATION There appears to be no general cause for concern. There has been a very small trade in mannikins from northern Irian Jaya, with birds being caught in the area from Jayapura to Wamena, flown to Biak and shipped to Europe and the United States from there. In CITES Annual Report data on non-CITES species traded from 1980 to 1992, apparently only 40 Hooded Mannikins were shipped in 1988 and 15 in 1989. Since I personally saw about 75 birds in one dealer's establishment in

the UK in 1987, these data are obviously unreliable. After an initial high demand in the 1980s, the prices stayed high and demand dropped off. In 1995 I noticed a comparatively free supply of Hooded Mannikins at a comparatively low price in the trade listings in continental Europe and in the UK. This suggests a significant supply response in northern Irian Jaya to an elastic demand for a very popular cage bird; it would be as well for the shipping data to be studied carefully in the future and any unhealthy trend noted.

REFERENCES Baptista (1990), Baptista & Horblit (1990), Clement *et al.* (1993), Coates (1990), Diamond (1967 & 1972), Goodwin (1982), Grant (1991), Gregory-Smith & Gregory-Smith (1989), Immelmann *et al.* (1968-72), Johnston (1990), Jonkers & Roersma (1990), Majnep & Bulmer (1977), Meyer (1930), Morris (1958), Neff (1971 & 1972), Restall (1995a).

29   HUNSTEIN'S MANNIKIN
Lonchura hunsteini   Plate 12

Described as *Lonchura hunsteini* Finsch
Other common names: Hunstein's Munia, New Ireland Mannikin, Black-breasted Mannikin (Clements 1981), Black-breasted Weaver-finch (Pratt *et al.* 1987), Lawyer Mannikin and Mottled Munia.

Hunstein's Mannikin, adult and juvenile.

TAXONOMY The form on New Hanover island is sometimes considered to be a separate species, *L. nigerrima* (Wolters 1979, Sibley and Monroe 1990).

FIELD CHARACTERS A small black munia with orange uppertail-coverts and a pale scaling pattern on the back of the head. Neither adult nor juvenile is likely to be confused with any other species.

STATUS Locally common.

HABITAT It is usually seen in huge flocks along roadsides, in grassy fields and in cultivated areas where it is considered to be a major agricultural pest (Pratt *et al.* 1987). Finch (1886) found the birds 'in high jungle grass' in the north corner of New Ireland. It is said to be found only in the lowlands (Coates 1990).

HABITS AND BEHAVIOUR Much the same as other mannikins (Coates 1990).

FOOD AND FEEDING Four specimens with stomach contents analysed in New Hanover (Heinroth 1903) had been feeding on grass seeds and had taken other unidentified seeds.

MOVEMENTS Not known, presumably sedentary.

CALL The voice is recorded by Pratt as a high, thin *peep-peep*, *peep*, and a flute like *pee* or *pee-up* and Gregory (1995c) records a metallic, rather paintive series of *see*.

SONG Nothing known.

COURTSHIP AND DISPLAY Nothing known.

BREEDING Nothing known.

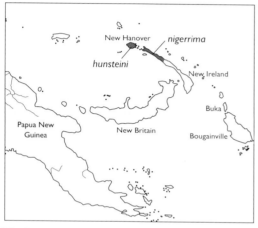

Distribution of Hunstein's Mannikin.

DISTRIBUTION The species is largely restricted to the Bismarck Archipelago, Papua New Guinea. The nominate race *L. h. hunsteini* occurs on the northern part of New Ireland, while *L. h. nigerrima* occurs on the adjacent island of New Hanover.

The species was apparently introduced to the island of Pohnpei (Ponape) in the 1920s. It was described 'from the grasslands of Ponape' by Yamashima in 1931 (Mayr 1945) and given the trinominal of *L. hunsteini minor*. It is not mentioned by Lever (1987) in his extraordinarily comprehensive *Naturalized Birds of the World* and remains a bit of a mystery as I can find no reference to it other than Pratt's "... abundant in the northern and eastern parts of the island." Mayr (1945) thought it occurred also on the Truk Islands, to the west of Pohnpei but Pratt *et al.* (1987) do not mention this.

DESCRIPTION

Three races are recognised by Paynter (1968) and I follow them here. I see no substance at all for the supposition by Sibley and Monroe (1990) that *L. forbesi* is conspecific.

HUNSTEIN'S MANNIKIN
L. hunsteini hunsteini

Former scientific name: *Donacicola hunsteini* Finsch, 1886, *Ibis*, p.1, pl.1.
Other common name: Lawyer Mannikin.
Adult male *c.*100mm. Finsch (1886) gave the measurements of the birds he found as being 3.3 inches, (85mm). Mayr (1947) records the species as being 3.5 inches (90mm), but from museum specimens I

have seen (always a most unreliable guide of body length) it could be 110mm and Clement *et al.* (1993) give 100 to 110mm as the length. Wing length 48–50mm, culmen 10mm, tarsus 11mm. Basically, the bird is entirely black except for dark brown wings and the rump, uppertail-coverts and broad edges to the tail which are almost reddish-orange. The feathers of the top and sides of the head have fuscous edgings. The feathers of the nape and sides of the neck have silvergrey edges. The bill is dark grey. The irides are dark brown. The thighs, legs and feet are black.

Adult female Similar, probably *c.*5mm shorter and can be distinguished by some pale barring or edging to the feathers of the belly and flanks (Goodwin 1982). However, of 10 skins that I studied in the Natural History Museum in Port Moresby, Papua New Guinea, the four females were indistinguishable from the six males, and showed no signs of any barring (see race *L. h. minor*, below). Finsch (1886) distinguishes the female as having the uppertail-coverts brighter (i.e. paler, or less richly coloured?).

Juvenile Entirely russet above, warmer on the rump and uppertail-coverts. The russet covers the entire head and breast and graduates into buffy-cinnamon on the belly, flanks, thighs and undertail-coverts. There is some faint irregular barring of the entire head and mantle with a darker brown. The young bird soon shows dark streaking on the head with paler edgings to the feathers. There is possibly considerable variation among juveniles, some birds having darker streaks on the breast and Clement *et al.* (1993) report some subadults being dull or dusky-brown with a pale head and face. The irides are dark brown. The bill is blackish. The legs and feet dark grey.

POHNPEI MANNIKIN
L. hunsteini minor

Former scientific name: *Munia hunsteini minor*, Yamashina, 1931, *Dobuts. Zasshi.*, p.600.
Adult *c.*90mm. The rump and uppertail-coverts are darker than on *L. h. hunsteini* and there may be some minor scalloping on the flanks; otherwise it is similar.

NEW HANOVER MANNIKIN
L. hunsteini nigerrima

Former scientific names: *Munia nigerrima*, Rothschild and Hartert, 1899, *Ornith. Monatsb.*,7, p.139. *Lonchura nigerrima*, Sibley and Monroe, 1990.
Other common name: (in Mayr 1945) Black-headed Weaver-finch.
Adult male 100–110mm. Wing length 50mm, culmen 10mm, tarsus 11mm. The entire head, back and lower back, and breast are jet black. The belly and flanks are black with buffish to pale grey edgings to the feathers, or only on the tips. The undertail-coverts are black. The wings are dark brown. The rump, uppertail-coverts and broad edgings to the tail are almost reddish-orange. The irides are dark brown. The bill is dark grey, slightly paler at the base of the lower mandible. The legs and feet are black, or slate-blue.
Adult female Similar to the male but is more prominently barred and streaked with buffish below.
Juvenile As for *L. h. hunsteini*.

HYBRIDS None recorded; the species is unknown in aviculture.

CONSERVATION No information on population levels or conditions relating to habitat.

REFERENCES Coates (1990), Clement *et al.* (1993), Clements (1981), Finsch (1886), Goodwin (1982), Gregory (1995c), Heinroth (1903), Lever (1987), Mayr (1945), Paynter (1968), Pratt *et al.* (1987), Sibley & Monroe (1990).

30   NEW IRELAND MANNIKIN
Lonchura forbesi   Plate 11

Former scientific name: *Munia forbesi* P. L. Sclater, 1879, *Proc. zool. Soc.*, London, p.449, pl.37, fig.3.
Other common name: Forbes' Mannikin, Buff-breasted Mannikin, New Ireland Munia or Finch.

New Ireland Mannikin

TAXONOMY On the basis of morphology and distribution, this species probably forms a superspecies with Grand Mannikin *L. grandis* and Buff-breasted Mannikin *L. melaena*. As can be seen from the paucity of notes below, very little is known about this species. It was listed by Sibley and Monroe (1990) as conspecific with *L. hunsteini* without any reference and in my judgement, without justification.

FIELD CHARACTERS Medium-sized brownish munia with a black head and yellow uppertail-coverts. Unlikely to be confused with any other species.

STATUS Scarce or locally fairly common (Coates 1990).

HABITAT It is widely distributed on the island, being found in grassland up to 1,000m.

HABITS AND BEHAVIOUR Usually seen in small groups. Finch and McKean (1987) found it common in rank grass around Mangai airstrip.

FOOD AND FEEDING It is known to feed on the seeds of grasses and other plants (Coates 1990). On a German zoological expedition to the South Seas at the turn of the century four specimens were collected (Heinroth 1903). The crops and stomachs of three contained grass seeds, other small seeds and fragments of mussel shell.

MOVEMENTS Not known.

VOICE Not known.

COURTSHIP AND DISPLAY Not known.

BREEDING The nest is undescribed but the egg is recorded as 15.0mm x 11.0mm (Reichenow 1899).

DISTRIBUTION The island of New Ireland, north-east of New Britain.

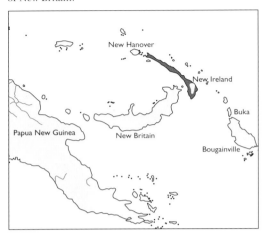

Distribution of New Ireland Mannikin.

DESCRIPTION
Monotypic.
Adult 115–120mm. Wing length *c.*53mm, culmen 12–13mm, tarsus 11–12mm. The thick bill is *c.*12mm in depth and consequently causes the larger head to give a stocky appearance. The entire head is black. The back and wings are russet, the rump, uppertail-coverts and edges of the tail orange-cream. The breast, belly flanks, and underwing-coverts are pale tawny to salmon. The thighs and undertail-coverts are black. The bill is dark grey above, paler blue-grey below. The legs and feet are grey. The irides are brown. There is no information about possible differences between the sexes; presumably males are larger with disproportionately larger bills as with *L. grandis*. I have not been able to study sufficient skins to more than generalise.
Juvenile Described by Clement *et al.* (1993) as being similar to the adult, but with head and face brown and forehead to nape streaked with buff-brown, or striped with dark brown and blackish (Hartert 1925). It soon shows signs of the adult's black on the head with dark centres to the feathers.

HYBRIDS Nothing recorded; the bird is unknown in aviculture.

CONSERVATION Insufficient information to draw even tentative thoughts. There is no trade in birds from New Ireland.

REFERENCES Clement *et al.* (1993), Coates (1990), Finch & McKean (1987), Hartert (1925), Heinroth (1903), Reichenow (1899), Sibley & Monroe (1990).

31   YELLOW-RUMPED MANNIKIN
Lonchura flaviprymna   Plate 9

Former scientific names: *Donacola flaviprymna* Gould, 1845, *Proc. Zool. Soc. London*, p. 80. *Munia flaviprymna.*
Other common names: Yellow-rumped Munia or Finch, Yellow-tailed Finch, Yellow-Rump.

Yellow-rumped Mannikin

TAXONOMY There has been speculation about this bird being conspecific with Chestnut-breasted Mannikin *L. castaneothorax* ever since it was discovered that the two species may hybridise freely in the wild. Chestnut-breasted Mannikin is an extremely promiscuous species that will also freely hybridise with Grey-headed Munia *L. caniceps* in Papua New Guinea and Scaly-breasted Munia *L. punctulata* in Australia, but it is unrealistic to conclude that all four species are conspecific. It is known to have hybridised with at least a dozen or more other species of estrildid finches in captivity. The Yellow-rumped Mannikin, were it conspecific with the far more numerous and widespread Chestnut-breasted Mannikin, would long ago have disappeared in an increasingly diluted gene pool. That it retains its specific identity despite being vulnerable to its more successful, adaptable and indiscriminate congener is a tribute to its genetic integrity.

Immelmann (1962) discussed the validity of Yellow-rumped Mannikin as a species at length and subsequently (1982) reaffirmed his belief in it. He repeated this to me personally when we met in Australia in 1987 and discussed this subject at length. He had thought at first that Yellow-rumped Mannikin might simply be a desert form of Chestnut-breasted Mannikin, which originated in the dry interior of northern Australia. It periodically spreads towards the coast, coming into regular contact with Chestnut-breasted when hybrids between the two occur. However, the two differ in several behaviour patterns and Immelmann postulated that they are distinct species which have reached Australia at different times and by different routes.

My feeling is that Yellow-rumped Mannikin is probably a geographic extension of Pale-headed Munia *L. pallida*. It most likely colonised Australia from Timor along with the Zebra Finch *Poephila guttata*, both birds being already pre-disposed to survival in arid country. Chestnut-breasted Mannikin probably arrived later, from New Guinea, together with Blue-faced Parrotfinch *Erythrura trichroa*.

After reaching Australia from two different directions, the two species extended their range and eventually met in the north and north-west of the continent, where they now occur together and where incomplete sexual isolation results in a large hybrid population. This was Immelmann's final opinion, and one I certainly agree with. It is interesting and may be relevant that whereas there have been several mutations of Chestnut-breasted Mannikin

developed in captivity, none have appeared in the captive populations of Yellow-rumped Mannikin, notwithstanding all the speculation about latent black faces and chest bars discussed in the early literature.

FIELD CHARACTERS It is a pale-headed bird, brown on the back with clear yellow rump and uppertail. Below, it is pale to buff with black thighs and undertail. The adult is quite distinct. However, some individuals of hybrid origin show a little black on the face and might be taken for Long-tailed Grassfinches *Poephila acuticauda* but once the white on the tail-coverts can be seen the two can be separated. Adult Yellow-rumped Mannikin can be told from the juvenile Pictorella Mannikin *Lonchura pectoralis* by the black undertail-coverts. Juvenile Yellow-rumped Mannikin is indistinguishable from juvenile Chestnut-breasted Mannikin in the field and easy to confuse with juvenile Pictorella Mannikin. The juvenile Star Finch *Neochima ruficauda* is another possible confusion species; it is slimmer, has a black bill and reddish uppertail-coverts.

STATUS Scarce to locally common.

HABITAT It is a bird of swampy grassland. It may be found in reedbeds, long grasses and similar habitat at the edges of water, swamps and marshes. It is found inland in scrub country with scattered trees and bushes, but it is not fully adapted to arid conditions and will always be found within reach of water. It will visit cultivated areas and will feed in rice paddies, and takes to cane beds readily.

HABITS AND BEHAVIOUR It is a highly social species that feeds and travels in groups or flocks. The flocks may number many hundreds of birds. In coastal areas it is often found in the company of Chestnut-breasted Mannikin but in the interior the flocks consist entirely of pure Yellow-rumped Mannikins. The flocks usually fly in close harmony, performing tight manoeuvres and changes of direction.

It has large feet and a robust bill and can climb among the stems of reeds and long grass with dexterity and agility. Social behaviour includes clumping and allopreening. Peering occurs, and one or more male birds will crowd close and listen intently whilst appearing to peer at the singer. In the mixed flocks, Chestnut-breasted Mannikins will peer at Yellow-rumped Mannikins and vice versa.

FOOD AND FEEDING It feeds on the half-ripe and ripe seeds of various grasses, taking seeds from the heads and climbing in a most agile manner among the stalks.

MOVEMENTS It is probably sedentary by nature but nomadic by force of local conditions, flocks moving inland with the wet and growth of grasses, and moving out towards the coastal areas as the dry increases. It is also found in coastal areas all year round.

CALL The contact note is a *teet* of varying degrees of loudness and length. Slater (1974) describes it as a bell-like *treet*.

SONG The song starts with a series of rhythmic clicks and some tweeks, then has a long, drawn out *weee*, and concludes with a short series of *tchuk, tchuk*. The song and performance is very much like those of the *L. atricapilla* group of munias (of which this species is undoubtedly the geographic representative). The song is different from that of Chestnut-breasted Mannikin.

COURTSHIP AND DISPLAY In undirected or advertisement display the male will perch still with neck stretched

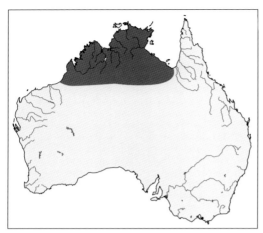

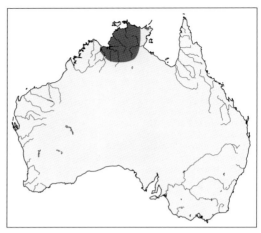

Range of Yellow-rumped Mannikin according to most sources.

Range of Yellow-rumped Mannikin after Fitzherbert and Baker-Gabb (in Goriup 1988).

a little, head pointed slightly downwards, bill held open, and feathers of the flanks and belly slightly erected. He will usually sing full song phrases but will cut off in mid song if disturbed or distracted.

In full courtship display, it is not uncommon for both sexes to carry stems of grass or similar material and hop or fly about near each other. The male will drop his straw and with body upright, head pointed down, bill open and feathers of the nape, rump, flanks and belly fluffed out begin to sing. He will bob up and down and hop towards her turning to look at her and twisting his head and, to a slight degree, his tail towards her at the end. If the performance does not result in copulation the male will beak-wipe a few times and begin again.

Young males are apparently quite precocious and begin singing while still in juvenile plumage, and it is most likely that pairing takes place at this time.

BREEDING The pair will select a site in tall growing grasses, and the initial procedure adopted by the birds is to shred the long leaves and while these are still attached to the main stem they are shaped into a shell to form the outer foundation of the nest. To this they will first add coarse grass and, as the nest nears completion, finer grass is used for lining. The nest is oval, not a ball. It is built with green grasses, but these quickly become dry and brownish, lined with softer fine stems and inflorescences. It is 130–140mm long, 120mm high and 90–100mm wide. The entrance is at the end but it does not have an entrance tunnel or porch. It seems that feathers might occasionally be used in the lining (Cayley 1932, Kingston *et al.* 1987) but their use might be a function of a limited variety or quantity of preferred material being available. The nest is placed low in a tussock of long grass, reeds or cane. Four or five white oval eggs are laid, but four seems to be the usual clutch. Incubation is about 13 days, the young fledging three weeks later. Both sexes incubate and brood during the day but the male roosts outside and nearby the nest at night leaving the female to brood alone.

The male is said to build a roosting nest above or below the main nest (Kingston *et al.* 1987). It is not clear whether these roosting nests are attached to the breeding nest or are quite detached. Their apparent proximity is of considerable interest. More information about this is

needed as it is extremely unusual for a *Lonchura*.

Immelmann (1982) quotes Teschemaker who wrote "I feel sure this species in a state of liberty rears its young on insect food, for which, as soon as the young are hatched, the parents are seen searching all day long and even hawking flies. I have seen as many as six gentles carried to the nest at one time". What I find noteworthy about this report is that munias do not carry food in their bills, but ingest and regurgitate it into the nestlings or fledglings crops subsequently.

According to Baxter (1985) the young take longer to fledge in early spring, when the days are comparatively shorter. With later broods when the days are longest, the young fledge in 3 weeks or less. On leaving the nest, they may be somewhat disorientated and the parents are very attentive calling them together. It is apparent that once they are fully independant they are very curious and may well interfere with ongoing breeding activities. The young return to sleep in the nest at night for a few days, up to as much as a week after fledging. However they soon flock with other immatures and go off in wandering groups.

Palate markings of nestling Yellow-rumped Mannikin.

DISTRIBUTION In most of the literature the distribution of the species is as shown in the map, being tropical grassland in northern Australia, from Derby in north Western Australia across the coastal area of Northern Territory possibly to north-western Queensland. The extent to which it penetrates the interior is not certain, neither does the eastern limit of its range seem clear, there being some doubt as to whether it reaches Queensland. However,

Fitzherbert and Baker-Gabb (in Goriup 1988) report a significantly reduced range, with known breeding only indicated in the region of Wyndham in the north-eastern part of Western Australia.

DESCRIPTION
Monotypic.
Adult male *c*.105mm. Wing length *c*.52mm, culmen 10mm, tarsus 12mm. The forehead and face is whitish, graduating into a suffused warm grey on the crown and nape, and sides of the neck. The back and wings are russet. The long uppertail-coverts are orange-rufous quickly becoming straw-yellow. The chin and throat are creamy-white graduating into creamy-buff that may border on salmon or faintly straw on the flanks and ventral area. The underwing coverts are buff. The thighs and undertail-coverts are black or dark brown. The irides are dark brown; the bill, legs and feet are blue-grey.
Adult female *c*.100mm. Wing length 50mm, culmen 9.5mm, tarsus 11mm. The sexes are very similar and it is not easy to tell male from female with certainty. In a well-defined pair the female will be seen to be greyer on the head and duller generally. The bill of the male is larger and the usual enlargement of the culmen of an adult male may be noticeable. It can be felt by gently rubbing the fingernail of the forefinger from the crown forwards to and over the edge of the culmen. The bill across the base is usually broader and deeper in the male, being about 9.5–10mm deep and 9mm across the base, compared to 9mm deep and 8.5mm across the base in the female.
Juvenile Sandy to olive-buff brown above with a tawny rump, paler below, greyish on the breast, darker on wings and tail. The bill is dark when the fledgling emerges but soon becomes grey once the bird is completely self-supporting. Adult plumage is attained at around six months.

CONSERVATION Yellow-rumped Munia is listed by the International Council for Bird Preservation (Collar and Andrew 1988) in the Near-threatened category. However, Fitzherbert and Baker-Gabb (in Goriup 1988) are in no doubt that it is truly threatened. At best it means that the species should be watched carefully. At worst it means that the population could be precipitated into a seriously threatened status by some catastrophe such as prolonged drought and a series of fires. It is not certain what is the cause for its listing by Collar and Andrew, but Fitzherbert and Baker-Gabb suggest that the repeated burning of grassland to force growth of tender green shoots for stock to graze is probably the most significant factor. Trapping for the bird trade is a well regulated and controlled activity in Australia nowadays and it is not suggested that this is a cause, although at some time in the past it might have had an impact on wild populations.

Populations of the species in captivity have never been high, not even in Australia. My conclusion from an ongoing survey of avicultural literature and correspondence with many aviculturists is that Yellow-rumped Munia is rare and captive populations in Europe are perilously close to such a low level that it is in danger of disappearing. The genetics of these birds is unknown and it is possible that most strains are inbred, with low reproductive capabilities.

REFERENCES Baxter (1985), Cayley (1932), Collar & Andrew (1988), Goriup (1988), Immelmann (1962 and 1982), Kingston (1987), Koepff (1984), Nachrichten (1978), Slater (1974).

32   CREAM-BELLIED MUNIA
Lonchura pallidiventer   **Plate 5**

Described as *Lonchura pallidiventer* Restall

Cream-bellied Munia

TAXONOMY During the seven years of dedicated study of the genus *Lonchura* for the preparation of this book I came across several new forms of munia. Some were eventually dismissed as probable hybrids, produced by bird keepers in Europe and imported into Jakarta along with stocks of domesticated Australian estrildids and canaries. Some were described as new subspecies (Restall 1995b). One, the subject of this chapter, has remained unexplained, and has now been proposed as a new species (Restall 1996).

FIELD CHARACTERS The rich chestnut coloration and pale bill suggest that the bird might be taken for the Chestnut Munia *L. atricapilla* despite lacking any black on the head, and assuming the cream belly and spotted flanks were not seen. In poor light, or if seen in the company of other munias, it might be taken for a White-bellied Munia *L. leucogastra*.

STATUS Unknown. The species has never been observed in the wild.

HABITAT Unknown.

HABITS AND BEHAVIOUR Unknown in the wild. In captivity it is gregarious. I have observed both clumping and allopreening. I have seen territorial aggression between individuals, and on one occasion a female attacked another species that failed to respond when she offered her nape for allopreening. They are lively and active birds, with loud calls, and are particularly vocal at dawn.

FOOD AND FEEDING Captive birds readily took all the varieties of fresh grasses that I offered, being particularly keen on *Panicum maximus* and fresh green wheat. They took different millets and other dry seeds without showing any bias or preference. They would not take any greens or fruits, nor any commercial soft foods.

CALL The contact note, when the birds are together, is *pip* or *chip*, and there are variations in tone from both sexes. The alarm call is a loud *tchek*! When nervous or apprehensive, such as when I am seen watching them through the window, the sentry bird will utter a rapid *tik tik tik tik*, accompanied by tail jerking from side to side and very quick wing flicking. The male, when calling its mate, utters a *pee*, *peet* or *cheet*; the female's reply is a *pip* or *chip*.

SONG In undirected advertisement song the male stands

at about 45° to the perch, head horizontal, and sings at first a quiet *tik tik tik tik tik tik tik* which changes to more of a *tuk tuk tuk tuk*. This becomes a few long *weeee* whistles, each tending to descend, changes to a long drawn out *weeeeeoooooooooo* legato, first rising then descending. It ends with several *wee wee wee wee* notes. The whole may last from 8 to 15 seconds and may be repeated many times. The legato is sometimes loud and penetrating. The song is similar in structure to that of Five-coloured Munia *L. quinticolor*.

Advertisement song of Cream-bellied Munia. The bird may bob up and down while bent over.

COURTSHIP AND DISPLAY When displaying to the female the male is slightly more hunched, with the bill pointing slightly downwards. The nape feathers are erected as is the bib and upper throat, but the chest is depressed. The rump is ruffled, and the flanks and belly fully erected showing the white spots on the black clearly. In high intensity display the bird stands well clear of the perch, with neck stretched and head almost horizontal, but moving from side to side as necessary to follow the female. During the performance the bill is opened wide and half closed in regular movements.

High intensity display of Cream-bellied Munia with directed song when a female is nearby.

I have seen the male take a length of grass, holding it at one end, and jerk his head upwards a couple of times. On this occasion the female approached but he dropped it and no display followed. On another occasion when a very active nest-building male saw his mate nearby he flew to her with a length of paper in his bill and went immediately into display song, dropping the paper as he opened his bill.

Cream-bellied Munia straw-carrying, before singing. The male will bob up and down while carrying the straw.

162

BREEDING Nothing known in the wild. With my captive birds, nest building occurred several times, when the active males would begin nests in both baskets and boxes. There was nothing in this behaviour to suggest any particular difference from, presumably, allied species such as Five-coloured Munia.

DISTRIBUTION From the statements of an importer and a trader in the bird market in Jakarta it seems that the birds come from the hinterland of Bandjarmarsin in southeast Kalimantan, Borneo.

DESCRIPTION   Plates 70–72
Monotypic.
A rich brown medium-sized munia with a cream belly, white-spotted black flanks, and golden uppertail-coverts. **Adult** 110–120mm. The crown, nape and sides of the head are raw umber or cinnamon. The mantle and wings are mid-brown but the wing coverts and flight feathers are edged with amber. The rump is orange-rufous changing to straw on the uppertail-coverts. The tail is mid-brown, the feathers edged with straw. The face, forehead, lores, base of mesial and bib are olive-brown. The breast is rich chestnut. The flanks, joining in a poorly-defined bar across the breast, are black with white spots and scallops. The inner flanks, hidden by the closed wings, are chestnut. The thighs are barred with black and chestnut or black and cream. The underwing-coverts are cream. The belly, ventral region and undertail-coverts are cream. There may be black subterminal crescents on the undertail-coverts. The irides are dark brown. The bill is pale violaceous-grey. The legs and feet are grey.

Males appear to have a few grizzled lines of black edging onto the upper part of the cream belly, which is absent in the female. They tend to be larger it seems, but not consistently so. The female has a slight pale barring on the lower rump. The colour plate also shows a difference in the inner flank spotting but this could be coincidental.
Juvenile The only individual I have seen is a bird that was well advanced into the moult into its first adult plumage and I have painted the juvenile based on this. This bird appears to be cinnamon to light drab above, a pale pinkish-buff on the lower face, throat and breast, and pale buff on the rest of the underparts.

REFERENCES Restall (1995b & 1996).

33   CHESTNUT-BREASTED MANNIKIN
Lonchura castaneothorax   Plate 10

Described as *Lonchura castaneothorax* Gould
Other common names: Chestnut-breasted Finch or Munia, Chestnut Finch or Bully Bird (Australia).

Chestnut-breasted Mannikin
L. c. castaneothorax

FIELD CHARACTERS It is a small brown-backed munia with a black face and greyish crown and nape, and a broad ferruginous breast bar above a white belly. The adult is unlikely to be confused with any other species, but the juvenile is very similar in the field to juveniles of other munias within its range. These are usually Yellow-rumped Mannikin *L. flaviprymna*, Scaly-breasted Munia *L. punctulata*, Grey-headed Mannikin *L. caniceps*, and Chestnut Munia *L. atricapilla*. Identification can only be ascertained by seeing the juvenile in the company of the relevant adult species.

STATUS Common, locally common or scarce.

HABITAT In Australia it is known as a bird of reed beds and rank grasses bordering rivers, in swamps, in grassy country, and mangroves. It is commonly found in cane fields and cereal crops, and the spread of irrigated cultivation has contributed significantly to the extension of the species' range. John Gould wrote of it (in Cayley 1932) "I had not the good fortune to meet with this bird in a state of nature, but I have been informed that it frequents reed beds bordering the banks of rivers and lagoons on the eastern coast, and that it much resembles the Bearded Tit *Panurus biarmicus*, of Europe in the alertness with which it passes up and down the upright stems of reeds, from the lower part to the very top, a habit for which the lengthened and curved form of its claws seem well adapted". In dry seasons it has been seen in arid or semi-arid country but always near water, unless actually in search of water. It is also found in grassy woodland (Slater *et al.* 1986).

In New Guinea it is a bird of drier areas and does not normally invade the jungle roads and clearings where other munias such as Grey-headed Mannikin are found. It is common in the Port Moresby area and will often form mixed flocks with Grey-headed Mannikins. I often saw it in the company of the latter which usually outnumbered it in a ratio of about two to one. On one occasion we netted 28 birds, about half of a flock, when for once Chestnut-breasted Mannikins outnumbered Grey-headed significantly. This was in July when flocks were composed equally of adults and juveniles.

In French Polynesia where it is well established as an introduced species, its habits have developed somewhat differently, indicating the adaptability of the species. It is widespread on bracken-covered hill slopes in the interior, in pastures and gardens (it is not a garden bird in Australia), on cultivated land and wasteland, in forest ecotones and coconut plantations (Lever 1989). It was found there as long ago as 1920, but on most islands the introductions appear to have been in the early 1970s.

HABITS AND BEHAVIOUR During the breeding season in Australia it is mostly seen in pairs, but in the late autumn and winter months it congregates in large flocks, at times eating the seeds of the different cereal crops. It is a highly sociable species, flocking in large numbers outside the breeding season. Breeding birds will join groups or flocks when foraging.

Chestnut-breasted Mannikins will clump, engage in allopreening and peering has been observed many times.

Single birds or small groups will usually fly with slight or marked undulations, while large flocks fly direct and fast (Goodwin 1982). In my observations, within the flock individual birds also fly with slight undulations. Birds in flight keep up a constant calling to each other as do most munias.

FOOD AND FEEDING It feeds on all manner of grass seeds. It has a distinct liking for barley seed and this is responsible for its local name of Barley Bird. "I have seen a flock of several hundreds of these finches settle on a crop of barley and noted the agility with which the birds moved among the stalks of the cereal, and the expert manner in which they separated the seed from the ear. It is really remarkable what havoc is caused in such a short space of time by a flock, if left undisturbed" (Cayley 1932).

The seeds of native grasses and small plants constitute its principal food, but it seems to be especially fond of paspalum grass *Paspalum longifolium*, bullrush millet *Pennisetum typhoedium* and *Sorghum* species. Immelmann (1962) saw them feeding on plum sorghum *S. plumosum*. I have offered captive birds partially ripe and ripe Guinea corn *S. bicolor* but they would not touch it. In the Port Moresby area I saw them feeding on *Rottboellia exaltata*, and in dense patches of *Setaria* spp. I also saw them feeding on the feral millet *Pannicum maximum*. Baptista (1990) records them feeding on the seeds of the wild sugar cane *Saccharum robustum* in Papua New Guinea and in Australia it is commonly found in sugar plantations. Goodwin (1982) lists wild rice *Oryza sativa* as an important natural food and Immelmann (1962) adds *Echinachloa colonum*, *Chloris virgata*, *Sehima nervosa* and *Pannicum zymbiformae*.

Their usual manner of feeding is to cling to the stem of grass or cereal just below the head and eat the seeds, or at least some of them. On several occasions in Queensland, I have seen a bird then reach out to a nearby stem with the bill, pull it close and grasp it with a foot and continue feeding from the new one. In Papua New Guinea I have seen them standing on the ground, jumping up a foot or more to grasp the heads of small seeding grasses, then stand on the head of the grass on the ground while chewing out the seeds.

Cayley (1932) noted it feeding in paddocks where the grass had been kept short by stock and showed no signs of seeding, and drew the conclusion it was seeking insect life. Immelmann (1982) and several others (presumably all drawing on Immelmann), have remarked how in Australia it catches termites on the wing at the beginning of the breeding season. It will in fact catch flying termites at any time during the breeding season and possibly at other times.

MOVEMENTS In eastern Australia it is more or less sedentary, while in the north it tends to be more nomadic. The two Papua New Guinea races are to some extent nomadic and I gained the impression when visiting Port Moresby that the birds of that area moved inland during the coastal dry season. Individuals have been known to travel up to 70km in the non-breeding season (Clement *et al.* 1993). It is found in hilly country up to 1,900m (Rand & Gilliard 1967) although it is primarily a bird of grassy lowlands.

CALL The sexes have different tones of contact call note, and a separated bonded pair will call constantly and loudly to each other until reunited. In this situation the different tone can be readily recognised. Thibault and Rives (1975) describe a loud contact call in flight as *pup-pup-pup*.

When studying the race *L. c. ramsayi* in Papua New Guinea (Restall 1990) I noted a wide vocabulary of different contact notes including a soft *weeee* which sounded intimate and comforting, and a very intimate *zeet-a-zeet-a-zeet-a-zeet-a-zeet* on a descending scale, like a subsong. When

5 birds in a cage roosted for the night they all snuggled together into the seed bowl as if it were a nest and indulged in a conversation of soft murmurings amongst themselves including a note like a short mew that I had not heard before. In contrast four *L. c. sharpii* kept in Hong Kong had a very limited vocabulary with their general conversation consisting essentially of variations on one note, that note being different for each sex.

SONG The song is preceded by some inaudible bill movements, probably clicks, then goes into a *weeee* and is followed by a series of *twee*, *tchuk* and ends with some bell-like *tching*. Morris (1958) describes the song thus: *weeeeee-eeeeeeeee-tuee-tuee-tuee-tuee-tuee-tuee-tuee-tuee-tuee-tuee-cheeouk-cheeouk-cheeouk-cheeouk-cheeouk-ching-ching-ching-ching-ching.* One singing bird in a group may set off other birds singing and a small 'concert' may well ensue. This is what Immelmann (1982) refers to as singing duets or trios. A singing bird may well attract another to peer, which will come close and lean forward, apparently listening very intently whilst appearing to peer hard at the performer's bill. Birds that peer are never paired to the singer. The peering bird is almost certain to be another male.

COURTSHIP AND DISPLAY In courtship there is no holding of nesting material by either sex. The male tucks his head in, inclined downwards a little, with the bill open. Then, with most of the feathers on the body erected will more or less bob up and down, in the inverted curtsey of Morris (1958). But the bobbing does not become jumping and the feet do not leave the perch. He may turn his head from side to side, or simply turn to face the female, then away, and back again. He edges towards her until they touch. If she is receptive, the female will bend forward into a more horizontal position at which the male will stop singing and also lean forward. At this point both birds have the feathers of the belly fully erected. They both move into an upright position together, and then bend forward again. Tails are pointed towards each other. This precedes any copulation that might take place.

Males in simple undirected advertisement song stand virtually motionless, with the neck stretched upwards, bill tilted down about 10° from the horizontal and kept open, and the feathers of the nape, flanks and belly held out from the body.

Baptista (1991) recorded a flight display, the first time such a display has been recorded for a *Lonchura* species. The bird flew in a mixture of fluttering flight and glides, head held down with bill wide open, uttering a loud series of *tik-tik-tik-tik-tik* and then dropped vertically into a patch of sorghum. The only other flight display recorded for an estrildid finch is of a Star Finch *Emblema ruficauda* (Immelmann 1982).

BREEDING The nest is usually built within a metre of the ground. It may be found in heavy grass, cane stands or maize, bamboo or a similar plant. It is a lateral oval, small by *Lonchura* standards, being about 10cm wide by 15cm long and 12–15 cm high. The entrance hole is about 3cm across at one end. There is no pronounced porch nor entrance tunnel (Immelmann 1982), but Cayley (1932) does refer to an entrance hood. Only green pliable grasses are used in the building of the nest walls and it is lined with softer small and finer grasses and inflorescences. The male brings most of the material to the nest, while the female does most of the building. If the nest is built in growing grass, which is the normal location, it is usual for

the leaves of the stems to be pulled into the structure. This serves to anchor the structure rather efficiently.

The species does not build roosting nests. Outside the breeding season birds gather in flocks and roost communally in reedbeds, cane breaks or suitable long grass.

The clutch is normally five or six, white, oval eggs, and narrower at one end. Incubation is 12–13 days and the young fledge at 20–21 days. Both sexes incubate and brood during the daytime but only the female is in the nest at night. The male roosts nearby.

The young are reared on a mainly vegetable diet of green seeds, but some insect food is taken. After fledging the entire family returns to the nest to roost at night for some days afterwards. Being very social birds they will nest close to each other, nests sometimes being less than a metre apart forming a regular colony. Once independent the young flock with other recently fledged juveniles and wander in groups of varying size. Meanwhile the adults continue breeding, raising up to three broods if conditions are favourable.

Palate markings of nestling Chestnut-breasted Mannikin.

DISTRIBUTION The six races are well defined in their distribution. The nominate *L. c. castaneothorax* ranges from Cape York down the north-east and eastern coastal edge of Australia through Queenland to New South Wales. The other Australian race *L. c. assimilis* ranges from Port Hedland (Carstens 1985) in Western Australia through the Kimberleys across the northern Northern Territory and occurs on Groote Eylandt and Melville Island. It does not meet nor intergrade with *L. c. castaneothorax* in the Cape York Peninsula. There are four subspecies distributed in New Guinea. The two widespread ones are *L. c. sharpii* which ranges from Humboldt Bay in Hollandia, on the easternmost part of north Irian Jaya eastwards to Astrolabe Bay in Papua New Guinea and *L. c. ramsayi* which is widespread in southeastern Papua New Guinea, from Hall Sound and the area of the Kumusi River, including Goodenough Island. Two extremely local races that occur in Irian Jaya are *L. c. uropygialis* at the head of Geelvink Bay and *L. c. boschmai* from around the Wissel Lakes and the Araboe River (Rand & Gilliard 1967).

It occurs on the Society and the Marquesas Islands (Lever 1989) and the race there is *L. c. castaneothorax*. It was first introduced to Tahiti at the end of the last century where the population appears to have evolved some discriminating plumage characteristics. Further birds were liberated on Tahiti in 1938. By 1972 it was abundant on Tahiti, Moorea, Raiatea, Tahaa, Bora Bora and Huahine (Long 1981). It was still abundant in gardens and coastal cultivation on Tahiti and Moorea in 1991 (Hicks *in litt.*). It has become established on the 52km² island of Eiao, where there has been major land clearance and overgrazing, which is limiting the occurrence of woody plants to a few groves. It will be interesting to note the extent to which these birds may evolve local characteristics in terms of size or plumage.

It is common in New Caledonia (Hannecart and

Letocart 1980), birds having been introduced from northern Australia, but whether these were *L. c. castaneothorax* or *L. c. assimilis* is not known, nor whether they have evolved modified plumage like the birds in Tahiti. It was common and numerous around Noumea in 1989 (Hicks *in litt.*).

Within Australia itself it seems to have been introduced into areas outside its natural range and is established as a local breeding bird in South Australia in the Finiss-Black Swamp area and possibly also around Perth in Western Australia.

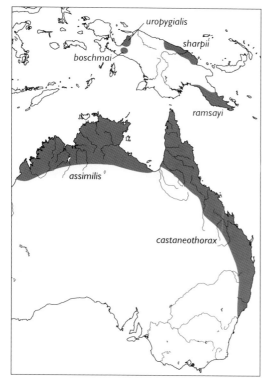

Distribution of Chestnut-breasted Mannikin.

DESCRIPTION Plates 73–74

Six races are recognised, two from Australia and four from New Guinea. The two Australian races are distinguished by having pale shafts to the ear-coverts. Of the four New Guinea races, Ramsay's has an all-black head with only vestigial paler edges to the feathers on the nape; the rump and short uppertail-coverts are orange. The Wissel Lakes race has a greyish crown and very pale rump and uppertail-coverts. Sharp's has a very pale grey crown and nape with dull maroon rump and uppertail-coverts. The Geelvink Bay race is also similar but can be distinguished by its duller grey nape and brighter, more orange uppertail-coverts.

EASTERN CHESTNUT-BREASTED MANNIKIN
L. castaneothorax castaneothorax Plate 73
Former scientific names: *Amadina castaneothorax* Gould, 1837, *Synops. Birds Australia*, pt. 2, pl. 21, fig 2. *Donacola castaneothorax northi* Mathews, 1923.
Other common names: Chestnut-breasted Munia, Chestnut Finch, Barley Bird, Bully Bird.

Adult *c.*110mm. Wing length 54mm, culmen 10mm, tarsus 11mm. The forehead is grey, becoming brown on the crown and nape with broad grey edges to the feathers. The entire face, lores, supercilium to the sides of the neck, bib and throat are black, tending to dark brown on the ear-coverts, the quill feathers of which are white. This gives a distinctive patterning to the cheeks only found on the two Australian races. The mantle, lower back and wings are cinnamon-brown. The rump and uppertail-coverts are warm straw, tending to orange-yellow on the rump. The breast is ferruginous (the word 'chestnut' is a misnomer), divided from the cream belly by a black line. This black continues on the flanks in the form of irregular barring, and contains some brown blotches. The thighs and undertail-coverts are black. The underwing-coverts are buffy-salmon to flesh. The irides are chestnut. The bill is steel-grey to bluish-grey. The legs and feet are mid-grey.

The sexes are superficially alike, but male birds tend to be a little larger and brighter. The base of the bill may be broader, the culmen slightly more pronounced. The black breast bar is usually thicker in the male. In a well-matched pair all the above differences may be seen, but there is considerable variation between individuals and it would be difficult to sex a single bird visually.

Juvenile Dull brown above with some darker streaking on the forehead and face. The wings are slightly darker than the back. The rump and uppertail-coverts tend to warm or cinnamon. The throat is pale buffy, occasionally having dark streaking. The underparts are light buff-brown with an ochraceous flush to the breast. The bill is dark horn or dark slate-grey, gradually lightening as the bird matures.

NORTHWESTERN CHESTNUT-BREASTED MANNIKIN
L. castaneothorax assimilis
Other scientific synonyms: *Munia castaneothorax assimilis* Mathews, 1910, *Bull. Brit. Orn. Club*, 27,p.28. *L. c. apsleyi*, Mathews, 1912. *L. c. gangi*, Mathews, 1912. *L. c. thorpei.*, Mathews, 1913.
Other common name: Western Chestnut-breasted Munia.

Adult *c.*110mm and similar to the above race but more richly coloured in every respect. The white striations on the cheeks are restricted to the centre of the ear-coverts, the back is russet (noticeably darker than on *L. c. castaneothorax*). The breast is darker cream, and the flanks are barred only black-and-white, with no brown. The upper rump is reddish-chestnut.

WISSEL LAKES CHESTNUT-BREASTED MANNIKIN
L. castaneothorax boschmai
Junge,1952, *Zool. Meded.* Rijksmus. Nat. Hist.Leiden, 31, p.29.

Adult *c.*105mm. Wing length 48–50mm, culmen 10mm, tarsus 11mm. From forehead to nape it is drab, with grey edgings to the feathers. The lores, supercilium and ear-coverts to the sides of the neck, chin and throat are black. The mantle and wings are medium brown to cinnamon. The rump and uppertail are yellow and the rectrices are slightly edged with yellow. The breast is cinnamon-rufous (not ferruginous as in *L. c. castaneothorax*) and darker than the other New Guinea races, being similar to the Australian *L. c.*

are white with irregular brown barring and occasional black spotting. The black bar dividing the breast from the belly is regular. The thighs and undertail-coverts are black.

GEELVINK BAY CHESTNUT-BREASTED MANNIKIN
L. castaneothorax uropygialis
Stresemann and Paludan, 1934, *Ornith. Monatsb.*, 42, p43.
Adult 100–105mm. Wing length 48–50mm, culmen 10mm, tarsus 11mm. This race is similar to *L. c. castaneothorax* but is distinguished by having the face entirely black and the belly and ventral area pale yellowish-white. The underwing-coverts are salmon. The rump is reddish-maroon, the uppertail-coverts and edges of the tail are orange.

Chestnut-breasted Mannikin *L. c. ramsayi*.

RAMSAY'S CHESTNUT-BREASTED MANNIKIN
L. castaneothorax ramsayi   Plate 74
Described as *L. c. ramsayi* Delacour, 1943
Former scientific name: *Donacola nigriceps*, Ramsay, 1877, *Proc. Linn. Soc.* New South Wales, 1 (1876), p.392.
Other common name: Black-headed Chestnut-breasted Mannikin.
Adult male *c.*110mm. Wing length 52mm, culmen 10mm, tarsus 12mm. It differs from the other New Guinea races in being larger and by having the entire head black, with some grey terminal edges forming variable V-markings from rear crown to nape. In birds I have examined in the field and kept briefly while in Papua New Guinea, males could be told from females by having fewer and smaller markings on the nape. Also, in most specimens I have seen, the flanks are more noticeably and regularly barred black-and-white than on the female. The underwing-coverts are white. The rump is orange, grading into yellow for the uppertail-coverts and edges of the tail feathers.
Adult female *c.*105mm. Wing length 48mm (Clement *et al.* 1993), 51mm (pers. obs.), culmen 10mm, tarsus 11mm.

SHARP'S CHESTNUT-BREASTED MANNIKIN
L. castaneothorax sharpii
Former scientific name: *Donacicola sharpii* Madarasz, 1894, *Bull. Brit. Orn. Club*, 3, p.47.
Other common name: Dwarf Chestnut-breasted Mannikin.
Adult male 98–103mm. Wing length 46–48mm, culmen 9–9.5mm, tarsus 11mm. From forehead to nape it is whitish, to pale grey on the nape with whitish edgings to the feathers. The underwing-coverts are salmon. The rump and uppertail-coverts are ma-

roon, with variable light orange edging to the uppertail-coverts. The legs and feet are variable from mid-grey to blackish.
Adult female 94–98mm. Wing length 45–46mm, culmen 9mm, tarsus 10mm. She is noticeably darker on the rear crown and nape. When several birds are together it is fairly easy to distinguish the males from the females.
Juvenile New Guinea races are alike. The typical juvenile is fawn on the head, clay-coloured above, fawn to buffish below, darkest on the wings and tail, warmest on the rump and palest on the chin. Recently fledged birds have a blackish bill, but this soon becomes a lavender blue-grey.

Three races of Chestnut-breasted Mannikin, *L. c. sharpii* on the left, *L. c. castaneothorax* centre and *L. c. ramsayi* on the right.

HYBRIDS In the Port Moresby area Chestnut-breasted and Grey-headed Mannikins will occasionally hybridise. In Australia Chestnut-breasted Mannikin will also hybridise naturally in the wild with Yellow-rumped Mannikin and Scaly-breasted Munia. Coates (1992) refers to Tolhurst's (1987) sighting of "a probable hybrid between *L. castaneothorax* and *L. grandis.*" I think it is unreasonable in the light of this to conclude as many writers (apparently uncritically passing on received wisdom) have done, that *L. castaneothorax* is conspecific with either *L. caniceps* or *L. flaviprymna*. To add *L. grandis* and *L. punctulata* to this melange brings the idea to the point of nonsense. A critical review of Tolhurst's report shows that it is extremely unlikely that the bird he saw was a hybrid, but was most likely a dark-breasted Chestnut-breasted Mannikin.

Immelmann (1962b) explains at length why he believes Yellow-rumped and Chestnut-breasted Mannikins are good species. He postulates the probability that Yellow-rumped Mannikin, being more completely adapted to the arid Australian environment, probably reached Australia from Timor comparatively early, Chestnut-breasted Mannikin reaching Australia from New Guinea somewhat later.

Peckover and Filewood (1976) comment, "Hybridisation between two species is unusual among birds or any animals. The fact that occasional hybrids occur does not detract from the definition of a species. Indeed, if Grey-headed Mannikin and Chestnut-breasted Mannikin were not different, they would mate at random and within a few generations they would all look like hybrids, whenever they occur together."

CONSERVATION The species appears not to be under any kind of pressure in Australia. The situation in New Guinea is less clear. *L. c. ramsayi* is under no threat. *L. c. sharpii* is being trapped in Irian Jaya in small numbers for the international bird trade, but this poses no threat for the major part of the population, which occurs in Papua New Guinea. *L. c. uropygialis* and *L. c. boschmai* appear to be uncommon to scarce, and nothing is known of their population densities, nor local habitat conditions. Neither appears to be of interest to the trappers.

REFERENCES Baptista (1990 & 1991), Carstens (1985), Cayley (1932), Clement *et al.* (1993), Goodwin (1982), Hannecart & Letocart (1980), Immelmann (1962b & 1982), Lever (1987), Long (1981), Morris (1958), Peckover & Filewood (1976), Rand & Gilliard (1967), Restall, R. (1991), Slater *et al.* (1986), Thibault & Rives (1975), Tolhurst (1987).

---

34 BLACK MANNIKIN
Lonchura stygia   Plate 14

Former scientific name: *Munia stygia* Stresemann, 1934, *Ornith, Monatsb.*, 42, p. 102
Other common name: Black Munia

Black Mannikin

FIELD CHARACTERS A medium-sized munia, entirely black with a yellow rump. The adult is unlikely to be confused with any other species.

The juvenile is virtually identical to juvenile Grey-crowned Mannikin *L. nevermanni* in the field. Neither the adult nor the juvenile is likely to be confused with Streak-headed Mannikin *L. tristissima* as suggested by Clement *et al.* (1993) since this species does not occur in the same area. It is possible for the juvenile to be to be confused with juvenile White-spotted Mannikin *L. leucosticta*, but this bird has a pale chin and some whitish spotting on the head and wings. It is similar to juvenile Crimson Finch *Neochmia phaeton*, with at times a rusty, almost reddish lustre to the body, but the Crimson Finch tail is long and pointed compared to the short blunt tail of the juvenile Black Mannikin.

STATUS Locally common.

HABITAT Lowland wet grassland, reedbeds and tall grasses. The Black Mannikin particularly favours floating mats of rice grass on lagoons and swamps. It is recorded visiting rice crops at Kurik, Irian Jaya (Coates 1990), and no doubt it will feed on paddy rice elsewhere. It is sometimes found in drier savanna country at sea level (Clement *et al.*).

HABITS This is a gregarious species moving around in small flocks. These may be of just a few birds (Gregory 1995a) or of a dozen to 20 or more birds, and these flocks stay intact while in flight (Coates 1990). It is sometimes found in mixed flocks with Grey-crowned Mannikin and Crimson Finch. It is a sociable species. Clumping has been recorded and I have seen allopreening. Peering has been recorded among captive birds by Oreste Piotto (pers. comm.).

FOOD AND FEEDING Black Mannikin feeds primarily on the seeds of grasses, both unripe and ripe on the stem, and dry when fallen to the ground. Gregory (1995a) saw it feeding on the seeding heads of *Oryza* and *Echinocloa* grasses, and tentatively identified *E. praestens*. It is an agile species well able to climb the stems and cling to the seeding inflorescences. It will cling to one stem and pull the seeding head of a nearby stem with its bill, grasp it with the foot, and then eat the seeds without having to climb from one stem to another. It feeds on the ground, picking up fallen ripe seeds. It also feeds on the seeds of weeds and other small plants, especially those that have fallen to the ground.

MOVEMENTS Mostly sedentary, moving in search of food. Juveniles are more mobile than the adults and will join up with wandering foraging groups with the other two estrildids found in this habitat.

CALL The quiet contact call is a *tyu tyu* or *tyiu tyiu*, which sounds the same from both sexes. Another soft contact note made when birds are in close proximity to each other is *quiet quiet*. I have noted several loud contact calls. One of these is *teeu! teeu!* uttered by the male and *tseeu! tseeu!* on a slightly lower note, uttered by the female. Another sounds to my ears like *quit! quit!* by the male, and *tuwit! tuwit!* by the female.

SONG The only song I have heard is a quiet series of burbling notes, with no distinguishing or audibly distinctive character, and lacking any significant legato or drawn-out *weee*. It lasts from two to three seconds. However, one male I acquired as a juvenile and kept only in the company of other Black Mannikins and Grey-crowned Mannikins, developed a very loud song that I transcribed as *tik-tik-tik-tik-tik-tewy-tewy-tewy-tewy-tseeeuu-tseeeu-tseeeu-tseeu*. The final series of *tseeu* notes was very loud and continued for up to 16 seconds, a remarkable length of time for a munia song.

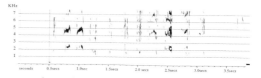

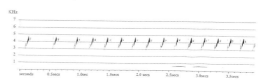

Sonograms of the songs of two different Black Mannikins. The upper row shows the typical song from one male. The lower row shows an unusual and remarkably extended song of a different male, which would run for 10–13 seconds.

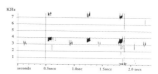

Loud calls of juvenile male Black Mannikin.

167

Male Black Mannikin singing in low intensity undirected song (left), and high intensity (right).

COURTSHIP AND DISPLAY The male stands fairly upright with the bill pointing directly forward or slightly downwards, bobbing up and down (pers. obs.) in the inverted curtsey (Morris 1958).This may be so strong as to become hopping clear of the perch (Michael Plose pers. comm.) which I have not seen in my own birds. Captive males deprived of contact with a female for any length of time will greet one within seconds of the meeting with a high intensity song and display, and attempts at rape that will continue for several minutes.

Black Mannikin nest, after Rand (1938).

BREEDING The nest is built fairly low down among the dense grasses that the birds inhabit. Rand (1938) appears to be the only source of observations of the bird breeding in the wild. He found nests up to 1.5m from the ground, a 'lop-sided flask-shaped' structure made of grass and well lined. There is a well-defined entrance neck to the nest. The lining is apparently normally formed of seedless inflorescences. Captive birds with unlimited and varied nesting material line the nest with fine grasses and construct a small neck with only a vestigial porch. The inner cavity usually measures about 8cm across.

Black Mannikin nest built in clump of bamboo in captivity (Michael Plose pers. comm.).

The clutch ranges from 3–7, with 4 or 5 being normal. The eggs are white. Those measured by Rand (1938) were 11mm wide with varying length of 16–17.5mm. Those laid by captive birds I have measured were all 11mm wide by 16mm long. Incubation lasts 15 days. Hofmann (in Nachrichten 1978) found incubation to last 14–16 days. The nestlings are brooded until they fledge, which is normally 21 days from hatching. The nestlings are light upon hatching, but turn dark within a few days and feathering begins at about five days.

Upon fledging the young birds appear a dark browny-charcoal. They begin to show the black of the adult at around 12 weeks. Full moult into adult plumage may not be completed before 6 months.

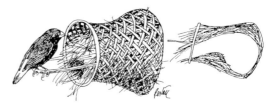

Nest built in a split-cane basket by a female Black Mannikin with cut-away side view to show construction of cavity.

DISTRIBUTION The species is restricted to the Trans-Fly region of southern New Guinea. It is essentially a bird of Irian Jaya. It is recorded in Papua New Guinea at Lake Owa, near Lake Ambuve (Gregory 1995a) and also from a small area east of Lake Daviumbu (Coates 1990).

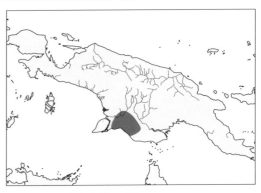

Distribution of Black Mannikin.

DESCRIPTION   Plate 75
Monotypic.
Adult male 105–110mm. Wing length 52–54mm, culmen 10–11mm, tarsus 12–13mm. The entire body, except rump and uppertail-coverts, is black often with a purple glossy shine. The underwing-coverts of several live birds I have examined are salmon with some black barring near the edges of the wing and elbow. Stresemann (1934) described the underwing-coverts as being fresh pale cream-buff. The rump, uppertail-coverts and edges of the tail are straw-yellow. The wing-coverts and flight feathers are actually very dark brown. The irides are dark brown. The bill is pale lilac-blue-grey. The legs, feet and nails variable pale grey to pale blue-grey.
Adult female 100–105mm. Wing length 50–53mm, culmen 9.5–10mm, tarsus 12mm. The entire body, except the

rump and uppertail-coverts, is very dark brown with black edges to the feathers of the head, mantle and breast, all with a purple-black gloss. The undertail-coverts are black. The underwing-coverts are beige-salmon with some black edging. The lower rump, uppertail-coverts and edges of the tail feathers are straw, tending to pale orange. I have examined several known females, both known for certain as first-year and known with certainty to be aged 2 years or more and never found one with the chestnut band across the upper rump described by Clement *et al.* (1993).

First-year Like the female but with more noticeably brown wings. From forehead to rear crown it is browner with more noticeable black edges on the feathers. It is less glossy than a second-year adult. A first-year male may be taken for a second-year female.

Juvenile Clay-coloured above, possibly a little lighter or brighter on the rump. The tail is darker with some yellowish edging. The ear-coverts are dark to blackish with whitish shaft streaks. Below it is pale clay or creamy-buff, palest on the bib, often with some dark mottling on the throat and breast. This throat and breast marking is highly variable, ranging from none at all to dark edges to the feathers or terminal streaks. The bill is dark upon fledging but lightens over the next few weeks and is largely grey by the time the birds are feeding independently.

HYBRIDS A specimen in the collection at Leiden Museum was assumed to be a hybrid with Grey-crowned Mannikin (Mees 1982). In my opinion, the Leiden hybrid, despite its appearance as a perfect halfway between the two, is very likely to be a melanistic Grey-crowned Mannikin. Goodwin (1982) suggests it may be possible that Black Mannikin is a black morph of Grey-crowned Mannikin, but offers no explanation for the significantly smaller distribution of *L. stygia*. Mees (1982) concludes his paper with the opinion that they are not conspecific because the juveniles of these two species are clearly different and that *L. nevermanni* is closer to *L. castaneothorax*. A comparison of sonograms of the vocalisations of the two species shows a basic difference in the structure of the song of Black Mannikin to that of Grey-crowned Mannikin.

Michael Plose (pers. comm.) successfully bred Black Mannikins and Grey-crowned Mannikins in adjacent aviaries and both Oreste Piotto and Colin Rowe (*in litt.*) bred them in cages. All three of these English aviculturists agree with my own conclusions from personal experience with captive birds that they are different species on the basis of observations of display and breeding behaviour.

CONSERVATION There is not enough information from Irian Jaya to judge whether the depredations of the bird trade is having an effect on the wild populations of Black Mannikin. The initial excitement over the species was brought about because it was being cross-bred with the Bengalese and the resulting hybrids were being used to produce new colour varieties of Bengalese. These 'Black Bengalese' are now established and self-perpetuating. The need for fresh blood from wild Black Mannikins has now passed and demand dropped off significantly by the end of 1994. The quantities I have seen in the trade pipeline in Indonesia recently are small, and seem most unlikely to be a serious threat to wild population levels. Similarly the quantities recently registered with CITES are insignificant, and there appears to be no threat to habitat now or in the forseeable future. Nonetheless, bearing in mind the comparatively restricted area Black Mannikin inhabits,

I feel this is a species that should continue to be monitored.

REFERENCES Clement *et al.*(1993), Coates (1990), Goodwin (1982), Gregory (1995a), Mees (1982), Morris (1958), Nachrichten (1978), Rand (1938), Restall (1989), Stresemann (1935).

35 BLACK-BREASTED MANNIKIN
Lonchura teerinki   Plate 15

Described as *Lonchura teerinki* Rand
Other common name: Grand Valley Munia, Grand Valley Mannikin, Black-breasted Reed-finch (from the German), Black-breasted Munia.

Male Black-breasted Mannikin, with typical irregular flank stripe.

FIELD CHARACTERS A small munia with black head, breast and an irregular line running down the flanks. Above, it is brown with yellowish rump and uppertail-coverts. Possible confusion in the field with Hooded Mannikin *L. spectabilis* suggested by Clement *et al.* (1993) is extremely unlikely as their respective ranges do not overlap. It might possibly overlap with Snow Mountain Mannikin *L. montana* but this latter species has a clearly defined black face mask with a tan breast that will facilitate sure distinction from *L. teerinki* where the black of the face extends down the breast onto the flanks.

STATUS Uncommon to scarce.

HABITAT It is a bird of the grassy scrub hillsides ranging from 1,200–2,300m. Rand and Gilliard (1967) say the habitat of the species is largely the extensive secondary grasslands resulting from native clearing. Old gardens growing up with weeds are especially favoured feeding places. It has a liking for cultivated ground that has been abandoned and become overgrown with scrub, weeds and grass. It is often found near to villages (Herwin Purwahariyanto pers. comm.) and can also be seen in clearings at the edge of scrub forest.

HABITS AND BEHAVIOUR It is quite shy, but foraging groups will venture onto cultivated ground and into native gardens. It is a highly sociable bird. Groups will roost together, clumping and allopreening. I have observed an interesting incident involving peering, that I have called peering-enforced singing. Peering is a common phenomenen in this species and a solitary male engaged in undirected advertisement song will often aquire a peer.

One particular male that sang frequently in one of my captive study groups was attracted to another bird, believed to be a female. He would fly to her side and clump with her. Another male would fly to perch alongside the first male and crowd up alongside it, sandwiching it in the middle. This was not clumping, for the attitude of the second male was intent and overbearing. He stood tall on the perch, his head slightly higher than that of the other, despite being lower because of the incline, and peered hard at the first male, the tip of his bill only a few millimetres from the other bird's lores. It seemed to me, after watching this happen half-a-dozen times, that the second male was demanding a song, for the hapless male in the middle always responded to this pressure by immediately raising his crown and nape, lowering his bill, puffing out his breast and belly and singing. The female showed little interest in the proceedings, peering half-heartedly the first time, barely at all the second, and ignored it all subsequently. This peering-enforced singing behaviour took place several times within about an hour and always involved the same three birds on the same perch. I have also seen the same behaviour in Grand Mannikin *L. grandis* and Hooded Mannikin *L. spectabilis*.

FOOD AND FEEDING The species feeds on the seeds of grasses, weeds and small seeding shrubs. It feeds both on the ground, taking fallen seeds, and clinging to the stem's inflorescences and seeding heads of plants. There are no records of the species of plant that the birds take or prefer. In captivity, birds will take a wide variety of seeds without any marked preference. There are no indications of the species taking insects either in the wild or captivity.

MOVEMENTS Not known.

CALL The soft contact note is a soft clear and bell-like *tseep*, but a bird separated from others of its kind will call a loud *tcheep*, becoming an insistent *tcheep*! The tone of this loud contact call is different between the sexes, the male's note being more of a *tcheerp*! while that of the female is slightly higher, sweeter and thinner, more like *tseep*! The male's reply to the female is a *tchirp*?, sometimes a strong querulous note. From my observations the male has a much more extensive vocabulary than the female. In a group they are very conversational, keeping up a constant twittering. They sound more like sparrows (*Passer*) than other mannikins.

SONG The song of the male is not described. Ironically, I have seen the birds sing several times, but have never been close enough to hear or record it.

Male Black-breasted Mannikin in advertisement song.

COURTSHIP AND DISPLAY In advertisement display the male will take a straw or fibre but drop it before singing. He perches upright, leaning forward slighly, not exaggerated in any way, but with the flank feathers sufficiently erected to be clearly defined. If the female or a prospective mate is nearby he turns slightly towards her in mid-song. She listens intently, leaning forward at a more horizontal angle than that of the male, in an apparently ritualised response posture, turned towards the male in a kind of begging/soliciting copulation manner. Either bird, usually the female, will break off this engagement by flying away at some distraction.

In high intensity display the male leans forward more and has most of the feathers of the body erected, from nape to rump and throat to belly and flanks. He leans towards the female singing all the while until he is both very fluffed up and is leaning over her. He will hop closer and she may hop or edge closer to him until they are touching. Meanwhile, the female has imperceptibly lowered herself and leans forward. If she actively solicits copulation by looking straight forward and quivering her tail, the male will mount and attempt coition. This is followed by low intensity bill-fencing. If she does not actually solicit, the male appears to become distracted by the female's forward-bent head and begins to preen her nape. This is followed by low intensity bill-fencing.

BREEDING An unattributed report in the Dutch bird magazine *Onze Vogels* in 1989 mentioned that both sexes build the nest, which is an oval structure with the entrance at one end, made of grasses and suitable fibres. Apparently it is usually placed in the fork of a bush. The clutch is 3–5 eggs and incubation by both sexes takes 13–14 days. The young fledge in 3 weeks.

DISTRIBUTION North-west central New Guinea. The race *L. t. teerinki* is found in the Grand Valley (cut by the Baliem and Bele Rivers) and the northern slope of Mt. Wilhelmina in the central Snow Mountains and Orange Mountains. The race *L. t. mariae* is found around Bokidini, 50km north of the Baliem Valley in the central Snow Mountains.

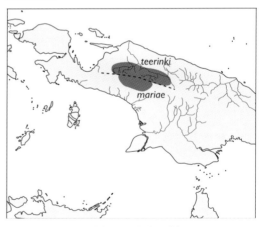

Distribution of Black-breasted Mannikin.

DESCRIPTION   Plate 76

There are two subspecies as described below.

BLACK-BREASTED MANNIKIN
L. teerinki teerinki
Rand, 1940, *Amer. Mus. Novit.*, no.1577, p.7.
Adult male 100–105mm. Wing length 50–52mm, culmen 10mm, tarsus 12–13mm. The entire head is black, merging smoothly into fuscous on the nape.

Black-breasted Mannikins. From left to right, adult male, adult female and juvenile.

The black of the face continues to the breast and abruptly graduates into an irregular line that runs down the side of each breast and onto the flanks. There is an irregular patch of white and rufous-chestnut at the sides of the breast. On the sides of the body beneath the folded wing it is white with an irregular flush of tawny or antique-brown, which runs around onto the rump. This tawny may be rich in colour and extensive. The black line along the flanks might contain patches or traces of this brown, especially at the end of the flanks, but it might also completely fill the area between the black and the underwing-coverts. The belly and the ventral region is white or perhaps tinged creamy-white. The underwing-coverts are pale pinky-buff. The thighs and the undertail-coverts are jet black. The back and wings are a rich uniform cinnamon-brown or mid-brown, and the flight feathers, including the tertials, are noticeably darker. The rump is cinnamon-rufous. The uppertail-coverts are straw-yellow. The tail is blackish in the centre of the inner feathers with a broad straw edging to the outer edges; the outer rectrices are dark brown with straw on the outer edges. The bill is stout, with the length of the culmen, lower mandible and the height of the bill all being 10mm. It is blue-grey, darker on the culmen, palest on the cutting edges. The feet and legs are dark leaden-grey.

Adult female *c*.100mm. Wing length 49– 50mm, culmen 9.5–10mm, tarsus 12mm. It is similar to the male but when a pair are seen side by side in good light, or compared in the hand, it may be seen to be slightly browner on the head. The back is a uniform cinnamon-brown. The rump is dark cinnamon which extends around the body under the wings. The uppertail-coverts are buff. The line of black-and-chestnut down the flanks is shorter, then becomes a series of black patches. As with the second-year male there may be some of the brown of the body under the wing and rump appearing in the lower end of the bar. The belly and ventral region are white. The thighs and undertail-coverts are jet black. The stout bill is slightly narrower than the males with the length of the lower mandible being fractionally longer than the culmen, and the height of the bill being fractionally less. It is dark blue-grey, darker on the culmen and paler on the cutting edge. The legs and feet are dark or leaden grey, or dark vinaceous-grey.

First-year Sexes are much more alike. The black of the face is duller, and graduates into the dark brown of the nape in scallops that begin on the crown. The back is lighter than in the older birds being an earthy-chestnut or deep raw sienna. The black of the breast forms into the bars on the sides of the breast and flanks but is invariably broken and then becomes an irregular trail of black, white and brown patches. The black usually stops shorter on the female, but it is not a reliable diagnostic feature. The upper rump is as the back, with only the lower rump being the brown of the underwing. The short uppertail-coverts are tawny-olive to buffy. The tail is dark brown with buffy edgings to the middle feathers, and only slightly on the rest.

Juvenile Clay-coloured above being lighter on the lower rump and uppertail-coverts, and creamy-cinnamon below, warmer on the chin and throat. There may be some light cinnamon on the flanks and rump. It soon acquires some adult plumage, first darkening on the face and streaking on the central upper breast, and becoming black on the thighs and undertail-coverts. At this stage the rump is light-cinnamon and the long uppertail-coverts are dark brown as is the tail. The bill is black upon fledging but gradually becomes blue-grey. The legs and feet are black.

BOKIDINI BLACK-BREASTED MANNIKIN
L. teerinki mariae
Ripley, 1964, *Bull. Peabody Mus.Nat. Hist.* (Yale Univ.), 19, p.74.

Adult Black on the entire head and breast, and the back and wings are chestnut, that is, deeper and richer brown than *L. t. teerinki*. In other respects it resembles the nominate race as described above, although Ripley (1964) says the black of the lower flanks, thighs and undertail-coverts appears denser, more truly black.

Juvenile Sightly darker than the young of the nominate race.

HYBRIDS No hybrids have been recorded. A single female in one of my study groups of captive birds bonded to a male *L. spectabilis* in preference to any other species of munia in the enclosure. They went to nest but did not breed.

CONSERVATION The species appears to be in no danger from change of habitat. Indeed, human destruction of the woodlands in the region could well benefit it. It is being trapped irregularly in small numbers in the vicinity of Wamena, for the bird trade, the birds finding their way to Europe and the United States. The birds do not do well in captivity and are very difficult to breed. The demand is small, since they seem to be somewhat of a specialist's species. The quantities that find their way into the trade are also small, however, usually only of a dozen or so birds at a time. This is unlikely to have any effect at all on local populations.

REFERENCES Clement *et al.* (1993), Goodwin (1982), Rand & Gilliard (1967), Restall (1989 & 1995a), Ripley (1964).

36 SNOW MOUNTAIN MANNIKIN
Lonchura montana   Plate 15

Other scientific name: *Munia montana* Junge, 1939, *Nova Guinea*, new ser., 3, p. 67.
Other common names: Western Alpine Mannikin.

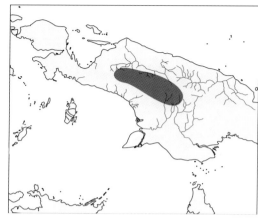

Distribution of Snow Mountain Mannikin.

Snow Mountain Mannikin

FIELD CHARACTERS A medium-sized munia with a black face and undertail-coverts with a barred pattern across the lower breast and flanks, otherwise brownish. It may be distinguished from the smaller Black-breasted Mannikin *L. teerinki* by its buff-yellow breast. The black of the breast of Black-breasted Mannikin is much more extensive than that of Snow Mountain Mannikin where it is restricted to the face. At a distance it could be taken for the smaller Hooded Mannikin *L. spectabilis* but the two do not overlap in range. Another rather similar lowland mannikin is Chestnut-breasted Mannikin *L. castaneothorax sharpii*, also smaller, and readily distinguished by the pale grey back of head and nape. The juvenile Snow Mountain Mannikin can be told from juveniles of other mannikins by its dark bib and throat.

STATUS Common or locally common.

HABITAT It inhabits alpine grassland, the edges of shrub-grown areas and, at least in the Ilaga Valley, cultivated fields (Ripley 1964).

HABITS AND BEHAVIOUR No information is recorded on social behaviour. Rand and Gilliard (1967) refer to the species as the Snow Mountain representative of Alpine Mannikin *L. monticola* of southeastern New Guinea, and having similar habits. Together with *L. teerinki* they probably form a superspecies.

FOOD AND FEEDING Ripley (1964) reports it feeding on weeds and grass seeds, flying from field to field in closely-packed flocks, and perching freely in alang-alang grass and trees. Rand and Gilliard (1967) found it in flocks of 6–20 birds but on examination these were not in breeding condition. Since some munias flock for feeding even when breeding it cannot be deduced that it only flocks out of season. On Mt. Capella it was recorded by Flannery (1987) as being a common camp visitor that fed on the seeds of grasses and herbs.

MOVEMENTS No information is recorded.

CALL No information is recorded.

SONG Nothing known.

COURTSHIP AND DISPLAY No information is recorded.

BREEDING It is reported to nest in grasses beside water (Beehler *et al.* 1986).

DISTRIBUTION Snow Mountains, Irian Jaya; recorded from 2,000m and upwards, but usually ranging between 2,900m and 4,000m. (Beehler *et al.* 1986) west of the Baliem gorge, western central New Guinea to Mount Capella, Papua New Guinea (Clement *et al.* 1993).

DESCRIPTION
Monotypic.
Adult male *c.*115mm. Wing length 60mm, culmen 13mm, tarsus 18mm (Rand and Gilliard 1967). The entire face from rear crown, ear-coverts to chin is black. The nape is pale cinnamon, extending in a broad collar to the breast; there is a continual graduation by flecking from the nape to the mantle which is earth-brown, as are the wings. The mantle and wing-coverts are barred with a darker brown, fine wavy lines of the same character as on the plumage of African Silverbill *L. cantans*. The rump, uppertail-coverts and edges of the tail feathers are buff-yellow. The breast is a warm buff-yellow. There is a bar of barred black-and-white across the lower breast, which continues in broad irregular bars along the flanks. The belly is cream. The thighs and undertail coverts are black. The slightly longish bill is pale blue-grey (described as pale grey or lead grey in Clement *et al.* 1993, black in Coates 1990). The legs and feet are grey. The irides are brown.
Adult female Paler straw-yellow on the breast, and the black face mask is more clear-cut on the throat and does not merge into the breast. The black on top of the head is restricted to the forehead (Clement *et al.* 1993).
Juvenile Dull earth-brown above, darker on the face. The rump and uppertail-coverts tend to straw. The chin is the dark earth-brown of the face, graduating to warm, almost cinnamon on the breast. There is no streaking on the throat or breast. The remainder of the underparts are dull creamy-buff. It has the iris light brown, bill black, and legs and feet brown.

HYBRIDS Nothing recorded.

CONSERVATION Insufficient information to draw even tentative conclusions. The species has never occurred in the bird trade, apparently being outside the range of the small-bird trappers from Wamena or Jayapura.

REFERENCES Beehler *et al.* (1986), Clement *et al.* (1993), Coates (1990), Flannery (1987), Rand & Gilliard (1967), Ripley (1964).

37 ALPINE MANNIKIN
Lonchura monticola

Plate 15

Described as *Lonchura monticola* De Vis.
Other common names: Eastern Alpine Mannikin or Munia.

Alpine Mannikin

FIELD CHARACTERS This is a large-bodied mannikin with a black face, black breast bar and flanks, brown above with straw rump and tail. The only possible confusion in the field could be with the variant of Hooded Mannikin *L. spectabilis guariae* which is cinnamon below and has barring along the flanks. However, this bird is significantly smaller. The juveniles of the two are quite similar, but the smaller size of *L. spectabilis* is diagnostic.

STATUS Common but local.

HABITAT Flocks ranging in size from 20 to 50 birds have been recorded in June and July. Immatures are often seen in separate and smaller flocks, and are much less shy of man than are the adult birds. A pair of Alpine Mannikins was seen at the edge of a flock of about 100 Grey-headed Mannikins *L. caniceps* at Myola airstrip, well below the previously-recorded altitude range for the species and, incidentally, well above the expected altitude range for *L. caniceps*. Two birds were subsequently seen on the grassland border of the moss forest, again in the company of *L. caniceps* (Hicks 1987). They are normally found in the vicinity of shrubbery, trees and rocks between 2,750m and 3,900m but will follow trails down through the forests to colonise grassy clearings at lower elevations (Coates 1990).

HABITS AND BEHAVIOUR The flight is described as being more direct than that of mannikins from lower elevations (Clement *et al.* 1993). The juveniles tend to form flocks by themselves (Mayr and Rand 1937).

FOOD AND FEEDING It feeds on the small seeds of grasses typical of the alpine grassland and rocky areas with small grassy patches (Rand and Gilliard 1967). It will cling to grass stems and pick seeds from the heads and will also hop around the ground picking up fallen seeds. Gregory (1995b) mentions watching it, in the company of Grey-headed Mannikins *L. caniceps*, feed on short turf around the village of Myola.

MOVEMENTS Not known.

CALL Beehler (1986) refers to the call while in flight as being a thin *see see see*, and a call note of "a distinctive rattling buzz similar to that of Plum-headed Finch *Aidemosyne modesta* of Australia, and unlike the typical *tyu* notes of other mannikins." Gregory (1995b) describes the call as

being quite harsh, a rather nasal and buzzy *tee tee*, and different to the plaintive note of the Grey-headed mannikin.

SONG The song is not recorded.

COURTSHIP AND DISPLAY The displays are not recorded.

BREEDING Alpine Mannikins have been found breeding at Myola (Gregory-Smith and Gregory-Smith 1990). Birds were seen carrying material from a patch of rushes on the village side of the stream at Myola and building about 3m from the ground in a small tree on the far bank. The nest appears to be fairly typical in size and form but is described as being more neatly woven than usual for *Lonchura*. The two nests described were made of rushes and grasses with a side entrance, but as described to me (Hicks *in litt.*), I inferred them to be a little smaller and neater than a typical munia nest, possibly more densly put together to protect against cold.

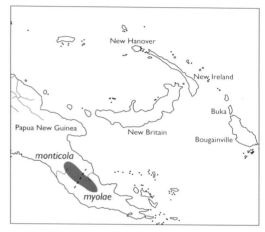

Distribution of Alpine Mannikin.

DISTRIBUTION A high altitude grassland species of southeastern Papua New Guinea, found between 2,800m and 3,900m, and truly an alpine bird. *L. m. monticola* occurs in the Wharton Range and *L. m. myolae* occurs in the Owen Stanley Range. The dividing line between the two races lies between the Murray Pass in the Wharton Range and Mt. Scratchley. It has been recorded at 2,080m at Myola, Hicks (1987), and Coates (1990) refers to it at Guari which is at 1,860m.

DESCRIPTION
There are two or three races. The Wharton Range birds are slightly creamy-yellow on the belly compared to the white of the Owen Stanley Range birds, and have fine barring on the mantle. The Owen Stanley Range birds are slightly richer in colouring on the back and rump. Birds from Guari are apparently distinct (Coates 1990), but are undescribed.

ALPINE MANNIKIN
L. monticola monticola
De Vis (1897). *Ibis*, p.387.
Adult *c.*120mm. Wing length 62–64mm (surprisingly long for a munia), culmen 13mm recorded by Rand and Gilliard (1967), but in museum specimens I measured the bill was surprisingly small, with a culmen of

9mm and 8–9mm deep. The entire front of the head, to the rear crown, ear-coverts and bib is dusky-brown to blackish. The nape is clay-coloured, forming a collar that covers the upper breast, and which may be scalloped or streaked with cinnamon. The mantle is dark earth-brown with the basal part of the feathers darker, giving the effect that the back is lightly scalloped with cinnamon. The wings are tawny with darker centres to the feathers. The rump, uppertail-coverts and edges of the blackish tail are straw-coloured. The upper breast is white with slight brown suffusions. A bar of white-scalloped black runs across the lower breast, and continues down the flanks. The thighs and undertail-coverts are black. The belly is pale yellowish-buffy. The irides are brown. The blue or blue-grey bill is small and conical. The impression of a typically munia-proportioned bill given in the illustrations in Beehler *et al.* (1986) and Clement *et al.* (1993) are misleading. The legs and feet are grey.

Juvenile *c.*115mm. It is fuscous on the face and upper head, graduating to hair-brown on the back and burnt umber on the wings and tail. It is dark tawny on the rump and uppertail-coverts. The bib is buffy, heavily mottled with black. The throat and breast are pale raw umber, the feathers having blackish centres. The sides of the breast, flanks and thighs are pale horn, the belly being paler. The ventral region and undertail-coverts were dark brown to fuscous on the single bird I examined in Papua New Guinea, but several juveniles I examined in the AMNH New York had pale spots on the dark undertail-coverts. The bill is grey to dark grey, and the legs and feet are grey. There is no racial difference between the juveniles.

MYOLA ALPINE MANNIKIN
L. monticola myolae
Restall, 1995, *Bull. Brit. Orn. Club.* 115 (3), 140 - 157.
Adult Similar to the nominate but differs in having the back clear chestnut without any mottling or scaling. The belly is the same clear, even white as the upper breast patch. The yellow of the uppertail-coverts is slightly richer than on *L. m. monticola*.

HYBRIDS Coates (1990) refers to Alpine Mannikin showing signs of hybridising with Grey-headed Mannikin at Guari, but gives no details. The implication is that the Guari population is visually different in some way and may represent an undescribed race.

CONSERVATION No information is available about the habitat and whether any significant changes are likely, or how they might affect the species. There is no legal activity by the bird trade in Papua New Guinea. Any illicit trade in birds would concentrate on species with a high market value, which mannikins do not have, and I have found no mention of the species in the trade at all.

REFERENCES Beehler *et al.* (1986), Coates (1990), Gregory (1995b), Gregory-Smith & Gregory-Smith (1989), Hicks (1987), Mayr & Rand (1937), Rand & Gilliard (1967), Restall (1995b).

38 THICK-BILLED MANNIKIN
Lonchura melaena   Plate 11

Described as *Lonchura melaena* Sclater
Former scientific name: *Munia melaena*
Other common names: Buff-bellied Black Mannikin, Thick-billed Munia or Mannikin, New Britain Mannikin (in Clements 1981) and New Britain Finch (in Clement *et al.* 1993), neither to be confused with the Hooded Mannikin *L. spectabilis* which is often referred to as the New Britain Mannikin.

Thick-billed Mannikin

FIELD CHARACTERS A large blackish munia with a large heavy bill, a cinnamon belly and reddish-orange uppertail-coverts. It is significantly bigger than Hooded Mannikin. The latter has a white or whitish belly and flanks and has a bill that is smaller both proportionately and absolutely.

STATUS Common or locally common.

HABITAT In New Britain it is a common bird of both open lowland grassland, and open broken woodland with grassy areas. It has been recorded up to 1,200m (LeCroy and Peckover 1983). In Buka it has been observed in grassy, swampy areas near the airstrip.

HABITS It moves around in small flocks of from 4–40 birds (Roger Hicks pers. comm.) and may be found amongst the swampy vegetation and trees, feeding on the seeds of the various grasses. Finch and McKean (1987) note seeing up to 20 birds frequenting rank grasslands near the radio tower just past the Local Government buildings in Hoskins. They described it as superficially like the Grand Mannikin *L. grandis* but felt it to be proportionally larger.

FOOD AND FEEDING Bishop (1987) watched a small group of about five birds feeding on sugar cane seeding heads *Saccharum* sp. Birds were also seen bathing in a small roadside puddle about 20km south of Hoskins in west New Britain. It has often been seen feeding on beaches bare of vegetation, but it is not known what it was feeding on. Immelmann *et al.* (1968-72) supposed it took mineral matter.

MOVEMENTS Possibly nomadic within its very limited range (Clement *et al.* 1993).

CALL The call is short and high-pitched (Coates 1990). I have a note (without source) that the call is apparently similar to that of *L. spectabilis*.

SONG Nothing recorded.

COURTSHIP AND DISPLAY Nothing recorded.

BREEDING Thick-billed Mannikins tend to nest colonially, usually in tall grass, and virtually all the year round.
Hadden (1981) found a nest in January being visited by a
bird which had led him to it. It was an untidy bundle of
grasses with a side entrance, well concealed, about 2m
from the ground in tall vegetation. Additional occupied
nests were seen in December 1980. Two had 2 eggs, one
held a single egg and another nest with 4 eggs was apparently deserted. Two of the occupied nests were within one
metre of each other. One egg measured 15.9mm x 11.0mm
and was off-white in colour. At this time birds were observed carrying nesting material.

The nest is built of grasses and is lined with finer panicles and florescences. The clutch is believed to be from
3–6 eggs. There is no information on brooding and incubation, nor feeding of the young.

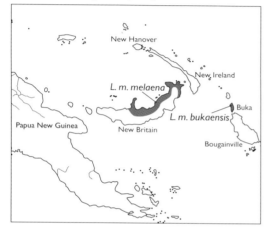

Distribution of Thick-billed Mannikin.

DISTRIBUTION *L. m.. melaena* is found on the northern
part of New Britain, and from Kimbe to Hoskins in West
New Britain (Bishop 1987). *L. m. bukaensis* appears from
local reports to occur in suitable habitat over the entire
island of Buka in the North Solomons.

DESCRIPTION
There are two races recognised. The New Britain race is
uniform brown from crown to lower back and has the
flanks black. The Buka race has the entire head black and
the rest of the upperparts are darker than the nominate.
The salmon belly extends to the flanks.

NEW BRITAIN THICK-BILLED MANNIKIN
L. melaena melaena
Former scientific name: *Munia melaena* Sclater, 1880,
Proc.Zool. Soc. London, p.66, pl. 7. fig 2..
Adult *c*.120mm. Wing length 54mm, culmen 13mm,
tarsus 16mm. The bill is larger and deeper than that
of most munias, being *c*.12mm deep; this causes the
head to be proportionally larger. In this it is very similar to Grand Mannikin *L. grandis*. The forehead, lores,
around the eye, ear-coverts, bib to breast, flanks,
thighs, ventral area and undertail-coverts are all black.
From the crown to the lower back it is dark olive-
brown, while the wings are dark brown. The rump,
uppertail-coverts and edges of the tail are chrome-

orange. The belly and underwing-coverts are pale cinnamon-rufous to salmon. The black of the flanks is in
the form of a series of thick irregular bars. The irides
are brown. The bill is black with pale blue at the base
of the lower mandible. The legs and feet are dark grey
to blackish.

There is no information about sexual differences. The
species appears to be the geographic representative
of Grand Mannikin which is significantly polymorphic
in some races, the males being up to 20% larger and
having noticeably larger bills with more curved cul-
mens than the females. It is therefore possible that a
series of measurements would show males being larger
than the females by 10% or more.

Juvenile Head dark brown, with pale streaking on the
chin. On the nape it becomes mid-brown, graduating
to paler brown on the rump and uppertail-coverts.
The breast is umber, graduating to cinnamon on the
belly and undertail-coverts. The underwing-coverts are
cinnamon. The bill is slightly smaller than in the adult
and the upper mandible is blackish while the lower is
grey.

BUKA THICK-BILLED MANNIKIN
L. melaena bukaensis
Restall, 1995, *Bull. Brit. Orn. Club* 115 (3), 140–157.
Adult *c*.120mm. Wing length *c*.54mm, culmen 12–
13mm, tarsus 15mm. This bird differs from *L. m.
melaena* in being much darker above. The black extends over the complete head and is washed over the
dark olive-brown back. The wings are dark brown. The
rump, uppertail-coverts and edges of the tail are dark
scarlet to chestnut (described by Hadden (1981) as
cinnamon-rufous, but in the specimens I examined
in Papua New Guinea they were definitely darker and
redder). The black of the breast is more extensive
than in the nominate race. The belly is buffy-salmon.
I was able to study two specimens of this race in the
collection of the National Museum in Port Moresby
and the colour plate of the bird is taken from these.
Juvenile Presumably similar to that of *L. m. melaena*.
Clearly more information about both is required.

CONSERVATION There appears to be no threat to the
habitat, nor is there any trapping for the bird trade.

REFERENCES Bishop (1987), Clement *et al.* (1993),
Clements (1981), Finch & McKean (1987), Hadden
(1981), Immelmann *et al.* (1968-72), LeCroy & Peckover
(1983).

39   PICTORELLA MANNIKIN
Lonchura pectoralis   Plate 16

Former scientific names: *Amadina pectoralis*, Gould, 1841,
Proc. Zool. Soc. London, 8, (1940), p. 127. *Heteromunia pecto-
ralis*, Matthews, 1913.
Other common names: Pictorella or Pectoral Finch, White-
breasted Finch, Mannikin or Munia, Pectoralis Finch,
Mannikin or Munia.

INTRODUCTION Goodwin (1982) suggests it is a primitive species in evolutionary terms and recognises the
supergenus *Heteromunia*. Kakizawa and Watada (1985)
place it as the most primitive estrildid of all the species

Pictorella Mannikins

they analysed, as did Christidis (1987). Sibley and Monroe (1990) follow Christidis in placing the Pictorella Mannikin in its own genus *Heteromunia*.

FIELD CHARACTERS A black-faced, grey-brown munia with a white breast slightly scaled with black. It is unlikely to be confused with any other bird. The black face recalls Chestnut-breasted Mannikin *L. castaneothorax* but the brown breast and white belly should quickly separate this bird. However the juveniles are very similar, as is the juvenile Yellow-rumped Mannikin *L. flaviprymna*.

STATUS Uncommon or locally common. It is declining in parts of its range, for reasons which are unclear.

HABITAT It is a nomadic bird that can be found in moist country with good vegetation, but may be found in dry country in the interior and also in true spinfex country. It inhabits open grassy plains dotted with trees and bushes, but prefers to nest near water, dams, creeks and waterholes.

HABITS AND BEHAVIOUR It travels in pairs or small parties but large flocks may occur near water at times of drought and it may form mixed flocks with other grass finches. From observations of captive birds, it appears to develop very strong pair bonding. Pairs that become separated, for whatever reason, do not usually pair again, and if so, only after a considerable period of what can only be described as mourning.

FOOD AND FEEDING It normally feeds on the ground taking fallen seeds, seeds from growing dwarf grasses and weeds and small insects. However, it is perfectly able to climb up and down the stems of grasses in true munia fashion to take the seeding heads. On occasions it is found in the rice fields feeding on the half-grown or half-ripe rice but is not devoted to this cereal to the extent of Chestnut-breasted and Yellow-rumped Mannikins. Grasses recorded in the species' list of preferences include *Echinachloa colnum*, *Chloris virgata* and several species of *Iseilema* (Immelmann 1965). It is known to take insects, including small spiders, flying ants, termites and small beetles.

It drinks in the usual way, but with quick sips, taking a bill-full and tilting the head up, in a much quicker sequence than seen in other mannikins. It has been seen drinking by sucking (Harrison, in Hall 1974) an interesting adaptation that allows the birds to draw moisture from tiny cracks and crevices (e.g. early morning dew) in the absence of open water. This ability has also evolved in the Zebra Finch *Poephila guttata castanotis* but not in any other *Lonchura* species to my knowledge.

MOVEMENTS It is a nomadic bird that wanders widely, particularly inland during the summer.

CALL The call is described as a double note *k-rt k-rt* (Slater 1974), or a low sparrow-like *chip* (Immelmann 1982).

There is a long sharp contact call given by a single bird seeking contact, described variously as *tleet*, *tlit* or *teet* which may be uttered by a bird on the ground or in flight.

SONG There is effectively no song, this being reduced to a simple two note performance, uttered 2 seconds apart, described by most writers after Immelmann as *gee* or *giee*. It may be given by a male alone on a perch, when the bird will bow forward with bill open a little, but usually during courtship display. Immelmann (1982) construes that the species might have had a song at one point because males will peer at singing males of other *Lonchura* species in captivity.

COURTSHIP AND DISPLAY The courtship of Pictorella Mannikin is unique among mannikins and bears some similarities to that of the Crimson Finch *Neochima phaeton* (Cayley 1932), possibly the result of convergence (Goodwin 1982). It takes place entirely on the ground and usually begins by both sexes making pecking movements and sometimes picking up and dropping small objects. The male might take up an item of nesting material in his bill, (some males do not), then, with bill pointing upward, body feathers fluffed and the tail fanned and pressed down, he hops back and forth in front of the female in ever-diminishing semi-circles until he is soon simply hopping in front of her. He then drops the grass or straw, if he had one, and hops around until he is alongside her, whereupon he bows. He then continues hopping around until he is alongside her other side, whereupon he bows again, quite deeply. He may continue around her several times until either the female quivers her tail to solicit copulation, or she flies away. The preliminary behaviour when the two birds peck at the ground, picking up small objects and letting them fall, may well take place without a following full courtship display by the male. During nest building the male often persistently chases the female in flight and then calls her to the nest (Guttinger 1976).

BREEDING The nest is usually built in a tussock of grass, or in a low bush or a tussock of spinfex, rarely more than 50cm from the ground, usually only a few centimetres from the ground. It is a rough ovoid built of fresh green and dried grasses, rootlets, twiglets and fibres, lined with finer pieces including feathers, with a small entrance hole at one end. It is described in Frith (1976) as bottle-shaped with a 10cm-long entrance tunnel. It has thick walls and is approximately 25cm long, 12cm high and 12cm wide. Four to six eggs form the clutch and as usual with *Lonchura* both sexes share incubation during the day with the female incubating at night.

Palate markings of the nestling Pictorella Mannikin.

Incubation is 12 or 13 days and the young naturally fledge in about 3 weeks. However, they will leave the nest from as early as 16 days if disturbed. When hatched, the nestlings are naked and dark with two luminous tubercules at the gape. The palate markings are very similar to those of the African *Spermestes* group of mannikins. The nestlings soon become dark-skinned. They are brooded during the day for the first two weeks, and then only at night. For the first few days after fledging the young return to the nest to roost. When begging for food they raise the far-side wing in the manner of the African mannikins. They begin to feed themselves within a few days and are independent about two weeks after this. They achieve adult plumage at about four months old.

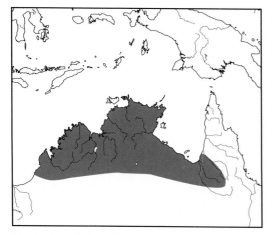

Distribution of Pictorella Mannikin.

DISTRIBUTION Tropical northern Australia. It is found within two areas (Blakers 1984). The first is bounded by a line from Derby in King Sound, Western Australia, south-eastwards across the Kimberly Plateau, possibly as far south as Lake Gregory in the summer, to the coast of the Gulf of Carpentaria around Limmen Blight. It then occurs again from the Robinson River south to the Barkly Tableland, across the Flinders network in Queensland to about Richmond, then north-west, east of Croyden and Vanrook, to about the Mitchell River. This is quite a reduction from the range shown on earlier distribution maps.

DESCRIPTION
Monotypic.
Adult male 110–115mm. Wing length 60mm (one individual I measured had the wing 66mm), culmen 11mm with a height of 9mm and the length of the lower mandible is 12mm, tarsus 13mm. The face and throat are black with a purple lustre. There may be a few white spots on the black on the sides of the throat. A crescent of pale cinnamon surrounds the black, from the nostrils, over the eye and round to the sides of the neck. From forehead to mantle, lower back and wings, it is a vinaceous-fawn with tiny white terminal spots on the median and greater wing-coverts. The rump and uppertail-coverts are plumbeous. The underwing-coverts are salmon. There is a broad band of white across the breast, in fact these feathers have black subterminal bands that are concealed by the large white spots at the end of each feather. The black shows sometimes in a slight and irregular scaling effect, most noticeable at the upper sides of the breast. The underparts are a delicate pale pinkish-hazel. Some of the feathers on the upper flanks have black spots with white spots within and grey edges, but these are largely concealed by the closed

wings. The undertail-coverts are barred blackish and white with pink-hazel edges. The bill is bluish-grey, darker on the culmen. It is proportionately longer and sharper than is usual for a munia. The legs and feet are flesh-coloured.
Adult female 105–110mm. Wing length 56–60mm exceptionally 64mm, culmen 10.5–11mm, the height of the bill at the base is 7.5–8mm and the length of the lower mandible is 11–12mm, tarsus 12–13mm. The face is black with brownish-grey mixed on the ear-coverts. The black subterminal bars on the breast feathers are more extensive and thus more noticeable, generally giving a mixed scaling and spotted effect to the white breast. The underparts are paler and more buffy than on the male. On all the skins I examined only the female had white terminal spots on the tertials as well as the greater wing-coverts. However, in an excellent photograph of a pair in Frith (1976) the male can clearly be seen to have white terminal spots on the tertials. Nicholas Day also illustrates white spots on the tertials of a male (Simpson and Day 1984).
Juvenile Dull brown above, darker on face and throat, wings and tail with reddish-buff tips and fringes to most wing feathers. The breast is dusky-grey and the rest of the underparts are pinky-buff. The brown, however, quickly fades to a pale buffish-brown above (Goodwin 1982). The bill is brownish-black, the legs and feet dark flesh.

HYBRIDS No hybrids have been recorded in the wild. In captivity it appears to have been crossed with Chestnut-breasted Mannikin and African Silverbill *L. cantans* (Grey 1958). Cayley (1932) writes of two hybrids, the first between Pictorella Mannikin and Diamond Firetail *Zonaeginthus guttata*, the second with Masked Grassfinch *Poephila personata.*

CONSERVATION It is listed as a Near-threatened species by Collar *et al.* (1994).

REFERENCES Blakers *et al.* (1984), Cayley (1932), Christidis (1987), Frith (1976), Goodwin (1982), Grey (1958), Guttinger (1976), Hall (1974), Immelmann (1982), Kakizawa & Watada (1985), Sibley & Monroe (1990), Simpson & Day (1984), Slater (1974).

40 JAVA SPARROW
Lonchura oryzivora   Plate 16

Former scientific names: *Loxia oryzivora*, Linnaeus, 1758. *Padda oryzivora.* Reichenbach, 1850.
Other common names: Rice Bird, Rice Munia, Paddy Bird, Temple Bird, Java Finch.

FIELD CHARACTERS A large grey munia with a black head and white cheek patch, and a pink bill. It is quite unlikely to be confused with any other species.

STATUS Scarce to uncommon (see remarks under Conservation).

HABITAT It is a bird of cultivated grassland with a marked preference for cereal crops, especially rice. It is most likely to be seen in the southern lowlands in Bali, where it may be seen in fields and gardens, and in cultivated areas scattered throughout Java.

HABITS AND BEHAVIOUR Flocks will gather in rice paddies, where they can consume considerable amounts of rice in a short time. Unlike Scaly-breasted Munia *L. punctulata* which is smaller and more cryptically coloured, Java Sparrow is easy to see. Flocks will gather in tall trees, or on the roofs of houses in the evening for up to half an hour or so before flying off to roost, conversing with various notes, but I have never seen singing or displays in this situation. In flight a flock will undulate and corkscrew, individual birds within the flock each following its own trajectory. This characteristic is the same regardless of the size of flock.

In disputes over nest sites protagonists are said to perform an elaborate body weaving display (MacKinnon and Phillipps 1994).

Bowing phase of greeting display of Java Sparrow.

There is a greeting display when a pair will bow their heads and, with bodies horizontal, each bird lifts its head, turned slightly towards the other, then the bow is repeated. This is similar to the greeting display of Timor Sparrow *L. fuscata*. There is a threat display, no doubt derived from a nest cavity defence posture such as that given by Great Tit *Parus major* where the bill is opened and the head turned from side to side while being pointed at the object being threatened or perceived as being a threat. The white cheeks are thus presented alternately. I have seen this performed by a bird in the nest box entrance and by a bird perching in a cage. In both cases the display was directed at me personally.

Head-twisting threat display of Java Sparrow.

Clumping and mutual preening occurs. The instinct to clump seems to be particularly strong in this species. Birds will sit or roost firmly pressed next to another. An interesting variation of this has been observed many times among domestic Java Sparrows and certain doves and pigeons (Goodwin 1952, 1963, 1965 and 1982, Morris 1956 and Brown 1963). Java Sparrows may roost at night or rest at day beside, underneath, or on top of certain doves that are kept with them. It has not been observed in the wild, but there are virtually no observations of Java Sparrows in the wild. I am not aware of any specific experiments designed to understand this behaviour. Obviously the instinct to clump is exceptionally strongly developed in this species and I suspect these particular doves, with their soft greys of plumage simply present an overwhelming offer-to-

clump stimulus. The contribution of this behaviour to the survival of the species has yet to be figured out.

Java Sparrow clumping alongside a Barbary Dove (after Morris 1956).

Java Sparrow attempting to roost underneath a Barbary Dove (after Morris 1956).

Java Sparrow roosting under a dove on the nest (after Goodwin 1982).

FOOD AND FEEDING When the rice is ripening it gathers in large flocks and obviously is capable of consuming considerable amounts, which naturally lead to its persecution. It wanders in small flocks, occasionally only in pairs, at other times of the year. It feeds both on the ground, and climbs stems to take seeds from the heads of various grasses and probably other seeding plants. Bernstein (1861) says it will take small fruits and possibly insects. I have hand-reared Java Sparrows, feeding them on a mixture of high-protein human baby food and hulled millet. The birds were reared indoors in a totally artificial environment and had never been exposed to a natural habitat nor to other Java Sparrows from which they might have acquired any feeding behaviour. When fully independent and several months old they immediately recognised stems of half-ripe seeding grasses as food, chewing on the milky seeds happily. Later, when given branches that were infested with greenfly they readily took the soft green insects and gobbled them up as well. I am not convinced this demonstrates a propensity to take insects. Rather I think the greenfly were seen as grass seeds, and happened to taste good as well. Java Sparrows normally rear their young entirely on vegetable matter in captivity, even when insects in various forms are available.

MOVEMENTS Generally sedentary, with local movements in response to the availability of cereal crops, rice in particular. There is some wandering by flocks that are composed mainly of juveniles and birds of the year.

CALL The call note is a kind of *tchuk*, and is slightly different between male and female. When a pair are calling to each other from a short distance apart this dissonance can be readily heard. However there is some variety of tone and intensity according to circumstances, and whether the bird is alarmed or not. A group in flight will call to each other with variations, and I have recorded *tik! tick! tek! teck! tuk!* and *tchuk!* all from the same group on one occasion. In a crowded gathering some birds will utter a rolling *crrrrrkk* or maybe *crrrrrkrkrkrkrkrkrkrk!* seemingly to assert social dominance. I have never heard this from a passive or submissive bird. I take this to be the growling or rattling aggression note mentioned by Goodwin (1982) but not heard by him. A typical situation when it is uttered would be when there is not enough room for all the birds at a feeding spot.

The mewing sound described in detail by Goodwin (1982) is uttered by many if not all munias, usually in the nest, when one bird is alone but aware the other is nearby, or when both are in the nest settling for the night. It may be uttered by a bird settling for the night outside the nest, and being forced to roost on a perch, but aware that others of its kind are close by. This is the kind of situation that occurs with captive birds. I have heard the mew from known male birds but have not heard it from known females. There is a short trilling call that is uttered after successful mating.

SONG The song is variable among individuals and may be described as a mixture of *diks*, *tchuks* and *wees* that are uttered at first slowly and then in a continual rattling or jangling song, usually ending in a drawn out *weeee*. The male may preceed the song with a clicking of the bill.

Male Java Sparrow at start of straw display.

COURTSHIP AND DISPLAY Java Sparrow exhibits most of the elements of the straw display (Baptista and Horblit 1990). A male will often carry a length of straw in the bill prior to singing and perfoming the inverted curtsey (Morris 1958) and twisting both head and tail towards the female but I have never seen the tail fanned. In beginning the advertisement display the male stands fairly upright, leaning forward slightly and singing with bill open. In courtship with a female nearby he will bend over in a hunched position, legs straight, bill clicking and head and

tail turned towards her and begin to sing. A receptive mate will bow, raising her body and maybe hopping in the air a few times before soliciting in the usual munia manner. If mating actually occurs, the male and maybe the female, may utter a short trilling call, as if to signal success. Mating is usually followed by bill-fencing, which may develop into a greeting display. Goodwin (1963 and 1982) describes the vocabulary and displays of Java Sparrow in considerable detail.

Male Java Sparrow bent over in courtship display.

BREEDING Java Sparrows naturally build a bulky spheroid or oval-shaped nest of grasses, fibres and fine strips, with a side entrance. The size appears to vary according to the location. Site-prospecting birds will readily inspect, and may take to a suitable ready-made aperture such as a hole in a tree, a gap beneath the eaves of a structure or a nest box. The nest is lined with finer fibres. Captive birds have been known to line their nests with feathers, but I do not think this has been recorded in field observations. The male is the senior architect, collecting most if not all the material and putting together the main structure. The female concerns herself with the inside. Both birds attend to the lining. The clutch of white oval eggs, broader towards one end is from 4–6, but from 3–8 eggs have been recorded.

Both sexes incubate during the day, taking it in turns, one brooding while the other one feeds, etc., but only the female broods at night. The incubation lasts 13 or 14 days and the young fledge in 3 weeks or so. Longer has been recorded with domestic birds. I have bred wild-caught grey birds, captive-bred grey birds and both domesticated white and fawn birds. The young pair that were hand-reared laid 3 in their first clutch, 4 in the second and 5 in the third. When I was able to record incubation and fledging reasonably accurately, the periods were consistently 14 days and 25 days respectively. The newly-hatched young are naked with a little down, and are dark flesh-coloured. The gape markings are a single dark inverted curve in the upper part of the palate. Fledglings begin picking up food for themselves quite soon, and may be weaned at about 2 weeks but continue to solicit food for up to 3 weeks and occasionally longer.

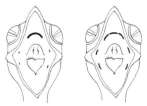

Palate markings of nestling Java Sparrow bred by the author, left, and after Immelmann *et al.* (1968-72), right.

Java Sparrows in captivity invariably choose a budgerigar or lovebird nest box in preference to a basket, which

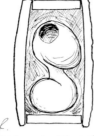

Spanish Oak bark nest box in which a pair of the author's Java Sparrows built a double-chamber nest.

they will stuff with hay and coconut fibre until only a small cavity remains. They will often line the cavity with feathers if available. A pair of South African fawn Java Sparrows I bred from, initially built a nest in a fake vertical tree trunk I had constructed with the use of Spanish Oak bark. The nest was intended for the use of a pair of Finch-billed Mynas *Scissirostrum dubium* who were very attracted to it. However once the Java Sparrows took an interest and decided to build in it, they easily unsurped the mynas. When I dismantled the nest later I found there were two cavities, one above the other looking very much like the cock's nest described for Timor Sparrow.

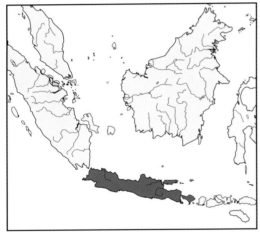

Natural distribution of Java Sparrow.

DISTRIBUTION The original range of Java Sparrow is Java and the adjacent islands of Bali and Kangean. However, this very popular cage bird has been exported widely and either escaped or been deliberately introduced into a large number of locations around the world. It is listed by MacKinnon and Phillipps (1994) as occurring in southern Sumatra, its adjacent islands and Borneo, but in small colonies that appear to be on the decline. Elsewhere in Indonesia it is established on Lombok and small populations appear to have shaky positions in Sulawesi, and a few other islands in the Moluccas and the Lesser Sundas (White and Bruce 1986).

I will never forget my surprise – and I must admit, pleasure – at recognising the bird when two heads were poking out of a nesting hole in the side of a building in suburban San Juan, Puerto Rico. Then I found a thriving colony in

the grounds of the University in north Bangkok and in January 1994 when visiting Venezuela, I learned from Miguel Lentino that it is apparently established and is breeding freely in the area around the university in Maracay.

It is thoroughly established in China where it has been a popular cage bird for several hundred years, and was probably deliberately released during the seventeeth century, or maybe earlier. It ranges from south Jiangsu and Zhejiang, Fujian to Guangdong and Guangxi (Meyer de Schauensee 1984) and Hong Kong. It is also found in Taiwan, Japan, and Vietnam where it has also been a popular cage bird for centuries. It is established in peninsular Malaysia, and Singapore. In 1993 a newspaper report in Singapore mentioned that a wealthy Chinese businessman had released 6,000 Java Sparrows as part of the celebrations at his daughter's wedding. Buddhists believe that it brings good fortune to release captive birds. This results in a thriving trade in estridid finches and sparrows by street traders outside Buddhist temples in Thailand and elsewhere and probably accounts for the thriving colonies of Java Sparrows in Thailand, Burma and other countries in Asia.

Java Sparrows were established in the Philippines before 1933 (Lever 1987) and the species has apparently colonised other islands in the archipelago since then. It has been recorded in India but the populations are largely ephemeral and it is not spreading. It seems to be established around Colombo in Sri Lanka but is local and not spreading. Sightings are reported elsewhere in Sri Lanka but of very few birds.

Further afield it is recorded in East Africa (Mackworth-Praed and Grant 1955) where it is something of a pest in the rice fields of Zanzibar and Pemba (Lever 1987). It has been introduced into the Seychelles and St. Helena (Mackworth-Praed and Grant 1955), but in the latter appears to have declined from being quite abundant due to reductions in the area of cultivated seed crops (Lever 1987). In the USA it is apparently stable in small numbers in Florida, being established around Miami (Peterson 1980) and it is established in Puerto Rico. Elsewhere, it is found on Christmas Island, where the small population is regularly supplemented by escapes or releases. It was introduced to the Cocos Islands but has apparently died out (Lever 1987). It is established in Fiji on the islands of Taveuni, Vanua Levu and Viti Levu, where it is a common bird of the lowlands, especially the rice fields and local gardens (duPont 1976). In Hawaii it is abundant and spreading from the Honolulu area on Oahu, is increasing in the Keauhou-Kona of Hawaii, and on Kauai. It survived for a while on Guam but died out (Pratt *et al.* 1987).

DESCRIPTION   **Plates 77–78**
Monotypic.

Adult male The adult male from Java is about 130mm long; the males of two wild-caught pairs from Luzon measured 135mm. Domestic birds commonly measure 140mm or more. The wing is 65–70mm. The culmen is 14–16mm. The tarsus is 15–16mm. From forehead over the top of the head, the lores, a line down the base of the bill, the bib, and a line running from the bib to the rear crown is black, totally encircling the snow-white ear-coverts. The primaries, rump, uppertail-coverts and tail are also all black. From the nape to the lower back, wings and entire breast it is a neutral grey with a bluish tinge on the breast; the back and wings tending to warm grey. The belly and flanks are a delicate flesh-colour, tending to vinaceous on the flanks. The underwing-coverts are pale grey, the ventral region and undertail-coverts white, the iris is dark brown, the skin around the eye, the bill, legs and feet deep pink. The eyelids and the base of the bill become swollen in a male in breeding condition and they become much redder then. The plumage is exceptionally smooth and well contoured, having a powdered silk-like appearance.

Adult female A Java-caught female was 126mm compared with females from Luzon which measured 125 and 128mm respectively. Similar to the male and it is not possible to tell the sexes apart on the basis of plumage. However, when in breeding condition the eyelids and base of the bill of the female are noticeably less swollen and not so red as on the male. The condition of the eyelids is a more reliable indicator of sex than that of the bill.

Comparison between bill and eye-ring in adult Java Sparrows in breeding condition, female on the left, male on the right.

Juvenile Length 110mm after fledging, to 120mm before the moult. From forehead to rear crown it is dark grey. The primaries and tail are also dark grey to blackish. The rest of the upperparts, from nape to uppertail-coverts and wings are neutral grey and there is a buffish edging to the feathers of the wings. The lores, ear-coverts and entire lower parts are light buff, with some grey streaking on the breast. The bill is horn-coloured, but this gradually lightens and becomes pink at the base. By the time of the first moult the bill is like that of an adult, and that of the males is already larger than of the females.

There are several colour variants that have been produced in captivity: a white, a pied grey-and-white known for some reason as calico, and a fawn. There are different strains of the fawn variant. The richly-coloured fawns that originated in South Africa seemed to me to be almost as lovely as the original grey, the blacks being replaced by dark brown, and the greys by subtle tones of fawn.

HYBRIDS No natural hybrids are recorded. In captivity it has cross-bred with at least three other munias, the Bengalese *L. striata*, African Silverbill *L. cantans* and Scaly-breasted Munia *L. punctulata*. It has been recorded as cross-breeding with both species of *Amadina*, Red-headed Finch *A. erythrocephala* and Cut-throat *A. fasciata* (Gray 1958) but no details are given.

CONSERVATION Whilst Java Sparrow is still widespread in its original habitat there is no doubt that it is significantly less common than before and on present rate of decline is destined to become Endangered. It is rated Vulnerable by Collar *et al.* (1994). Thanks to having been introduced in many places and becoming domesticated, it will survive as a species. But being introduced into a new location does not in itself guarantee survival. The species is apparently dependent on cereal crops and the absence of generous supplies of cultivated grains appears to inevitably result in declining numbers of birds.

Conversely, the irony is that where the feral Java Sparrow is abundant, it is a pest to rice farmers and invites persecution.

In 1993 Indonesia became a net importer of rice for the first time, and the resultant pressure on the rice farmers to significantly increase yields has been intense, particularly in Bali. Every method possible is being used to this end. Under these circumstances the combined actions of the bird trade trappers and the rice farmers could well prove to be fatal. In Bali and Java the rice farmers pay small children to hunt out the nests of Java Sparrows and other rice birds and clean out the eggs. In the past I have seen youngsters with jars full of eggs and marvelled at the resilience of the birds to hold up respectable numbers in the face of such depredation. In 1992 I stayed in a cottage among paddy fields outside Ubud, in Bali, where I spent a lot of time studying Scaly-breasted Munias *L. punctulata* and Javan Munias *L. leucogastroides* and I was disappointed in not seeing any Java Sparrows at all. An old man told me that the Jelatik, as it is called locally, is now scarce because of persistent hunting by men with guns. Years ago, he told me, it was continual war of boy against bird, but then the bird always stood a chance. Nowadays they are too easy to kill, he said, and that is very bad. Other locals during more recent visits to Bali have told me that the Java Sparrows are now hunted regularly by men with air rifles. Guns are illegal in Indonesia, but air rifles are on open sale in the streets of Jakarta and elsewhere. Using them to hunt Java Sparrows has the dual appeal of being a competitive game and having real utility.

A further cause of predation by man in addition to protecting the rice, and trapping for the bird trade, is catching them for food. There are times when 'Rice Birds' are on offer in restaurants in Hong Kong, Singapore, Jakarta and no doubt elsewhere. The entire bird, suitably cleaned, is served in a rich brown sauce.

Java Sparrow has been a popular cage bird for a long time. In the east it has been domesticated for centuries. In the west it is usually kept as a decorative addition to a mixed collection of birds in garden aviaries. The 6,000 Java Sparrows released at a wedding in Singapore were apparently wild caught birds from Java. The quantity of birds in this single incident is remarkable, but the incident itself is not. The official figures from the Indonesian Department of Forest Protection and Nature Conservation (PHPA) as quoted in a TRAFFIC report (Nash 1993), show an annual exportation of over 20,000 Java Sparrows each year for recent years, declining to over 17,000 in 1993. This is almost certainly a serious underestimate of the actual number, but the decline is significant. During three visits to the bird market in Denpasar in 1995, I found just one Java Sparrow. Most of the sellers told me it was 'now gone'. One man said he had some at home and offered to sell them at 35,000 rupiahs each. That was roughly US$18, a higher price than grey Java Sparrows in the trade in Europe. Another man offered to get some, quoting 80,000 rupiahs a pair, the same price as domesticated white Java Sparrows.

The toll of the bird trade in Java Sparrows has been ferocious for decades but the impact has probably not had a seriously negative effect on populations until comparatively recent times when, no doubt enhanced by other factors, it has precipitated the present serious situation when the species might well be on the brink of losing critical mass. In my judgement it is wise to regard the Java Sparrow as being Seriously Vulnerable.

REFERENCES Baptista & Horblit (1990), Bernstein (1861), Bond (1971), Brown (1963), Collar *et al.* (1994), duPont (1976), Goodwin (1952, 1963, 1965 & 1982), Gray (1958), Lever (1987), MacKinnon & Phillipps (1994), Mackworth-Praed & Grant (1960), Meyer de Schauensee (1984), Morris (1956 & 1958), Nash (1993), Peterson (1980), Pratt *et al.* (1987), White & Bruce (1986).

41   TIMOR SPARROW
Lonchura fuscata   Plate 16

Former scientific names: *Loxia fuscata*, Vieillot, 1807 *Padda fuscata*, Reichenback, 1850.
Other common names: Timor Munia, Kupang Sparrow or Munia, Brown Rice Bird, Brown Sparrow, Timor Dusky Sparrow.

Adult and juvenile Timor Sparrows

FIELD CHARACTERS A large greyish-brown munia with white cheek patches and white belly. The adult is unlikely to be confused with any other species within its range. The drab juvenile, if a single bird is glimpsed, might be mistaken for a cisticola, but is bulkier and has a comparatively massive bill. If the juvenile is seen in the company of other species of munia, most likely *L. molucca* or *L. pallida*, it can be identified by its larger size, larger bill and dark lores.

STATUS Local or locally common.

HABITAT It is usually found in grassy areas with scattered scrub, bushes and trees, and saltflats. It may be found around areas of cultivation and has a particular affection for rice paddies. When the rice is not in season it wanders in small parties around grassy areas, and through open grassy woodland.

HABITS AND BEHAVIOUR It is a gregarious species, and while it may generally be found in pairs or small groups up to 12 or so, it is often seen in mixed flocks with the Red Avadavat *Amandava amandava* (Clement *et al.* 1993) and sometimes other *Lonchura* (Linda Santosa pers. comm.).

FOOD AND FEEDING It feeds on the seeds of various grasses, seeding weeds and apparently thistles (Clement *et al.* 1993). Seeds are taken from the inflorescences on the stem, and the bird climbs about with great agility. It also feeds on the ground. Insect food appears to play no part in the diet (Restall 1975, Burkhard 1980a).

Recently-caught birds that the trappers have kept on a diet of plain dry paddy rice immediately show an interest in a variety of foods if given the opportunity, and may sample fruit and take green foods such as chickweed and lettuce, but after a while settle down into conservative eating habits, preferring dry seeds and grass seed on the stem, especially those of cereals such as rice, oats, wheat, etc.

CALL The call or contact note is a *tchik*, often repeated, and a more explosive *tchuk!* when the bird is alarmed. There are also a series of soft chip notes uttered by the birds when at rest together (Restall 1989).

There is a piercing somewhat ventriloqual *wheeee* uttered by the male of a pair when inside the nest. If the female does not respond by entering the nest the male repeats it, moving around inside the nest. Further failure to entice his mate to join him, usually results in the male leaving the nest to join her. If she does join him they appear to move around inside, settling down, both uttering a short series of churring noises.

SONG The undirected song is performed with the male standing clear of the perch, moving slightly from side to side but not pointing at any other bird in the vicinity. It goes *chip chip chip chip chipchipchipchip* (gurgling, gargling *chip*). The note rises as the *chip* is repeated more rapidly and runs into a continual *chip*. The song is usually repeated many times. An unpaired male will also sing from a chosen nesting site, or an old nest that he is trying to attract a female to, leaning forward, looking for a female and singing repeatedly.

The song is quite distinct from that of the closely related Java Sparrow *L. oryzivora*.

Greeting display of Timor Sparrow, male on the left, female on the right.

COURTSHIP AND DISPLAY There is a greeting display, when a courting or bonded pair upon reuniting will bow deeply one to the other. The birds bend forward, bills opening and closing, uttering a quacking contact note. The angle of the body of both birds is about the same as that of a female soliciting copulation. The birds are always positioned head to tail in this display. Should a bird alight facing the same way as its mate it will hop about-face before the two of them indulge in the greeting display. The display may last up to 20 seconds. It is usually followed by mutual preening.

Song and dance of male Timor Sparrow.

LIST OF MEASURED DRAWINGS

Note: on the measured drawings, the word 'heel' refers to the thigh.

These are birds that have been bred in captivity over many generations. The adults have lost the reddish to the lower mandible, are paler grey on the head and more dense, even pink below.

Madagascar Mannikin
Lonchura nana

The juvenile is significantly darker than in the wild.

7 birds bought from an importation of 22 birds from Germany, 1985.

Immature ♂

Very lively and active little birds, seem to get on well together in a colony, but often some serious chasing which subjugates the loser to a state of dullness and inactivity.

Males

Length	wing	culmen	tarsus
92	46	8	11
92	45	8	11
92	46	8	11
87	47	8	11

Females

Length	wing	culmen	tarsus
98	47	9	11
91	46	9	11
91	46	8	11

young adult ♂

culmen curved and entire bill cone-shaped.

Juvenile ♂

slight pink tinge

Juvenile ♀

← Pale pink

Full adult ♂ definitive plumage

The difference in plumage between the juveniles is not diagnostic

Adult ♀

Plate 17

African Silverbill
Lonchura cantans

Four adult birds
bought from a pet shop
in London, probably
bred in captivity

Young birds
have pale edges
to rectrices →

← apparently
black but in
reality deep
fuscous

2 Adult males:

	Length	114	and 115 mm
	wing	53	53
	culmen	11	12
	tarsus	12	11

slight exaggeration
of the difference
between the central
rectrices of ♂ and ♀

2 adult females:

	Length	109	and 113
	wing	53	54
	culmen	9.5	12
	Tarsus	10	10

♂   ♀

♂   ♀

edges of central
rectrices of the male
had a definite deep red
lustre.

♂♀ have different tone
call/contact notes.

edges of central
rectrices dead black

This female, thought to
be a young bird, is
noteworthy for the
clear white patches
above and below the lores,
which were darker than normal.

— Barring on flanks variable and are no
indication of either sex or age.

Plate 18

Indian Silverbill
Lonchura malabarica

uppertail-
coverts have
progressively
less black on
the outer
edges

The central rectrices actually
lie together to
form a single point
as in the birds
below

origin north-
western
India

bill pale grey with
a hint of blue

Four males were studied –
their overall length varied according to
the wear (?) of the central rectrices

Length 113 114 115 116 mm
wing   53   53   53   53   mm
culmen 10   12   12   9   mm
tarsus 10   11   10   10   mm

legs and feet
rich vinous.

Three females were studied –

Length 109 113 114 mm
wing   53   54   53   mm
culmen 9·5 12   9·5 mm
tarsus 10   10   10   mm

white of
long uppertail-coverts
seems to abraid or shorten quickly.
It is rare to see them so long.
This bird is in fresh plumage.

Plate 19

Bronze Mannikin
Lonchura cucullata

Length 92mm
wing 47 mm
culmen 9mm
tarsus 10 mm

L.c.cucullata

interesting double barring of undertail-coverts

intermediate from western Tanzania

Length 90mm
wing 47 mm
culmen 8mm
tarsus 10 mm

L. cucullata scutatus

L.c.cuculleta Senegal

location of origin of these birds

intermediates around Lake Victoria

L.cucullato scutatus Natal

juvenile

flank feathers inner ones (to belly) tipped with black, those nearer the wing brown, tipped with white.

Plate 20

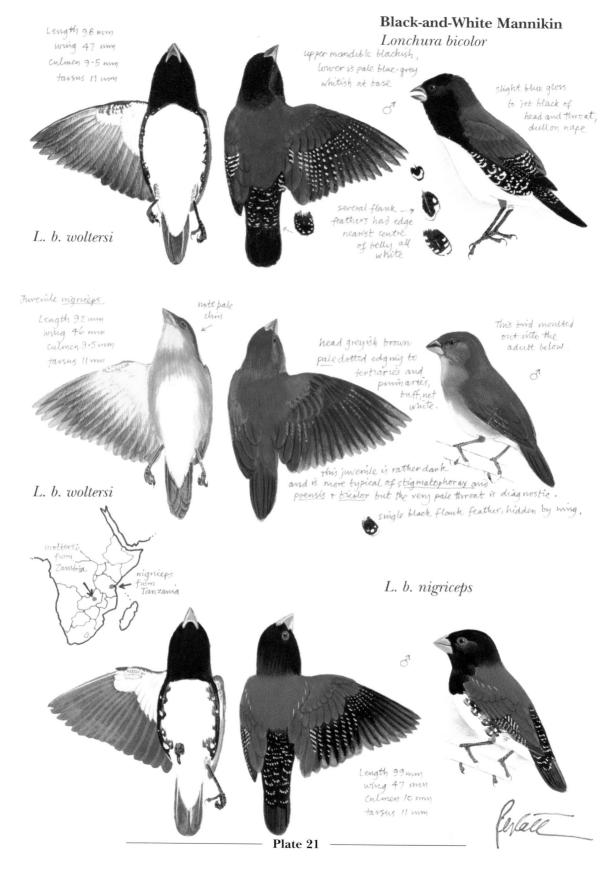

Black-and-White Mannikin
Lonchura bicolor

Length 98 mm
wing 47 mm
culmen 9·5 mm
tarsus 11 mm

upper mandible blackish,
lower is pale blue-grey
whitish at base

♂

slight blue gloss
to jet black of
head and throat,
dull on nape

L. b. woltersi

several flank
feathers had edge
nearest centre
of belly all
white

Juvenile *nigriceps*

Length 92 mm
wing 46 mm
culmen 9·5 mm
tarsus 11 mm

note pale
chin

head greyish brown
pale dotted edging to
tertiaries and
primaries,
buff, not
white.

This bird moulted
out into the
adult below.

♂

L. b. woltersi

this juvenile is rather dark
and is more typical of *stigmatophorax* and
poensis + *bicolor* but the very pale throat is diagnostic.

single black flank feather, hidden by wing.

woltersi
from
Zambia

nigriceps
from
Tanzania

L. b. nigriceps

♂

Length 99 mm
wing 47 mm
culmen 10 mm
tarsus 11 mm

Plate 21

Magpie Mannikin
Lonchura fringilloides

Length 115·0 mm
wing 59·0 mm
culmen 15·0 mm
tarsus 10·0 mm

L. f. fringilloides

origin of these specimens

L. f. fringilloides
Senegal

L. fringilloides
pica
Tanzania

note broader
markings along
the flanks

white lines of quill
shafts of scapulars
very marked on
both birds

Length 114·0 mm
wing 59·0 mm
culmen 14·0 mm
tarsus 11·0 mm

Plate 22

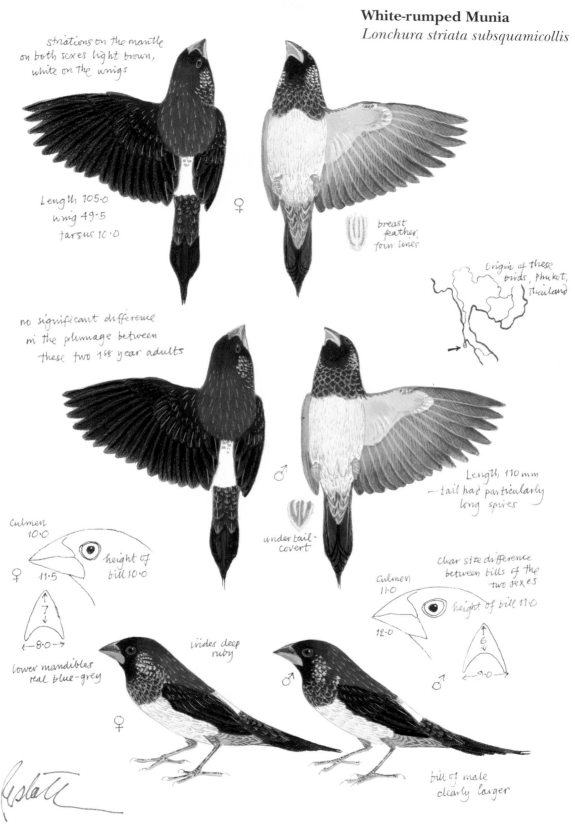

White-rumped Munia
Lonchura striata subsquamicollis

striations on the mantle
on both sexes light brown,
white on the wings

Length 105·0
wing 49·5
tarsus 10·0

♀

breast
feather,
four lines

Origin of these
birds, Phuket,
Thailand

no significant difference
in the plumage between
these two 1st year adults

♂

Length 110 mm
— tail had particularly
long spires

under tail-
covert

culmen
10·0

♀

11·5

height of
bill 10·0

↑
7
↓

← 8·0 →

lower mandibles
real blue-grey

irides deep
ruby

♀

char size difference
between bills of the
two sexes

culmen
11·0

height of bill 11·0

12·0

↑
6
↓

← 9·0 →

♂

♂

bill of male
clearly larger

Plate 23

White-rumped Munia
Lonchura striata subsquamicollis

ear-coverts hardly spotted at all

irides ruby

black face

Two separate shipments of birds in a pet-shop in Kuala Lumpur, March 1989.

This is the bird from the north of peninsular Malaysia. It is more contrasting in colouring with a clear cream rump

apparent origin of these two types

heels all brown

undertail-coverts uniform cinnamon with only faint pale edging

heels only barred at lower part

irides ruby

This bird is from the lot said to be from the southern part of the peninsula, Johore

dark brown face

All upperparts of southern bird darker

Clean clear rows of white dots on the ear-coverts, very noticeable.

legs and feet delicate, feet small

The northern bird is very similar to skins from Laos in the Brit. Mus. (Nat. Hist.), at Tring, but the Johore bird is very close to *explita* from Sumatra. Could it in fact be *explita*?

Plate 24

White-rumped Munia
Lonchura striata subsquamicollis

breast of ♀ slightly
creamier than ♂

♀

Adult female,
compare undertail-coverts
with those of
the
juvenile

These
three birds
are from
Ho Chi Minh
City, Viet nam

clear rump on all
three birds

Length 105 mm
Wing 51 mm
Culmen 10 mm
height of bill 8 mm

white dots
on auriculars

♀

Length 106 mm
Wing 51 mm
Culmen 10 mm
height of bill 8 mm

? No significant difference between
the sexes other than size of bill of the
male

♂

Length 105 mm
Wing 49 mm
Culmen 11 mm
height of bill 9 mm

♂

undertail-coverts slightly
more richly coloured.

Plate 25

White-rumped Munia
Lonchura striata swinhoei

Adult, possibly ♀, Length 115 mm, wing 50 mm

January 1992

. note pale leading edge to base of primaries ↓

trailing edges noticeably pale ↑

very clean rump, not noticed when wings are folded

precise location of origin unknown, bought in Hong Kong as 'local'

flank from adult —

flank from immature

This young bird was actually moulting into first-year adult plumage.

note that bill of adult bird is smaller

10.5 9mm
11.5

10.5 10mm
12mm

bill of the young bird is heavier and wider. It is probably a male

Length 115mm
wing 54 mm
tarsus 12 mm

Plate 26

Javan Munia
Lonchura leucogastroides

origin Bali, Indonesia.

striations very faint

feather of side of neck

This adult is in definitive plumage 2nd year plus. Under parts off white, striations on mantle almost completely gone.

Length 103 mm
wing 50 mm
culmen 9.5 mm
tarsus 10 mm

on this bird the striations show quite clearly

This is an adult in its first year basic definitive plumage.

Length 99 mm
wing 48 mm
culmen 9 mm
tarsus 9.5 mm

white — 14 mm long 10 mm wide

the black on all the birds is actually very dark brown — appearing black.

In some lights the black bill has a purple lustre.

Full adult, 2nd year or older. All brown plumage is darker — and no striations on the back.

Juvenile — bill dark horny to black above

paler horny below, palest at base.

Two first-year adults — note creamier underparts with distinctive flank markings

♀   ♂

heels dark

Juvenile — dark creamy underparts — back is dull

uppertail-coverts softly barred

undertail-coverts barred in pairs of spots

Plate 27

Moluccan Munia
Lonchura molucca molucca

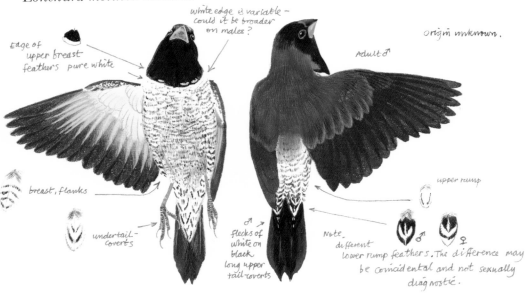

Edge of upper breast feathers pure white

white edge is variable – could it be broader on males?

origin unknown.

Adult ♂

breast, flanks

undertail-coverts

♂ Flecks of white on black long upper tail-coverts

upper rump

Note, different lower rump feathers. The difference may be coincidental and not sexually diagnostic.

Adult male, above: Length 110 m
                           Wing 52 mm
                           culmen 9.5 mm
                           tarsus 10 mm

Two females were aquired, the one below measured:
    Length 108 mm
    wing 49 mm
    culmen 9.5 mm
    Tarsus 10.0 mm

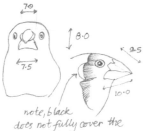

note, black does not fully cover the auriculars.

with both females, the long uppertail-coverts were pure black, while those of the male had flecks of white.

Adult ♀

Adult ♂

Adult ♀

central pair of long uppertail-coverts darker on the inner webs.

Exaggerated to show "golden triangle" on side of male's neck

Plate 28

upper mandible
black

Moluccan Munia
Lonchura molucca molucca

Two birds from "Maluka"
November '93. 1st-year
adults, both males

undertail-covert

white shafts
to upper-tail coverts

flank

upper flank

upper mandible
dark grey

lower
flank

spot of brown remaining from
juvenile plumage

Plate 29

Spot-sided Munia
Lonchura sp.

Adult in first-year plumage, painted January 1991

Length 110.0 mm
Wing 51.0 mm
Tarsus 11.0 mm
Culmen 13.0 mm

Origin uncertain, believed to be not far from Bandjamarsin, south-eastern Borneo

call note a rasping *tzizt!*

♀

irides dark brown

heel mottled and barred

rich reddish-chestnut edges to uppertail-coverts

White double barred crosses on flanks hidden by folded wing

x x x

reddish chestnut edges merge into near-black undertail-coverts

12
11 height
13 mm
10 mm across base of bill

♀ second year

upper flank
mid-flank
lower flank

Paler edges to uppertail-coverts visible in first year, now barely visible at all

same bird following a total moult in May '91. The face, throat and breast are warm vandyke that is almost purple.

Plate 30

Scaly-breasted Munia
Lonchura punctulata punctulata

extremely well marked
underwing-coverts

faint striations on
mantle

irides deep ruby

These are 2
of 6 birds
obtained in
the Bombay
area

♂

flank

note intense orange edging
to the uppertail-coverts and undertail,
and the extent of the markings

♂ length 110 mm
wing 54 mm
culmen 12 mm
height of bill 11 mm

• female also well coloured on undertail
but without any ticking
at all!

♀ length 110 mm
wing 54 mm
culmen 12 mm
height of bill 10 mm

irides deep ruby

flank

♀

white edging to tertiaries
forms more often on females.

- rich dull orange

Plate 31

Scaly-breasted Munia
Lonchura punctulata punctulata

Almost certainly a bird in 1st year adult plumage – ? female

striations run from forehead to rump, and cover auriculars

painted in Colombo April, 1993

pale blue grey at base of lower mandible

clear undertail-coverts

rump has striations, each 3 short lines, with some black barring.

much weaker orange than on the other bird.

origin – south-west Sri Lanka

♀?

Length 107 mm, Wing 53 mm Culmen 12 mm

legs and feet blue-grey

heel brown and black

middle flank feather from female(?).

lot of black on upper breast, and brown flush

no striations on head

note fine dark barring on mantle and wing-coverts

note white fringe. This is from the male (?)

ticking on undertail-coverts

rump has a narrow band of white dots with black underlining these become the spot of the lower flank

lower flank

bill ridged and old-looking.

legs and feet vinous.

♂?

Appears to be a mature bird in 2nd year plumage. Compare to punctulata from Bombay.

heel black and white

Length 112, wing 52 Culmen 12.5

Plate 32

Length 112 mm
wing 52 mm

Length 114 mm
wing 55 mm

20 January '92
Bought in the bird
market, Hong Kong,
locally caught.

emerging flank

all three have
square tails

Length 107 mm
wing 51

11.5
11
12 · 7
← 8.75 →

10.5
9
11 · 6.5
8.5

11
9.5 · 6.5
11 · 8 →

This bird
sang a
sweet sub-song
in the dark
in the studio

This bird
singing
often

bill now black on
this bird

31 March '92

note tails
beginning
to lengthen

note well
marked
undertail-cov's

these two have
identical call
notes

flank

bills on all
three now black

flank

5 July '92
(then all 3
released).

flank

rump

① ♂

② ♂

③ ♀

These three birds were painted at 3-monthly intervals over 6 months to compare
rate of moult and individual differences. They were colour banded for ease
of recognition ① and ② both males by song. ③ Main discriminator (only?) is
smaller bill size.

Jeslen

Plate 33

Scaly-breasted Munia
Lonchura punctulata topela

irides dark ruby

Length 113 mm
Wing 57 mm
culmen 11 mm

tawny leading
edges to
primaries

underwing-coverts
light cream

note barring across
mantle and wing-coverts

outer ear-coverts
light tawny

uppertail-coverts buff-yellow
edges on sepia, not yellow as might be
expected.

olive-grey
barring

flank feathers.

interesting to note that
the bill of the juvenile is
all black

legs and feet
dark grey

heels barred

note pattern
on ear-coverts
of juvenile

irides dark
brown

legs and
feet black

Length 105
wing 50
culmen 10

origin of these
birds: Kanchana Buri.
Thailand

Plate 34

note the underwing-coverts on both birds are dark

irides deep ruby

Scaly-breasted Munia
Lonchura punctulata topela

bill of the male is larger and broader

♂ Length 115 mm
wing 54 mm
tarsus 11 mm

tail of male longer than female's

typical flank feather

♂

These birds were obtained on the island of Phuket, Thailand, Sept. '91

bill of all birds jet black

note yellow only on long uppertail-coverts - not higher

typical flank feather

♀

The female is slightly smaller and a little paler

note the strong striations on both birds, and the fine barring across all upperparts

undertail-coverts paler than males, and ticking less marked

tail shorter by 3 mm.

tail 8 mm across when folded

♀ Length 100 mm
wing 52 mm
tarsus 11 mm

Plate 35

Scaly-breasted Munia
Lonchura punctulata cabanisi

♂ Length 97.0
wing   49.0
culmen 10.0
tarsus 10.0

♂ Length 100.0
wing   48.0
culmen 11.0
tarsus 10.0

Very fine barring across
upper surfaces

26 [mm

♂

30 [mm

First year
adult

Juvenile

Response call note of this
bird to the other, a clear note
lower, however both birds soon began singing

Length 105.0
wing   49.0
tarsus 11.0
culmen 10.5

fine barring on the mantle,
wing-coverts and
tertianies, amber
edging to tertianies.

Origins of these birds:

central
LuZon

note bill all pale blue-grey,
with blackish at base of
upper mandible only

breast feather

flank

32 [mm

♂

slight warm
straw edging to
long uppertail-coverts
and tail

rear
flank
behind the
heel.

This is the male,
upper right, in 2nd-
year adult plumage

Plate 36

note complete lack of
striations above

Scaly-breasted Munia
Lonchura punctulata fretensis

irides ruby red

Adult bird
  Length 110 mm
  wing 52 mm
bill short and deep
  - culmen 10mm
  - height 10mm
  - width at base 9mm

bill dark
above, pale
below

none of flank
feathers has double
markings

Juvenile
length 98 mm
wing 52 mm
culmen 11 mm

This 1st year bird
was moulting into its
adult plumage, but looked
particularly dull and drab.
Note, head unmoulted.

flank

rump pattern
distinctive, and
typical of first-
year adults

The flank feathers
on this
bird were
mostly double
marked.

This young bird in first-year
adult plumage. It is
particularly orange on the face,
note the striations.

selection
of patterns
from breast
and flanks

All three
birds from
southern
Sumatra,
1990

Plate 37

Scaly-breasted Munia
Lonchura punctulata holmesii

Fine barring across all upper surfaces on all birds

This is one of nine birds received from Pontianak, West Kalimantan, September, 1990.

All are in first adult plumage. The sexes are quite alike but there is a distinct difference in the length of the tail

Average length from
5 males   111·0 mm
4 females 106·0 mm
Average wing length ♂♂ 52 ♀♀ 50
Average culmen ♂♂ 11 ♀♀ 10·5
Width of lower mandible ♂♂ 8·5 ♀♀ 7·5
    Tarsus ♂♂ 11 ♀♀ 10

35 mm or 36 mm

♂

uppertail-coverts and tail brownish-olive to grey with very pale straw edging

upper mandible dark grey

lower mandible pale grey

underwing richer cream to salmon

undertail-coverts completely clear

29 mm

origin in Borneo

♀

upper breast

middle flank

legs & feet blackish

Plate 38

Scaly-breasted Munia
Lonchura punctulata nisoria

Adult male in very clear new plumage
Length 114 mm
wing 53 mm
culmen 12 mm

wider deep ruby eyering black

very fine striations on mantle (and faint)

note cream centre to belly and cream undertail-coverts
base colour of flanks is white.

— black uppertail-coverts edged straw

— black tail, edged straw

35mm

origin central Java

cream fringe —

bill vinaceous blue-grey below and only truly black above at tip

note white spots on brown, effectively the brown extends well onto the breast

heels barred black and straw

males' tails up to 5 mm longer than on females

rump and uppertail-coverts uniform with back

juvenile very warm colouring below

no striations at all

12 10
9·5

Length 102 mm
wing 53 mm
tarsus 14 mm

Plate 39

Scaly-breasted Munia
Lonchura punctulata blasii

bill black above,
blue-grey below

Length 113 mm
Wing 52 mm

flank   lower breast

This male sang sweetly and often —
between calling to both females.

♂

strongly marked
undertail-
coverts

uppertail-coverts broadly
edged with olivaceous
cream

culmen
pronounced and
curved

♂

typical from side
of flank

Two females were identical.

· bill blue-grey, darker
above, violaceous below

Three birds acquired
in Kupang,
West Timor

♀

Length 100 mm
Wing 49 mm

completely unmarked on the
belly, vent and undertail-coverts.
- on both females.

Plate 40

Unknown Munia Probable hybrid
Lonchura stygia x Bengalese

no striations at all

♀

Length 109
wing 51
culmen 10
tarsus 11

31mm

flank feather. The smallest, inner U is concealed by the overlapping feather.

upper breast feather

lower breast and belly

Both birds bought in Jakarta bird market, origin unknown. Female Nov. '89, male January '91. Dealer regularly receives birds from Borneo and says they are from Bandjamarsin.

The female is in its 2nd-year adult plumage

uppertail- and undertail-coverts appear to be black but are fuscous

iris deep ruby

appears black

bright umber

♀

legs and feet dark blue-grey

scalloping on flanks of the male with white shaft lines breaking U into []

♂

face of male blacker than on female

Length 115
wing 50
culmen 10
tarsus 11

1st year adult

note pattern on lower back

36 mm

tail longer and darker than that of female

dark-edged feathers with white striations and dots on male only

iris ruby

sides of neck noticeable pale patch

legs and feet vinous-grey

Plate 41

White-bellied Munia
Lonchura leucogastra smythiesi

No striations on head or nape

in behaviour remarkably similar to *L. striata*.

irides deep ruby

♀

Female length 107 mm
        wing   49 mm
        culmen 11 mm
        tarsus 10 mm

rather more spotting on belly

↑ dark brown

contact note of female tit! a full note higher than male's call of chup!

Long call note ♂ twyst? reply of ♀ teetee!

These birds came from district of Semitan in Kalimantan Barat, west central Borneo

♂

male length 112 mm
      wing   51 mm
      culmen 11 mm
      tarsus 12 mm

six birds from this area, shipped from Pontianak

bill of male noticeably deeper and culmen more swollen

12 mm ♂   10 mm ♀

9 mm   8.5 mm

Plate 42

Four birds, ♂♂♀♀, from near Wamena.

underwing same colour as uppertail

second-year adults

Edges to median and greater wing-coverts are black in the male

10 mm
9 mm
10 mm

♂ 115 mm long
50 mm wing
culmen 10 mm

♂

paler or brighter on the male

← From breast and flanks to undertail-coverts, the black feathers have shiny "silken" edges on all four birds.

Dark edges to median and greater wing-coverts are very dark brown on female

← note brown streaks more extensive on face of female, and on sides of breast.

♀

♀ Length 110 mm
wing 50 mm
culmen 10 mm

10 mm
9 mm
10 mm

underwing paler than uppertail

shiny silken edges to black underparts look pale in some lights

♀

black bar of rump fades into brown of lower back

Note colour is darker than on male and has minor black infusion

Collected at same, or near same location as L. teerinki!

Plate 43

Streak-headed Mannikin
Lonchura tristissima calaminoros

Length 108 mm
wing 52 mm
Culmen 10 mm
tarsus 15 mm

Adult,
sex not known

← black long uppertail-coverts

← note, no black above straw rump, indicating
race <u>calaminoros</u>

origin Hollandia
W. Irian Jaya

Juvenile

violaceous tint to bill

short uppertail-
coverts
hazel

Length 100 mm
wing 51 mm
culmen 10 mm
tarsus 15 mm

Plate 44

White-spotted Mannikin
Lonchura leucosticta leucosticta

bill of this old male has a solid lilac colouring, only pale blue at base of lower mandible

Length 105 mm
wing 50 mm
culmen 9.5 mm
tarsus 17 mm

origin Merauke, W. Irian Jaya

Adult male definitive plumage, 2nd year.

note black longer uppertail-coverts →

black vent is sex diagnostic ←
♂

blackish heels

legs long at 17 mm

♂

In comparison, females are slightly lighter both above and below, and not so heavily spotted

bill pale blue

black longer uppertail-coverts

First-year adults are less heavily spotted; this ♀ could be taken for a young, 1st year ♂

♀

note — BROWN on heels and vent

Length 100 mm
wing 48 mm
culmen 9 mm
tarsus 16 mm

This juvenile drawn from one of six in Patrick Tay's collection in Singapore

bill pale grey, not bluish

note longer uppertail-coverts are much darker.

No trace of straw on rump or uppertail-coverts

Plate 45

Tricoloured Munia
Lonchura malacca

8.5mm

8mm

bill 8.5mm high
upper mandible
8mm wide

Typical breast feather,
it is *not* a solid
brown as in the breast
vermiculation of
L. punctulata.

The condition is
permanent, the birds
moulting true.

Length 116 mm
wing 57 mm
culmen 13 mm
tarsus 12 mm

This adult is
typical of a small
percentage with a brown
patterned breast. This is
not absolutely consistent
bird to bird. Some are more
boldly barred, some rather "loose"
and irregular.

Perfectly normal
L. malacca with
pure white
breast

Juvenile from the same batch,
only a couple of months old.
Note feet darker than those of adults.

Two juveniles were
measured —

Length: 96   93 mm
wing   55   50 mm
culmen 10.5 10.5 mm
tarsus 14   12.5 mm

Plate 46

Tricoloured Munia
Lonchura malacca

young adult,
1st year plumage

Length 118 mm
Wing 54 mm
Tarsus 12 mm
Culmen 12 mm

rich lustrous deep maroon

♂

This bird was obtained
in the open market
in Madras,
December 1991.

origin of the juvenile, near Bombay

origin of the young adult ♂ near Madras

faint lustrous reds and orange

This colour morph is found over the
entire range. I subsequently saw it
in Bombay and in Sri Lanka.
It moults true, being a permanent condition.

Length 112 mm
Wing 52 mm
Tarsus 12 mm
Culmen 10.5 mm

note the rich cinnamon
rump and uppertail-coverts;
very interesting to compare to the
juvenile atricapilla.

Plate 47

Chestnut Munia
Lonchura atricapilla sinensis

Maroon of belly and undertail
replaces black of other
races.

note unusual
contrasts of colours
on back and wings.

Length 115 mm
wing 52 mm
culmen 11 mm

♂

lack of
maroon on
rump

♂

maroon not so
extensive as on ♂
and flanks
edged paler

Length 98 mm
wing 45 mm
culmen 9.5 mm

Length 108 mm
wing 49 mm
culmen 10 mm

♀

note mottling on
mantle and
wing-
coverts

origin of
these birds
Kanchana Buri,
Thailand

compare this pale
underside with warmer
darker juvenile *minuta*
from Borneo

Plate 48

Chestnut Munia
Lonchura atricapilla sinensis

Length 100 mm
Wing 47 mm
tarsus 12 mm

pale silky edging very noticeable on mantle and breast

belly and undertail-coverts blackish

10.5 mm
10
11 mm

♂

← 9 →

Bill larger than ♀

head shiny black

rump and short uppertail-coverts rich lustrous chestnut

long uppertail-coverts and entire tail golden

note black on heels

head dull brownish-black

heels all brown

♀

Length 98 mm
Wing 46 mm
tarsus 12 mm

First-year female belly dark brown with blackish

9 m
10
11 mm

← 8 →

most of head brownish-black

lower rump and short uppertail-coverts chestnut

origin Sumatra

Plate 49

Chestnut Munia
Lonchura atricapilla formosana

♀ length 115 mm
wing 49 mm
tarsus 12 mm
culmen 11 mm

Side by side ♀ is noticeably smaller
and paler, and less bold on the head.
– back is less rich chocolate
and the rump, uppertail-
coverts and tail less richly
coloured.

Of the four birds studied,
♀♀♀♂ only the male
had black heels

The sexes of this munia
are clearly distinct.
In the field the different
shades on the head
are diagnostic.

Head of adult male is
a little darker than
that of the
female

dark grey
chest →

♂

blackish
heels

♂ flanks noticeably more
rich chestnut

mantle slightly
more chocolate

Length 117 mm
♂ wing 52 mm
culmen 11 mm
tarsus 12 mm

♂

note lack of any yellow or orange

Plate 50

Chestnut Munia
Lonchura atricapilla deignani

This juvenile showing an extraordinary moult pattern unfortunately died on the 3rd day

Note the very pronounced and curved culmen

very rich underparts

Length 108 mm
Wing 56 mm
Culmen 11 mm

Immature painted June 1992

Three adults caught locally were aquired in Ho Chi Minh City, June '92. The male was distinct and atypical in the strong and extensive black — but the two females were typical *deignani*.

♂

	♂	♀	♀
Length	105	110	108
Wing	52	52	54
Culmen	11	10	10

♂

uppertail-coverts and edges of tail deep reddish-orange

Ho Chi Minh City, South Viet Nam

origin

Plate 51

Chestnut Munia

Lonchura atricapilla brunneiceps

Length 95 mm
wing 49 mm
tarsus 10 mm

dark brown

olive only on nape

deep luscious maroon

Origin, Makasar in Sulawesi

♂

rich salmon underwing-coverts

dark brown

pale tuft on vent

Length 100 mm
wing 49 mm
tarsus 10 mm

♀

the dark brown of the belly and undertail-coverts is broader on this bird.

medium-orange on tail only, not long uppertail-coverts

♂

This is the top bird

Fuscous of throat merges with sides of breast

heel brown

olive extends to crown

brighter chestnut

legs and feet pale blue-grey

heel very dark brown

♀

Plate 52

This race differs from the typical Philippine *jagori* in having the entire rump and uppertail-coverts brick-red, amber edging on the tail and edging of orange-maroon on older birds

Chestnut Munia
Lonchura atricapilla selimbauensis

Origin Selimbau in West Kalimantan

Borneo

most females has the nape dark to raw umber

two females kept in 1990

length	105	108
wing	51	53
culmen	10	11
tarsus	11	12

These birds moulted heavily in October

♀

uppertail-coverts deep brick-red

orange on edges of tail only

bar across chest and flanks same chestnut as back

♀

head all black on all birds

back chestnut

edges of flanks and belly, irregular in all birds

uppertail-coverts lustrous maroon

This male is from the second lot of birds from Selimbau and is typical

♂

flanks and breast bar brick-red

Length 106, wing 52 culmen 11, tarsus 12

The differences shown between male and female - more black on belly of male, darker flanks and narrower breast bar were constant on both lots of birds.

Males also had longer tails. Females' tails averaged 23 mm from wing tip; males' tails averaged 27 mm from wing tip.

Lustrous deep orange-maroon on edges of tail, but none on uppertail-coverts

Plate 53

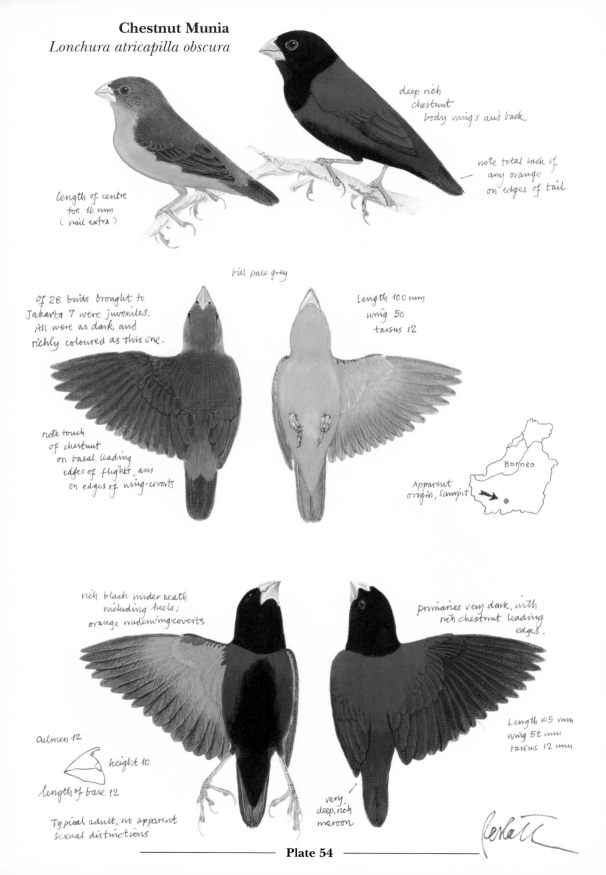

Chestnut Munia
Lonchura atricapilla obscura

deep rich
chestnut
body, wings and back

note total lack of
any orange
on edges of tail

Length of centre
toe 16 mm
(nail extra)

bill pale grey

Of 28 birds brought to
Jakarta 7 were juveniles.
All were as dark and
richly coloured as this one.

Length 100 mm
wing 50
tarsus 12

note touch
of chestnut
on basal leading
edges of flights, and
on edges of wing-coverts

Borneo

Apparent
origin, Sampit

rich black underneath
including heels;
orange underwing-coverts

primaries very dark, with
rich chestnut leading
edges.

Culmen 12

height 10

length of base 12

Typical adult, no apparent
sexual distinctions

very
deep, rich
maroon

Length 105 mm
wing 52 mm
tarsus 12 mm

Plate 54

Belly and undertail not black but blackish

Chestnut Munia
Lonchura atricapilla

Length can be affected by the development of the central tail feathers and the straw fringes which may add 5mm or more to overall length.

Three adults measured

	♀	♀	♂
Length	104	103	97
wing	46	49	52
tarsus	12	12	14
culmen	10	9·5	9

legs black & grey as adults

Pallid Munia
Lonchura pallida

fat round body, 28mm across

The bird sang a sweet and soft song at night, in a cage in the studio - triggered by two other munias

12 11 6 12 ← 9 →

Length 112 mm
wing 54 mm

long uppertail covert.

♂

tarsus 11·0 mm - centre toe 15 mm plus the nail.

Plate 55

Black-throated Munia
Lonchura ferruginosa

Length 113 mm
wing 50+ (tips frayed)
culmen 12 mm
tarsus 13 mm

origin central Java

Adult bird in worn plumage,
very dull, with frayed ends

Top of
Culmen quite
prominent;
significantly more
than on female.

bill height
9.5

♂

bill 8.0 width at base

note mix of brown
into the mesial

Height of bill
11.0 mm
Culmen 13.0 mm

Length 105 mm
wing 53 mm

Adult male with
all-black
front

♂

♀

female showing
"dirty" crown and nape

maroon breast
band same
width as on
male

Height of bill 9.5 mm
Culmen 11.5 mm

Length 103 mm
wing 54 mm

♀

Plate 56

Five-coloured Munia
Lonchura quinticolor

Length 125 mm
Wing 54 mm
Tarsus 14 mm
Culmen 12.5 mm

L. q. quinticolor

orbital ring deep reddish-grey
base of bill lilac

grey U markings
on nape and
irregularly on
upper
mantle

This golden-rumped bird is a
typical example of a thousand or
so birds examined in Singapore,
February 1989. They were from Timor.

There are many differences between this
and the maroon-rumped L. q. wallacii

All the birds in the shipment
had glossy white breasts with white-on-
white shiny scalloping, as if the
feathers were fringed with silk

L. q. sumbae

note darker
head and
pink/darker
ear-covert
striations

This race is apparently
smaller and darker than
quinticolor.

This is one of a small
shipment of birds in Jakarta
apparently received from
Sumba.

note strong
orange

Length 120mm
Wing 54 mm
tarsus 12 mm
culmen 10 mm

Plate 57

Five-coloured Munia
Lonchura quinticolor sumbae

Length 113 mm
Wing 52 mm

10   12
     12

♀
No yellowish
on rump

Onigm.
Kupang.
West Timor

This female is in its first-year
adult plumage. In bright
light the crown
and nape have
a lovely chestnut
gloss

♀

♂

Overall, the male is
larger and more richly
coloured than the female

This bird is an adult
male in first-year
adult plumage, with
cinnamon flush to the
breast and barring on
the flanks. July '92.
It moulted in March '93
to a paler version

Length 120
Wing 57

Note band of light orange
on the rump, which does
not notice when wings closed.

♂

10   12.5
     12.5

Egg - nicely oval,
rounded at one end.

12 mm x 17 mm

Plate 58

Five-coloured Munia
Lonchura quinticolor wallacii

The ear coverts are glossy, almost metallic with pale shafts

underparts - snow white slightly creamy on underwing coverts.

Undertail-coverts glossy black

heels normally all black ...??

rump rich reddish with some golden tinges to the uppertail-coverts

♂ probably a first year adult - note heels and lack of V on nape.

Length 115 mm
wing 58 mm
culmen 12.5 mm
tarsus 14.5 mm

Country of origin - Indonesia Island of Lombok.

Immature, virtually indistinguishable from immature *L.maja* or *L.ferruginosa* but pale shafts on ear-coverts may be noticeable and are diagnostic.

These particular adults lacked the grey broken V marks on the nape of other races; sometimes it is faint on this race

Ear-covert striations near white and noticeable on most juveniles

First adult plumage usually creamy breast with brown parts duller and lacking silky gloss.

Plate 59

White-headed Munia
Lonchura maja

Length 112 mm
wing 52 mm
culmen 12 mm
– bill 11mm high
– width at base 9mm

♀

Young bird just completing
the moult into first adult
plumage – see vestigial juvenile
feathers on belly and flanks

bar of
brown

♀

Young, 1st year, adult male,
note black extending up to breast

♂

Length 115 mm
wing 52 mm
Culmen 12 mm
– height of bill 11 mm
– width at base 8mm

♂

These two birds selected
from a box full in Jakarta
June '91. released after painting.

origin of this
pair

central Java

Plate 60

White-headed Munia
Lonchura maja

beginnings of richer chocolate brown of adult plumage on shoulder

note beginning of brown on breast

From central Java

This miniature was taken as a corpse from a local trapper's cage in the bird market, Jakarta, April 1985.

Length 96mm
Wing 51·5mm
culmen 11mm
Tarsus 13mm

note black undertail-coverts starting:

← black centres, broad buff edges

Length 110 mm
wing 52 mm
culmen 11 mm
tarsus 14.5 mm

♀

This bird was also taken locally in the Jakarta region – June 1985

bill blue-grey

From behaviour and voice I took this bird to be ♀

note feet of juvenile are blacker than those of the adults

this juvenile is warmer above, greyer on head than juveniles of *atricapilla*

Plate 61

White-headed Munia
Lonchura maja

Deep maroon-crimson of rump graduates into lower back

First-year adult male

♂

↙ pure white

note richer and more extensive breast ♂

Length 115 mm
Culmen 13 mm
Wing 53 m
Tarsus 13 mm

13
11
13·5

←9→

Edge of central tail feathers almost orange

Flanks of both birds more like milk chocolate than dull chestnut of the wings and back

origin Jawa

↙ crown pale straw, less white than on male

♀

12
11
12·5
←8→

First-year adult female

♀

deep maroon-crimson of uppertail-coverts only reaches up to level of middle tertiary

Length 110 mm
Wing 53 mm
Tarsus 13 mm

Plate 62

White-headed Munia
Lonchura maja vietnamensis

First-year ♂
length 106 mm
wing 55
tarsus 13

note touch of
hazel at base
of mesial

♂
breast
hazel or
cinnamon-
brown.

back of female
noticeably darker
than male.

♀
breast →
greyish
vinaceous-pink

origin of these
three birds
vietnam
♀ juv. Da Lat
♂
Tay ninh

Juvenile ♂
(sing mg)
length 104
wing 53
tarsus 13

second-year ♀♀ (identical)
length 105, 106
wing 52 56
tarsus 14 · 15

Plate 63

Pale-headed Munia
Lonchura pallida

Length 105 mm
Wing 55 mm

Bought in Bali, Denpasar bird market, June '92. Claimed by vendor to have been caught locally. Probably from Lombok

11 12 11·5 ♀

first signs of adult plumage on undertail-coverts.

♀

11 12 12 ♀

note darker bill than usual

♀

Adult female

underparts noticeably duller than on the male

note face is whiter than female's

11 12·5 12·5

Length 105 wing 54

♂

♂

paler

brighter

Adult male

edges of central rectrices brighter, tinged orange.

Plate 64

Grand Mannikin
Lonchura grandis destructa

Four birds were studied, ♀♀♀♂

Female #1 Length 130 mm
wing 53 mm
culmen 15 mm
tarsus 13.5 mm

Origin Hollandia,
West Irian Jaya

chestnut of flanks
largely covered by folded
wing, more so on the female.

♀

feet are large
and strong

9
8
7
6
5
4 3

5-8 primaries
← clearly notched

orbital skin
dark grey

bills pale blue with
white cutting
edges

♀

green gloss to black of head
and throat

The male
is a larger bird
with a noticeably
larger and deeper
bill.

Irides chestnut.

Female #2 length 125 mm
wing 55 mm
culmen 14 mm
tarsus 14 mm

♀

♂

♂♀ have different
tone of contact call notes

Female #3 Length 135 mm
wing 56 mm
culmen 14 mm
tarsus 14 mm

♂ Length 142 mm
wing 62 mm
culmen 19 mm
tarsus 14 mm

Plate 65

Grand Mannikin
Lonchura grandis heurni

♀ bill is 12·5 mm
high from base
to culmen

10 mm wide
at base

Total head is
large but body
in fact is normal munia

♀ length 115 mm
wing 53 mm
tarsus 12 mm (centre
toe another 15 mm)
culmen 13 mm

This is my last pair from the
importations of 1984 and '85.
Died in London, January '89.

female is
much lighter
chestnut above than
male

♀

central
rectrice
33 mm long
and 7 mm wide
All rectrices brown
but appear to be
black with straw
edging

black of body is very dark
brown in parts of the
belly and ventral area,
but has slight green
gloss in some
lights

♀

♂

length 130 mm
wing 54 mm
tarsus 15 (with
centre toe
another 17mm)

culmen 16 mm

♂

green gloss is on edgings of
feathers

bill is 15 mm
high

12·5 mm
wide at base

four
distinct
bars of
colour.
rump darker
than mantle.

underwing-coverts darker
and more richly coloured on
male

central rectrice brown
35 mm long, 8 mm wide

Plate 66

Adult male length 110·0 mm
        wing 52·0 mm
        culmen 10·5 mm
        tarsus 13·0 mm

Grey-headed Mannikin
Lonchura caniceps caniceps

several birds caught, measured and compared, Port Moresby, 1990.

♂

underwing coverts, axillaries, of female darker
♀

♂

colour of rump of male is higher note in relation to tertiaries

♀

upportail-coverts of female duller orange when compared side by side

length 105·0 mm
Adult wing 48·0 mm
female culmen 9·5 mm
        tarsus 11·0 mm

eyering blue-grey

♀
(juvenile)

Length 102·0 mm
wing 46·0 mm
culmen 11·0 mm
tarsus 12·0 mm

juvenile, probably only a few weeks old -

    Length 100·0 mm
    Wing 50·0 mm
    culmen 9·0 mm
    tarsus 11·0 mm

♀

not far from Moresby, July 1990

Plate 67

Grey-crowned Mannikin
Lonchura nevermanni

Young bird obtained April 1983 from Germany. It died within the week. Length 112, wing 53 culmen 10, tarsus 12.

bill has distinct lilac tinge to the blue.

shipped from Merauke

Startlingly rich colour of rump of two females, both moulting heavily, showing black. One female also had black scallops on the belly

velvety black undertail-coverts

young adult in its first year.

bill blue above, white at base of lower mandible.

bill grey

one of 60 birds examined in Singapore – sept. '89

legs and feet pale grey

♂ Full adult male in definitive plumage — 2nd or 3rd year.

legs and feet dark grey

Length 118 mm wing 55 mm ♂ culmen 11 mm tarsus 16 mm

Plate 68

Hooded Mannikin
Lonchura spectablis mayri

Young adult (just completing moult into first-year adult plumage

cream below "dirty" breast with streaks and slight barring

♀

shiny black legs & feet

black dots

Length 92.0 mm
wing 45.0 mm
culmen 9.0 mm
tarsus 14.0 mm

Juvenile, showing typical dark streaks on ear-coverts

Length 30.0 mm
wing 45.0 mm
culmen 9.0

legs and feet grey

♂

second year adult showing two variations, pale tips to median wing-coverts and yellowish tinge to underparts.

legs and feet bluish-grey
Length 110.0 mm

Normal second-year adult with white below

♂

legs and feet violaceous & lavender

Length 112 mm
wing 47mm
culmen 10 mm
tarsus 13 mm.

clear colour of rump and uppertail typical of all 2nd year birds.

location of origin, near Jayapura, Irian Jaya

Tips of central rectrices may be 3 mm longer than body of tail

Plate 69

Cream-bellied Munia
Lonchura pallidiventer

This bird acquired May '90

♀ length 115 mm
wing 53 mm
culmen 11 mm
tarsus 11 mm

Female, slightly greyer on nape and less warm on mantle

♀

irregular and light barring on rump only on female

♂ length 115 mm
wing 53 mm
culmen 12 mm
tarsus 11 mm

absence of lines on inner flanks

♂

almost clear of any ticking

bill of male significantly larger

When closed the wings do not appear to be as deep and rich a brown as on the flanks

This bird acquired April '91

BORNEO

origin somewhere in the region of Bandjamarsin, Borneo

♂

richer coloured rump and uppertail-coverts

Plate 70

Cream-bellied Munia
Lonchura pallidiventer

Young female in 1st year adult plumage — May 1990

Two birds bought in Jakarta bird market from the Bandjamasin dealer. The Juvenile in heavy mid-moult died before my arrival, the other bird thrived and proved eventually to be a female.

white quills on tertiaries

length 115 mm
wing 53 mm
culmen 12 mm
tarsus 11 mm

♀

sides of rump barred

flanks painted paler to show complexity of pattern

belly

Length 107 mm
wing 52 mm
culmen 10 mm
tarsus 10 mm

Juvenile in heavy moult, October 1990

note orange and yellow coming through

outer four rectrices are new

long undertail-coverts

Plate 71

Cream-bellied Munia
Lonchura pallidiventer

These two are painted from 5 in the possession of Sami Susanto, Jakarta, 1990. He received them from Bandjamarsin, Kalimantan Selatan. (Borneo).

undertail-coverts clear cream

length 120 mm
wing 58 mm
culmen 11 mm
tarsus 13 mm

Length 115 mm
wing 55 mm
culmen 10 mm
tarsus 13 mm

cream is slightly paler on centre of belly and undertail-coverts

heels barred brown and black

flanks entirely black

heels barred cream and black on outside only, inner heel black

undertail-coverts ticked with black

Plate 72

Chestnut-breasted Mannikin
Lonchura castaneothorax

L.C. sharpii

length 101
wing 47.5
culmen 9.5
tarsus 11

origin northern
Coastal areas of New Guinea

sharpii

uropygialis

rump reddish-chestnut
uppertail-coverts only
slightly paler

note barring on
inside of heel, black
on outside on both
races

the only differences between these two races is
the paler greyer head in sharpii (but this is variable)
and the orange uppertail-coverts in uropygialis.

rump orange-chestnut
with uppertail-
coverts more
yellowish

L.C. uropygialis

Length 102
wing 48
culmen 10
tarsus 11

another identical bird measured length 100,
wing 48, culmen 11 and tarsus 12.

Plate 73

Chestnut-breasted Mannikin

Lonchura castaneothorax ramsayi

Many birds caught and compared, Port Moresby July 1990.

breast had pale silken edges, giving clear scaled impression in the hand

males averaged:
Length 110.0 mm
wing 52.0 mm
culmen 10.0 mm
tarsus 12.0 mm

flank feather from beneath the wing - note the brown, which is seldom if ever noticed

♂

rump and uppertail-coverts identical in both sexes

rump normally covered by closed wings, and not showing at sides of the flanks

♂

This immature Length 105.0 mm wing 51.0 mm culmen 10.0 mm tarsus 11.0 mm

adult plumage comes through quite irregularly on body first, then flight feathers predictably.

Of two matched pairs, in both cases the female was more clearly marked on the rear crown and nape

♀

Females averaged:
Length 105.0 mm
Wing 51.0 mm
Culmen 10.0 mm
tarsus 11.0 mm

♂

Young bird feeding independently (bill blue-grey) Length 107. mm wing 49.0 mm culmen 9.5 mm tarsus 13.0 mm

juvenile recently fledged -- dark beak Length 104.0 mm Wing 51.0 mm Culmen 10.0 mm tarsus 11.0 mm

origin of these birds

Plate 74

This bird was acquired as an adult
November '85. Died Dec. '88, and
was then painted here.

Black Mannikin
Lonchura stygia

Length 100mm
wing 51 mm
culmen 10 mm
tarsus 12 mm

♀

wings dark brown
with black edgings

breast
very shiny black

♀

undertail-
coverts dead
black

These birds
came
from
Merauke, West Irian Jaya

note yellow brighter
and more
extensive

Heads of two of Patrick
Tay's birds when newly arrived.
Singapore, '90

legs and feet
pale blue-grey,
nails grey

♂

no brown on mantle

bill paler
than females

Males of Tay's
newly arrived birds
had yellow brighter and
sexes very easy to
distinguish.

♂

Plate 75

Black-breasted Mannikin
Lonchura teerinki teerinki

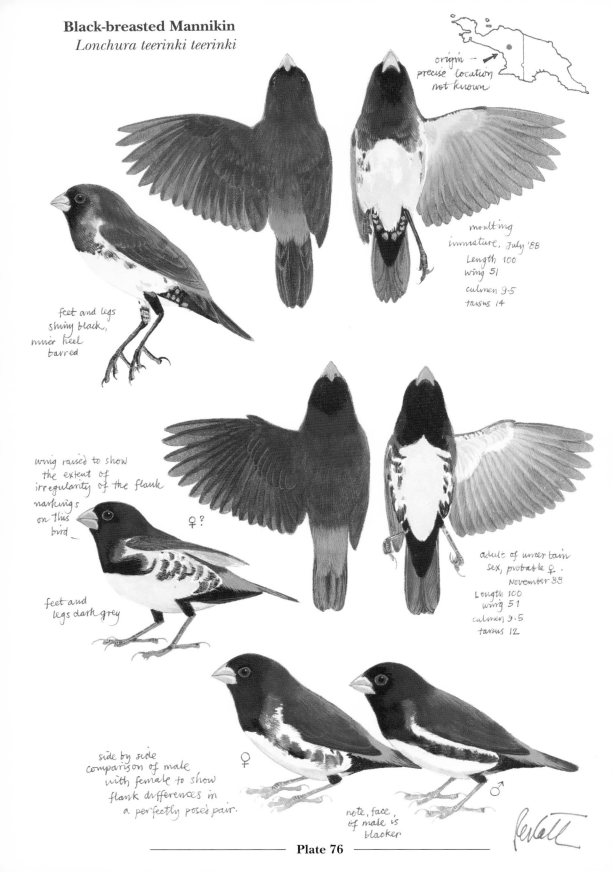

origin →
precise location
not known

feet and legs
shiny black,
inner heel
barred

moulting
immature, July '88
Length 100
wing 51
culmen 9·5
tarsus 14

wing raised to show
the extent of
irregularity of the flank
markings
on this
bird

♀?

feet and
legs dark grey

adult of uncertain
sex, probable ♀.
November 88
Length 100
wing 51
culmen 9·5
tarsus 12

side by side
comparison of male
with female to show
flank differences in
a perfectly posed pair.

♀

♂

note, face
of male is
blacker

Plate 76

origin of these birds, central Luzon — philippines

Java Sparrow
Lonchura oryzivora

warm dark brown flights with grey leading edges

8th – 5th primaries notched

Two adults caught near Manila, more or less identical. Male & female:

♂ Length 136 mm ... ♀ 125 mm
♂ wing 70mm · · · ♀ 67 mm
♂ tarsus 16 mm · · · ♀ 15 m

irides bright ruby

bill 10 mm high
10 mm wide
♂ culmen 15
♀ culmen 14

dark tip on bill

5 months

one month

flanks under the wings are grey

clay and buff edges to wing-coverts and secondaries

plumage perfectly tight with no feathers' edges perceptible

Juvenile at 3 months

brown centres to undertail-coverts

Plate 77

Java Sparrow
Lonchura oryzivora

Fawn mutation

snow-white under-
wing-coverts.

Feet very red.

♀

Adult birds bred in South Africa by P.R.earden,'85.
Juvenile one of my breeding in London 1986.

Key discriminator when
in breeding condition is
swollen red eyering and
base of bill. Eyering is
a clearer
sign and
more
noticeable.

♂ in breeding
condition

♀ in breeding
condition

♀ Length 140 mm
wing 68 mm
tarsus 17 mm
culmen 13 mm

fledgling snow-white
underwing-coverts

Juvenile at one
month after fledging

Length 115 mm
wing 68 mm
tarsus 14 mm
culmen 10 mm

Plate 78

Timor Sparrow
Lonchura fuscata

9
8
7
6
5

6, 7 + 8th primaries notched

Juveniles
Length 118 120 mm
wing 64 65 mm
tarsus 15 15 mm
culmen 12.5 13 mm

When juvenile begins the moult, the forehead and crown become blackish-brown, leaving the pale front of superciliary

1st year adult moulting - note change of cheek patch

dark lores with pale spot at base of superciliary very distinctive

Note mesial stripe is buffish, not white like chin.

underparts warm buffy-white

'second-year adult'

Sides of breast are last to moult into adult plumage.

breast has distinctict plum-purple bloom, almost iridescent.

Adult pair
 | ♀ | ♂
Length | 120 | 126
wing | 62 | 65
tarsus | 14 | 14
culmen | 13 | 14

Eggs laid by these birds varied in size from 20mm x 13mm to 19mm x 12.5mm

Plate 79

Timor Sparrow
Lonchura fuscata

brown of breast is slightly more brown than the upperparts

total plumage has a silken almost silvery lustre similar to that of Java Sparrow.

This drawn from a single museum skin, sex unknown

Length 130 approx
wing   67
tarsus 16
culmen 13

sexes alike

Brown has an odd colour, almost a dark grey

culmen not on continuous line with skull

note line of black feathers along base of lower mandible

Plate 80

BIBLIOGRAPHY

Ali, S. & Ripley, S. D. 1987. *Handbook of Birds of India and Pakistan.* Oxford Univ. Press, Oxford.

Andrew, P. & Holmes, D.A. (Eds.). 1990. Sulawesi Bird Report. *Kukila* 5: 44-26.

Archer, G. & Godman, E.M. 1961. *The Birds of British Somaliland and the Gulf of Aden.* Oliver & Boyd, London.

Baker, E.C.S. 1925. *Bull. Brit. Orn. Club.,* 45: 58.

— 1926. *The Fauna of British India.* Taylor and Francis, London.

— 1934. *The Nidification of the Birds of the Indian Empire,* vol. 3. London.

Bannerman, D.A. 1949. *The Birds of Tropical West Africa.* Oliver & Boyd, London.

— 1953. *The Birds of West and Equatorial Africa.* Oliver & Boyd, London.

Baptista, L. 1990. Observations on the feeding habits of some New Guinea birds in Madang Province. *Muruk* 4 (2).

— 1991. Field Observations on some New Guinea Mannikins (*Lonchura* spp.). *Avic Mag.* 97: 141-152.

— 1995. A Guide to the Study of Estrildids. *The Estrildian,* 3(1): 12-24.

— & Horblit, H.M. 1990. The Inheritance and Loss of the Straw Display in Esrildid Finches. *Avic. Mag.* 96: 141-152.

Barnes, H.E. 1897. *The Birds of India.* Bombay.

Bartlett, E. 1896. Notes on Birds. *Sarawak Gazette* 66: 240-241.

Batchelor, D.M. 1959. North Borneo Bird Notes. *Sarawak Museum Journal,* 9: 13-14, 263-266.

Bates, G.L. 1930. *Handbook of the Birds of West Africa.* London.

Baxter, E. 1985. *The Avicultural Writings of Eric Baxter.* Avic. Soc. of S. Australia, Adelaide.

Beehler, B.M., Pratt, T.K. & Zimmerman, D.A. 1986. *Birds of New Guinea.* Princeton Univ. Press, New Jersey.

Benson, C.W. 1941. Further notes on Nyasaland Birds (with particular reference to those of the Northern Province). Part IV. *Ibis* Ser. 14, 5: 1-55.

Bernstein, H.A. 1861. Ueber Nester und Eier Javascher Vogel. *J. Orn.* 9: 177-192.

— 1952. Notes from Nyasaland. *Ostrich* 23 (3): 144-159.

— & Benson, F. M. 1977. *Birds of Malawi.* Montfort, Malawi.

— & White, C.M.N. 1957. *Checklist of the Birds of Northern Rhodesia.* The Government Printer, Lusaka.

Bishop, K.D. 1987. Interesting Bird Observations in Papua New Guinea. *Muruk* 2: 52-57.

— 1992. New and interesting records of birds in Wallacea. *Kukila* 6: 8-34.

Blakers, M., Davies, S.F.J. & Reilly, P.N. 1984. *The Atlas of Australian Birds.* RAOU & Melbourne Univ. Press.

Bond, J. 1971. *Birds of the West Indies.* Houghton Mifflin, New York.

Brickell, N. 1986. *An introduction to South African Cage and Aviary Birds,* Vol.1. Nadine, South Hills, South Africa.

— & Konigkramer, T. 1994. *African Aviculture,* Vol. 2. Avicultural Publications, Durban.

— Huntley, B. & Vorster, R. 1980. Observations on Wild and Captive Pied Mannikins. *Bokmakierie,* 32 : 9-12.

Britten, R.J. 1989. Comment on a criticism of DNA hybridization measurements. *J. Human Evol.* 18:163-166.

Brooksbank, A.1949. *Foreign Birds in Cage and Aviary.* Cage Birds, London.

Brown, R.E.B. 1963. Java Sparrows. *Avic. Mag.* 59: 239.

Burkhard, R. 1980a. Von eininger Seltneren Psittaeiden und Prachtfinken. *Gefiederte Welt* 1980: 1-2.

— 1980b. Notizen uber das Verhalten meiner Funffarbennonnen.*Gefiederte Welt.* 1980: 39.

Burton, J.E. 1993. White-backed Munia feeding on algae. *Hong Kong Bird Report 1992.* Hong Kong Birdwatching Society, Hong Kong.

Butler, A.G. 1899. *Foreign Finches in Captivity.* Brunby and Clark, London.

Caldwell, H.R. & Caldwell J.C. 1931. *South China Birds.* Shanghai.

Carstens, A.D. 1985. The Chestnut-breasted Finch *Lonchura castaneothorax.* *The Grassfinch,* 9: 12-13.

Cayley, N.W. 1932. *Australian Finches in Bush and Aviary.* Angus & Robertson, Sydney.

Clancey, P. 1964a. *The Birds of Natal and Zululand.* Oliver & Boyd, London.

— 1964b. Occas. Papers Nat. Mus. Southern Rhodesia, 27B: 28.

Clements, J.F. 1981. *Birds of the World: A checklist.* Croom Helm, London.

Clement, P., Harris, A. & Davis, J. 1993. *Finches and Sparrows.* Helm, London.

Christidis, L. 1987. Biochemical systematics within Paleotropic Finches. *Auk*: 104: 380-391.

Coates, B.J. 1990. *The Birds of Papua New Guinea,* vol. 2. Dove, Brisbane.

Collar, N.J. & Andrew, P. 1988. *Birds to Watch. The ICBP World Checklist of Threatened Birds.* ICBP Technical Publication No. 8, Cambridge, UK.

Collar, N.J., Crosby, M.J. & Stattersfield, A J. 1994. *Birds to Watch 2.* BirdLife International, Cambridge, UK.

Corbin, K.W. 1977. Genetic Diversity in Avian Populations. Pp. 291-30 in *Endangered Birds* (ed. S.A. Temple) Madison, Wisconsin.

Cramp, S. 1994. *Handbook of the Birds of Europe the Middle East and North Africa,* Vol 8. pp 437-439. Oxford Univ. Press, Oxford.

Daisaku, E. 1981. *Birds of Tokyo.* Tokyo.

Deckert, H. 1980. Zucht des Wellen-Bronsemanchen (*Lonchura molucca*). *Gefiederte Welt,* 1980: 184-185.

Dee, T.J. 1986. *The Endemic Birds of Madagascar.* ICBP, Cambridge, UK.

Delacour, J. 1943. A revision of the subfamily Estrildinae of the family Plocidae. *Zoologica* 28: 69-86.

De Zylva, T.S.U. 1984. *Birds of Sri Lanka.* Trumpet, Colombo.

Diamond, J.M. 1967. New subspecies and records of birds from the Karimui Basin, New Guinea. *Amer. Mus. Novit.* No. 2284.

— 1972. *Avifauna of the Eastern Highlands of New Guinea.* Publ. Nuttall Orn. Club no. 12. Cambridge, Mass.

— & LeCroy, M. 1979. Birds of Karkar and Bagabag Island, New Guinea. *Bull. Amer. Mus. Nat. Hist.* 164: 467-531.

duPont, J.E. 1976. *South Pacific Birds.* Delaware Mus. Nat. Hist., Delaware.

— & Rabor, D.S. 1973. South Sulu Archipelago Birds. *Occ. Papers Delaware Mus. Nat. Hist.,* no. 9.

Eisner, E. 1960. The Biology of the Bengalese Finch. *Auk* 77: 271- 287.

— 1963. A Quantitative Study of Parental Behaviour in the Bengalese Finch. *Behaviour* 20: 134 - 206.

Etchécopar, R.D. & Hüe, F. 1967 *The Birds of North Africa.* Oliver & Boyd, London.

Faulkener, J. 1986. Breeding the Moluccan Mannikin (*Lonchura molucca vagans*). *Avic. Mag.*, 92: 235-236.

Filewood, L.W. 1979. (No title) *PNG Bird Society Newsletter* 47: 3.

Finch, B.W. & McKean, J.L. 1987. Some notes on the Birds of the Bismarcks. *Muruk* 2: 3-28.

Finsch, O. 1886. On two new species of Birds from New Ireland. *Ibis*, ser. 5, 13: 1-2.

Flannery, T. 1987. Journey to the Stars. *Aust. Nat. Hist.* 22: 245-249.

Frith, H.J. (ed.), 1976. *Complete Book of Australian Birds.* Readers Digest, Sydney.

Gallagher, M. & Woodcock, M.W. 1980. *The Birds of Oman.* Quartet, London.

Gibson-Hill, C.A. 1950. *A Check-list of the Birds of Singapore Island.* Bull. Raffles Mus., 21: 132-183.

Gilliard, E.T. & LeCroy, M. 1966. Birds of the Middle Sepik Region, New Guinea. Results of the American Museum of Natural History Expedition to New Guinea in 1953- 54. *Bull. Amer. Mus. Nat. Hist.* 132: 245-276.

Goodwin, D. 1952. Recollections of some small birds. *Avic. Mag.* 58: 24-29.

— 1963. Observations on Java Sparrows. *Avic. Mag.* 69: 54-69.

— 1965. *Instructions to Young Ornithologists*, VI: Domestic Birds. Museum Press, London.

— 1982. *Estrildid Finches of the World.* British Museum (Nat. Hist.) London.

Goriup, P.D. (Ed.). 1988. *Ecology and Conservation of Grassland Birds.* ICBP Tech. Pub. No.7., Cambridge, UK.

Grant, P. 1991. Natural Selection and Darwin's Finches. *Scientific American* 265: 60-65.

Gray, A.P. 1958. *Bird Hybrids.* Commonwealth Agricultural Bureau, Farnham, Surrey.

Green, R. 1986. Breeding the Five-coloured Munia. *Avic. Mag.* 92: 181-183.

Gregory, P. 1995a. Notes on the Black Mannikin (*Lonchura stygia*) and other mannikins (*Lonchura* sp.) at Lake Owa, Middle Fly River. *Muruk* 7 (3).

— 1995b. Memorable Myola. *Muruk* 7 (3).

— 1995c. More from Manus. *Muruk* 7 (3).

Gregory-Smith, R. & Gregory-Smith, J. 1989. Eastern Alpine Mannikin *Lonchura monticola* nesting. *Muruk* 4 (2).

Guttinger, H.R. 1970. Zur Evolution von Verhaltensweisen und Lautausserungen bei Prachtfinken (Estrildidae). *Z. Tierpsychol.* 27: 1011-1075.

— 1976. Zur systematische Stellung der Gattungen, *Amadina*, *Lepidopygia*, und *Lonchura* (Aves, Estrildidae). *Bonn. Zool. Beitr* 27: pp. 218-244.

Hadden, D. 1981. *Birds of the North Solomons.* Wau Ecology Institute, Handbook no. 8, PNG.

Hahn, Maj. J.C. 1988. Bird Watching in Hong Kong. *Army Bird Watching Bulletin*, Annex B: B1-B4.

Hails, C. & Jarvis, F. 1987. *Birds of Singapore.* Times Editions, Singapore.

Hall, B.P. (Ed.) 1974. *Birds of the Harold Hall Australian Expeditions 1962-1970*: 326-327. Brit. Mus. (Nat. Hist.), London.

Hall, M.F. 1962. Evolutionary Aspects of Estrildid Song. *Symp. Zool. Soc. London*, 8: 37-55.

Hannecart, F. & Letocart, T. 1980. *Oiseaux de Nouvelle Caledonie et Les Layautes*, vol.1. Les Editions du Pacifique, Singapore.

Harrison, C.J.O. 1964. The taxonomic status of the African Silverbill *Lonchura cantans* and the Indian Silverbill *Lonchura malabarica*. *Ibis* 106: 462-468.

Harrisson, T.H. 1950. Bird Notes from Borneo. *Bull. Raffles Mus.* 23: 328-335.

Hartert, E. 1925. A collection of Birds from New Ireland (Neu Mecklenburg). *Novit. Zool.* 32 : 115-136.

Harvey, W.G. & Holmes, D.A. 1976. Additions to the Avifaunas of Sumatra and Kalimantan, Indonesia. *Bull. Brit. Orn. Club* 96: 90-92.

Heinroth, O. 1903. Ornithologische Ergebrisse der "1 Deutschen Sudsee-Expedition von B. Mencke". *J. Orn.* 51: 65-125.

Henry, G.M. 1955. *A Guide to the Birds of Ceylon.* Oxford Univ. Press, London.

Hicks, R.K. 1987. An extension of altitude range for two mannikin species. *Muruk* 2 (2): 60.

Hoogerwerf, A. 1949. *De Avifauna van de Plantentuin te Buitenzorg.* Buitenzorg, Java.

Immelmann, K.J. 1962a. Biologische Bedeutung optischer und akustikher Merkmale bei Prachtfinken (Aves Spermestidae). *Verh. Deutsche Zoel. Ges.*, 369-374.

— 1962b. Beitrage zu einer vergleichenden Biologie australischer Prachtfinken. *Zool. Jb. Syst.* 90: 1-196.

— 1969. Uber den Einfluss Fruhkindlicher Erfahrungen auf die geschlechtliche Objektfixierung bei Estrildiden. *Z. Tierpsychol*, 26: 677-691.

— 1982. *Austalian Finches in Bush and Aviary.* Angus and Robertson, Sydney.

— & Immelmann, G. 1967. Verhalten Sokologiische Studien an afrikanischen und australis chen Estrilden. *Zool. Jb. Syst.* 94: 609-686.

— , Steinbacher, J. & Wolters, H. E. 1972. Vogel in Kafig und Voliere. *Prachtfinken* 3: 431-440.

Irwin, M.P.S. 1956. Field Notes on a Collection from Mozambique. *Ostrich* 27: 28-39.

Jackson, H.D. 1972. The Status of the Pied Mannikin, *Lonchura fringilloides* (Lafresnaye) in Rhodesia and its association with the bamboo *Oxytenanthera abyssinica* (Munro). *Rhod. Sci. News*, 6: 342-348.

Johnston, R.F. 1990. Variation in Size and Shape in Pigeons *Columba livia*. *Wilson Bull* 102: 213- 255.

Jonkers, B. & Roersma, H. 1990. New subspecies of *Lonchura spectabilis* from East Sepik province, Papua New Guinea. *Dutch Birding*, 12: 22-25.

Junge, G.C.A. 1939. The Birds of South New Guinea, part III. *Nova Guinea*, new ser. 3: 66-67.

Kakizawa, R. & Watada, R. 1985. The Evolutionary Genetics of the Estrilidae. *J. Yamashina Inst. Orn.*, 17 : 143-158.

Kigomo, B.N. 1988. Bamboo Resource in the East African Region. *Proc. Int. Bamboo Workshop*, Nov 14-18, 1988. Cochin, India.

King, B. 1979. New Distributional Records and Field Notes for some New Guinea Birds. *Emu* 79: 146-148.

Kingston, R. (Ed.) 1987. *The Finch Breeders Handbook, Vol.1: The Australians.* Queensland Finch Society, Woolloongabba, Queensland.

Kinnear, N.B. 1929. On the birds collected by Mr. M. H. Stevens in Northern Tonkin in 1923-24. *Ibis* 71: 107-150.

Koepff, C. 1984. *The New Finch Handbook.* Barron's, New York.

Kunkel, P. 1965. Verhaltensstudien an den Kontinentalafrikanischen Elterschen. *Vogelvelt* 86: 161-178.

Langberg, W. 1955. First breeding in confinement of the Brown or Black Munia, *Lonchura fuscans. Avic. Mag.* 51: 229-230.

— 1963. Breeding of the Grey-headed Silverbill *Odontospiza caniceps. Avic. Mag.* 69: 97-101.

LeCroy, M. & Peckover, W.S. 1983. Birds of the Kimbe Bay Area, West New Britain, Papua New Guinea. *Condor* 85: 297-304.

Legge, V. 1880. *A History of the Birds of Ceylon.* Dehiwala, Ceylon. (Reprinted in facsimile by Tisara Prakasayo Press, Colombo, 1983).

Lekagul, B. & Round, P. 1991. *A Guide to the Birds of Thailand.* Saha Karn Bhaet Bangkok.

Lever, C. 1987. *Naturalized Birds of the World.* Longman, Harlow, Essex.

Lim Kim Seng. 1992. *Vanishing Birds of Singapore.* The Nature Society, Singapore.

Lindgren, E. 1975. *Papua New Guinea Birds.* Robert Brown, Port Moresby.

Lodge, W. 1991. *Birds alternative names: a checklist.* Blandford, London.

Long, J. 1981. *Introduced Birds of the World.* David and Charles, Newton Abbot.

MacKinnon, J. 1988. *Field Guide to the Birds of Java and Bali.* Gadjah Mada Univ. Press, Yogyakarta.

— & Phillipps, K. 1993. *A Field Guide to The Birds of Borneo, Sumatra, Java, and Bali.* Oxford Univ. Press, Oxford.

Mackworth-Praed, C.W. & Grant, C.H.B. 1960. *The Birds of Eastern and Northeastern Africa.* Volume 2. Longman, London.

Maclean, G.L. 1985. *Roberts' Birds of Southern Africa.* Voelker Bird Book Fund, Cape Town.

Madoc, G.C. 1956. *An introduction to Malaysian Birds.* The Malayan Nature Society, Kuala Lumpur.

Majnep, J.S. & Bulmer, R. 1977. *Birds of my Kalam Country.* Oxford Univ. Press, London and Auckland.

Majumdar, N. 1978. On the Taxonomic Status of the Eastern Ghats Rufous-bellied Munia, *Lonchura kelaarti vernayi* (Whistler and Kinnear, 1933) [Aves: Ploceidae]. *Journ. Bombay Nat. Hist. Soc.* 75: 493 - 495.

Mason, C.W. & Le Froy, H. 1912. *The Food of Birds in India,* Memoirs of the Department of Agriculture in India. Dept. Agric. India, Calcutta.

Mason, V. & Jarvis, F. 1989. *Birds of Bali.* Periplus, Singapore.

Mayr, E. 1938. Birds from South Borneo. *Bull. Raffles Mus.,* 14: 45.

— 1945. *Birds of the Southwest Pacific.* Macmillan, New York.

— 1970. *Populations, species, evolution.* Belknap Press, Harvard Univ., Cambridge, Mass.

— & Rand, A.L. 1937. Results of the Archbold Expeditions, 14: Birds of the 1933-1934 Papuan Expedition. *Bull. Amer. Mus. Nat. Hist.* 73: 1-248.

McClure, F.A. 1993. *The Bamboos.* Smithsonian, Washington, DC.

Mees, G.F. 1958. Een bastaard tussen *Lonchura tristissima* (Wallace) en *L. leucosticta* (D'Albertis and Salvadori). *Nova Guinea,* new ser. 9: 15-19.

— 1982. Birds from the Lowlands of Southern New Guinea (Merauke and Koembe). *Zoologische ver Handlingen* 191:154-158.

Meinertzhagen, R. 1954. *Birds of Arabia.* Oliver & Boyd, London.

Meyer, E. 1930. Uebersicht uber die Brutzeten der Vogel auf der Insel Vuatom (New Britain). *J. Orn.* 78 : 19-38.

— 1978. Zucht der Nevermann - oder Weissscheitelnonne (*Lonchura nevermanni*). *Gefiederte Welt* 102 : 161-162.

Meyer De Schauensee, R. 1984. *The Birds of China.* Oxford Univ. Press, Oxford.

Mitra, G.N. & Nayar, Y. 1972. Chemical composition of bamboo seeds (*Bambusa arundinacea* Willd). *Ind. For.* 98: 479-481.

Morris, D.1956. The feather postures of birds and the problem of the origin of social signals. *Behaviour* 9: 75-113.

— 1957. The reproductive behaviour of the Bronze Mannikin (*Lonchura cucullata*). *Behaviour* 11: 156 - 201.

— 1958. The comparative ethology of grassfinches (Erythrurae) and mannikins (Amadinae) *Proc.Zool. Soc. London* 131: 389-439.

— 1970. *Patterns of Reproductive Behaviour.* Jonathan Cape, London.

Motley, J. & Dillwyn, L.L. 1855. Contributions to the Natural History of Labuan, and the Adjacent Coasts of Borneo. *Birds,* 8-38, 53-62.

Moynihan, M. & Hall, M.F. 1954. Hostile, Sexual, and other Social Behaviour Patterns of the Spice Finch *Lonchura punctulata* in Captivity. *Behaviour* 7: 33-76.

Nachrichten, A.L. 1978. *Gefiederte Welt* 103: 1.

Napper, D.N. 1965. *Grasses of Tanganyika.* Ministry of Agriculture, Forests and Wildlife, Tanzania.

Nash, S.V. 1993. *Sold for a Song....The Trade in Southeast-Asian Non-CITES Birds.* TRAFFIC International, Cambridge.

Neff, R. 1971. Die Prachtnonne (*Lonchura spectabilis*). *Gefiederte Welt* 95: 232-236.

— 1972. Weitere Beobachtungen ander Prachtnonne (*Lonchura spectabilis*). *Gefiederte Welt* 96: 68.

— 1979. Ehrfahrungen mit der Weissscheitelnonne (*Lonchura nevermanni*). *Gefiederte Welt* 103: 61-63.

Newman, K. 1983. *Birds of Southern Africa.* Southern Book Pub., Johannesburg.

Oberg, H. 1975. Gesangs und Zuhorverhalten bei Prachtfinken (Estrildidae). Dissertazion, Technischen Universitat Carolo-Wilhelmina zu Braunschweig.

Oberholser, H.C. 1926. New East Indian Passerine Birds. *Journ. Washington Acad. Sci.,* 16: 521.

Oppenborn, H. 1987. *Gefiederte Welt* 111: 52-53.

Parkes, K.C. 1958. Taxonomy and Nomenclature of three species of *Lonchura* (Aves, Estrildinae). *Proc. U. S. Nat. Mus.* 108: 279-293.

Paynter, R.A.1968. Family Estrildidae, in *Check-list of the Birds of the World.* Vol. 14. Mus. Comp. Zool., Cambridge, Mass.

Peckover, W.S. & Filewood, L.W.C. 1976. *Birds of New Guinea and Tropical Australia.* Reed, Sydney.

Peterson, R.T. 1980. *A Field Guide to the Birds East of the Rockies.* Houghton Mifflin, Boston.

Phillips, W. A. 1948. Nest and Eggs of Ceylon Birds. *Ceylon Journ. Sci.* (B) XXIII: pt. 3.

Pratt, H.D., Brunner, P.L. & Berrett, D.G. 1987. *The Birds of Hawaii and the Tropical Pacific.* Princeton Univ. Press, New Jersey.

Queensland Finch Society. 1987. *The Finch Breeder's Handbook.* Volume 1: The Australians. Wooloongabba, Queensland.

Rand, A.L. 1936. Distribution and Habits of Madagascar Birds. *Bull. Amer. Mus. Nat. Hist.,* 72: 143-499.

— 1938. Results of the Archbold Expeditions, No. 20: On

some Passerine New Guinea Birds. *Amer. Mus. Novitates* 991:1-20.

Rand, A.L. 1942. Results of the 1938-39 Archbold Expeditions, No. 43. *Bull. Amer. Mus. Nat. Hist.* 79: 425-516.

— & Gilliard, E.T. 1967. *Handbook of New Guinea Birds.* Wiedenfeld and Nicholson, London.

Ratti, J.L. 1980. The classification of avian species and subspecies. *American Birds* 34: 860-866.

Reichenow, A. 1899. Die Vogel der Bismarckinseln. *Mitt. Zool. Mus. Berlin*, 1 : 1-106.

Restall, R.L. 1975. *Finches and Other Seedeating Birds.* Faber & Faber, London.

— 1987. The Javan or Javan Munia *Lonchura leucogastroides*. *Avic. Mag.* 93: 130-135.

— 1989. Reminiscences of Rare Munias. *Avic. Mag.* 95: 129 - 141.

— 1990. Reminiscences of Rare Munias. *Avic. Mag.* 96: 192-209.

— 1991. Observations on the Grey-headed Mannikin (*Lonchura caniceps*) and the Chestnut-breasted Mannikin (*L. castaneothorax*) in the Port Moresby area. *Muruk* 4: 3

— 1993. White-crowned Mannikins. *The Estrildian* 1(2): 15-17.

— 1994a. The Tricoloured Munia and the Chestnut Munia – two good species? *Avic. Mag.* 100: 192-194.

— 1994b. Munias and Mannikins. *The Estrildian*, 2(1): 8-25.

— 1995a. Observations of unusual behaviour in munias, genus *Lonchura*. *Avic. Mag.* 101: 63-74.

— 1995b. Proposed additions to the genus *Lonchura* (Estrildidae). *Bull. Brit. Orn. Club.* 115: 140-157.

— 1996. A proposed new species of munia, genus *Lonchura* (Estrildinae). *Bull. Brit. Orn. Club.* 116: 137-142.

Riley, J.H. 1938. Birds from Siam and the Malay Peninsula in the United States National Museum collected by Drs Hugh M. Smith and William L. Abbott. *Smithsonian Inst. U.S. Nat. Mus. Bull.* 172.

Ripley, S.D. 1964. A Systematic and Ecological Study of the Birds of New Guinea. *Peabody Mus. Nat. Hist., Yale Univ. Bull.* 19.

Roberts. T.J. 1974. Interesting Distributional Records for Pakistan. *J. Bombay Nat. Hist. Soc.* 77: 12-20.

— 1992. *The Birds of Pakistan.* Oxford Univ. Press, Karachi.

Robinson, H.C. & Chasen, F.N. 1927-29. *Birds of the Malay Peninsula*, 4 vols. H. F. & G. Witherby, London.

Rudiger, N. 1981. *Gefiederte Welt* 105: 61-62.

Rutgers, A. & Norris, K. A. 1977. *Encyclopaedia of Aviculture.* Blandford, London.

Salomonsen, F. 1953. Miscellaneous notes on Philippine Birds. *Vidensk. Medd. Dansk. Naturh. For.*, 115: 205-281.

Sarich, V.M., Schmid, C.W. & Marks, J. 1988. DNA hybridization as a guide to phylogeny. *J. Human Evol.* 17: 769-786.

Scally, P. 1967. Breeding the Pearl-headed Silverbill (*Odontospiza caniceps*). *Avic. Mag.* 73:3.

Schafer, E. 1938. Ornithologische Ergebnisse Zweier Forschungreisen nach Tibet. *J. Orn.* 86, Sonderheft.

Sclater, W.L. & Moreau, R.E. 1933. Taxonomic and field notes on some birds of north-eastern Tanganyika Territory (Part V). *Ibis* 75: 399-440.

Sibley, C.G. & Ahlquist, J.E. 1985. The phylogeny and classification of the passerine birds, based on comparisons of genetic material, DNA. Pp 83-121 in *Proc. 18th Intl. Ornithol. Congress*, Moscow 1982. Nauka Publ., Moscow.

— & — 1990. *Phylogeny and Classification of Birds: A Study in Molecular Evolution.* Yale Univ. Press, New Haven and London.

Sibley, C.G., Ahlquist, J.E. & Monroe, B.L. 1988. A classification of the living birds of the world based on DNA hybridization studies. *Auk* 105: 409-423.

Sibley, C.G. & Monroe, B.L. 1990. *Distribution and Taxonomy of Birds of the World.* Yale Univ. Press, New Haven and London.

Sinclair, I. 1984. *Field Guide to the Birds of South Africa.* Collins, London.

Simpson, K. & Day, N. 1984. *The Birds of Australia.* Lloyd O'Neill, Victoria.

Slater, P.J.B. 1970. Nest building in the Bengalese Finch. *Behaviour* 36: 300-319.

Slater, P. 1974. *A Field Guide to Australian Birds.* Rigby, Adelaide.

— , Slater, P., & Slater, R. 1986. *The Slater Field Guide to Australian Birds.* Rigby, Dee Why West, NSW.

Smith, T.B. 1991. A Double-billed Dilemma. *Natural History*, 1, 91: 41-16.

Smithe, F. 1975. *Naturalist's Color Guide.* Amer. Mus. Nat. Hist., New York.

Smythies, B.E. 1981. *Birds of Borneo.* The Sabah Society with the Malayan Nature Society, Kuala Lumpur.

— 1986. *The Birds of Burma.* Nimrod, Liss, UK.

Soderberg, P.M. 1956. *Foreign Birds for Cage and Aviary.* Cassell, London.

Spavin, S. & Spavin, K. 1991. Striated Munias. *Foreign Birds* 57: 8-9.

Sproule, M. 1994. The Five-coloured Mannikin. *The Estrildian.* 2(1): 4-6.

Steiner, H. 1960. Klassifikation der Prachtfinken, Spermestidae, auf Grund der Rachenzeichnungen ihre Nestlinge. *J. Orn.* 101: 421-447.

— 1966. Atavismen bei Artbastarden und ihre Bedeutung zur Feststellung von Verwanschaftbeziehungen. Kreuzungsergegebnisse innerhalb der Singvogelfamilie der Spermestidae. *Rev. Suisse Zool.* 73: 321-337.

Strange, M. & Jeyarajasingam, A. 1993. *Birds. A Photographic Guide to the Birds of Peninsular Malaysia and Singapore.* Sun Tree, Singapore.

Stresemann, E. 1935. Zwei neue Webervogel aus Sud-Neuguinea. *Orn. Mber.* 35: 87.

— 1939. Die Vogel von Celebes. *J. Orn.* , 88: 1-135.

Tay, P. 1989. *My Mannikin Collection.* Sing. Avic. Soc., Singapore.

Tewari, D.N. 1993. *A Monograph on Bamboo.* Dehra Dun, India.

Thibault, J-C. & Rives, C. 1975. *Birds of Tahiti.* Times Editions, Singapore.

Tolhurst, L.P. 1987. Bird-watching Observations. *Muruk* 2: 72-73.

Tweedie, M.W.F. 1960. *Common Birds of the Malay Peninsula.* Longman, Kuala Lumpur.

van Marle, J.G. & Voous, K.H. 1988. *The Birds of Sumatra.* BOU Check-list No. 7, BOU, Tring.

Viney, C., Phillipps, K. & Lam Chiu Ying. 1994. *Birds of Hong Kong and South China.* The Government Printer, Hong Kong..

Ward, P. 1968. The origin of the avifauna of urban and suburban Singapore. *Ibis* 110: 239-54.

Watling, D. 1983. Ornithological notes from Sulawesi. *Emu* 83: 24-261.

Whistler, H. 1928. *Popular Handbook of Indian Birds.* Oliver & Boyd, London.

— Kinnear, N.B. 1933. The Vernay Scientific Survey of the Eastern Ghats, Ornithological section. *Journ. Bombay Nat. Hist. Soc.*, 36: 835.

White, C.M.N. & Bruce, M.D. 1986. *The Birds of Wallacea.* BOU Check-list no. 7. BOU, Tring.

Whitehead, J. 1893. *Exploration of Mount Kinabalu, North Borneo.* London.

Wijesinghe, D.P. 1994. *Checklist of the Birds of Sri Lanka.* Colombo.

Wilkinson, R., Dutson, G., Sheldon, B., Noor, D. & Noor, Y. R. 1991. The Avifauna of the Barito Ulu Region, Central Kalimantan. *Kukila*, 5: 99-116.

Wolters, H.E. 1957. Die Klassifikation der Weberfinken (Estrildidae). *Bonn. Zool. Beitr.*, 2: 90-129.

— 1979. *Die Vogelarten der Erde.* Paul Parey, Hamburg and Berlin.

Yoneda, T. & Okanoyo, K. 1991. Ontogeny of sexually dimorphic distance calls in Bengalese Finches, (*Lonchura domestica*). *J. Ethology* 9: 41-46.

INDEX OF SCIENTIFIC AND ENGLISH NAMES

Species are listed by their vernacular name (e.g. Scaly-breasted Munia), together with alternative names where relevant, and by their scientific names. Specific scientific names are followed by the generic name as used in the book (e.g. *punctulata, Lonchura*) and subspecific names are followed by both the specific and generic names (e.g. *topela, Lonchura punctulata*).

Numbers in italic type refer to the first page of the systematic entry, those in bold type refer to colour plate numbers and those in bold italic type to the plate numbers of the coloured measured drawings.